Douglas Pass.
From his Aunt Ina Hie.
May 14th 1903.

THE DESCENT OF MAN,

AND

SELECTION IN RELATION TO SEX.

UNIFORM EDITIONS.

WORKS BY CHARLES DARWIN, F.R.S.

LIFE AND LETTERS OF CHARLES DARWIN. With an Autobiographical Chapter. Edited by FRANCIS DARWIN. Portraits. 3 vols. 36s.

NATURALIST'S JOURNAL OF RESEARCHES INTO THE NATURAL HISTORY AND GEOLOGY OF COUNTRIES VISITED during a VOYAGE ROUND THE WORLD. With 100 Illustrations by PRITCHETT. 21s. *Popular Edition.* Woodcuts. 3s. 6d.

*ORIGIN OF SPECIES BY MEANS OF NATURAL SELEC-*TION; or, THE PRESERVATION OF FAVOURED RACES IN THE STRUGGLE FOR LIFE. Large Type Edition, 2 vols. 12s. *Popular Edition*, 6s.

VARIOUS CONTRIVANCES BY WHICH ORCHIDS ARE FERTILIZED BY INSECTS. Woodcuts. 7s. 6d.

*VARIATION OF ANIMALS AND PLANTS UNDER DO-*MESTICATION. Illustrations. 15s.

DESCENT OF MAN, AND SELECTION IN RELATION TO SEX. Illustrations. Large Type Edition, 2 vols. 15s. *Popular Edition*, 7s. 6d.

EXPRESSION OF THE EMOTIONS IN MAN AND ANIMALS. Illustrations. 12s.

INSECTIVOROUS PLANTS. Illustrations. 9s.

MOVEMENTS AND HABITS OF CLIMBING PLANTS. Woodcuts. 6s.

EFFECTS OF CROSS AND SELF-FERTILIZATION IN THE VEGETABLE KINGDOM. Illustrations. 9s.

DIFFERENT FORMS OF FLOWERS ON PLANTS OF THE SAME SPECIES. Illustrations. 7s. 6d.

LIFE OF ERASMUS DARWIN. Portrait. 7s. 6d.

POWER OF MOVEMENT IN PLANTS.

FORMATION OF VEGETABLE MOULD THROUGH THE ACTION OF WORMS. Woodcuts. 6s.

FACTS AND ARGUMENTS FOR DARWIN. By FRITZ MÜLLER. 6s.

The above works are Published by JOHN MURRAY.

STRUCTURE AND DISTRIBUTION OF CORAL REEFS.
SMITH, ELDER, & CO.

GEOLOGICAL OBSERVATIONS ON VOLCANIC ISLANDS AND PARTS OF SOUTH AMERICA. SMITH, ELDER, & CO.

MONOGRAPH OF THE CIRRIPEDIA. Illustrations. 2 vols. 8vo. RAY SOCIETY.

*MONOGRAPH OF THE FOSSIL LEPADIDÆ, OR PEDUN-*CULATED CIRRIPEDS OF GREAT BRITAIN.
PALÆONTOGRAPHICAL SOCIETY.

*MONOGRAPH OF THE FOSSIL BALANIDÆ AND VER-*RUCIDÆ OF GREAT BRITAIN. PALÆONTOGRAPHICAL SOCIETY.

THE

DESCENT OF MAN,

AND

SELECTION IN RELATION TO SEX.

By CHARLES DARWIN, M.A., F.R.S.

SECOND EDITION, THIRD IMPRESSION.

IN TWO VOLUMES.—Vol. I.

WITH ILLUSTRATIONS.

LONDON:

JOHN MURRAY, ALBEMARLE STREET.

1898.

UNIFORM WITH THE PRESENT WORK.

THE ORIGIN OF SPECIES, BY MEANS OF
NATURAL SELECTION; or, The Preservation of
Favoured Races in the Struggle for Life. *A New
Library Edition in large type.* 2 vols. Crown 8vo. 12s.

LONDON: PRINTED BY WILLIAM CLOWES AND SONS, LIMITED, STAMFORD STREET
AND CHARING CROSS.

PREFACE TO THE SECOND EDITION.

DURING the successive reprints of the first edition of
this work, published in 1871, I was able to introduce
several important corrections; and now that more
time has elapsed, I have endeavoured to profit by the
fiery ordeal through which the book has passed, and
have taken advantage of all the criticisms which seem
to me sound. I am also greatly indebted to a large
number of correspondents for the communication of a
surprising number of new facts and remarks. These
have been so numerous, that I have been able to use
only the more important ones; and of these, as well as
of the more important corrections, I will append a list.
Some new illustrations have been introduced, and four
of the old drawings have been replaced by better ones,
done from life by Mr. T. W. Wood. I must especially
call attention to some observations which I owe to the
kindness of Prof. Huxley (given as a supplement at the
end of Part I.), on the nature of the differences between
the brains of man and the higher apes. I have been
particularly glad to give these observations, because
during the last few years several memoirs on the
subject have appeared on the Continent, and their
importance has been, in some cases, greatly exaggerated by popular writers.

I may take this opportunity of remarking that my
critics frequently assume that I attribute all changes
of corporeal structure and mental power exclusively to
the natural selection of such variations as are often
called spontaneous; whereas, even in the first edition
of the 'Origin of Species,' I distinctly stated that
great weight must be attributed to the inherited
effects of use and disuse, with respect both to the
body and mind. I also attributed some amount of
modification to the direct and prolonged action of
changed conditions of life. Some allowance, too,
must be made for occasional reversions of structure;
nor must we forget what I have called "correlated"
growth, meaning, thereby, that various parts of the
organisation are in some unknown manner so connected, that when one part varies, so do others; and
if variations in the one are accumulated by selection,
other parts will be modified. Again, it has been said
by several critics, that when I found that many details
of structure in man could not be explained through
natural selection, I invented sexual selection; I gave,
however, a tolerably clear sketch of this principle in
the first edition of the 'Origin of Species,' and I there
stated that it was applicable to man. This subject of
sexual selection has been treated at full length in the
present work, simply because an opportunity was
here first afforded me. I have been struck with the
likeness of many of the half-favourable criticisms on
sexual selection, with those which appeared at first on
natural selection; such as, that it would explain some
few details, but certainly was not applicable to the
extent to which I have employed it. My conviction of
the power of sexual selection remains unshaken; but it

is probable, or almost certain, that several of my conclusions will hereafter be found erroneous; this can hardly fail to be the case in the first treatment of a subject. When naturalists have become familiar with the idea of sexual selection, it will, as I believe, be much more largely accepted; and it has already been fully and favourably received by several capable judges.

DOWN, BECKENHAM, KENT,
    September, 1874.

First Edition Feb. 24, 1871.
Second Edition Sept., 1874.

TABLE

1st Ed., 1871. In 2 Vols. VOL. I.	2nd Ed., 1874. In 1 Vol.	2nd Ed., 1888. In 2 Vols. VOL. I.	
Page	Page	Page	
94	117, note	179, note	Suicide amongst savages.
97	120, note	184, note	The motives of conduct.
112	28	42	Selection, as applied to primeval man.
122	35, 36	53, 54	Resemblances between idiots and animals.
124, note	39, note	58, note	Division of the malar bone.
125, note	36–38, note	54–56, note	Supernumerary mammæ and digits.
128, 129	41, 42	62, 63	Further cases of muscles proper to animals appearing in man.
146	55, note	82, note	Broca: average capacity of skull diminished by the preservation of the inferior members of society.
149	57	86	Belt on advantages to man from his hairlessness.
150	58, 59	87, 88	Disappearance of the tail in man and certain monkeys.
169	134, 135	207, 208	Injurious forms of selection in civilised nations.
180	143	220	Indolence of man, when free from a struggle for existence.
193	151	234	Gorilla protecting himself from rain with his hands.
208, note	161, note	250, note	Hermaphroditism in fish.
209	163	252	Rudimentary mammæ in male mammals.
239	188–190	292	Changed conditions lessen fertility and cause ill-health amongst savages.
245	195, 196	303	Darkness of skin a protection against the sun.
250	199–206	309–318	Note by Professor Huxley on the development of the brain in man and apes.
256	209, 210	323	Special organs of male parasitic worms for holding the female.
275, 276	224, 225	346, 347	Greater variability of male than female; direct action of the environment in causing differences between the sexes.
290	235	363	Period of development of protuberances on birds' heads determines their transmission to one or both sexes.
301	243, 244	376, 377	Causes of excess of male births.

1st Ed., 1871. In 2 Vols. VOL. I.	2nd Ed., 1874. In 1 Vol.	2nd Ed., 1888. In 2 Vols. VOL. I.	
Page	Page	Page	
314	254	391	Proportion of the sexes in the bee family.
315	255, 256	393, 394	Excess of males perhaps sometimes determined by selection.
327	264	406, 407	Bright colours of lowly organised animals.
338	272	418, 419	Sexual selection amongst spiders.
339	273	420	Cause of smallness of male spiders.
345	277	426	Use of phosphorescence of the glow-worm.
349	280	431	The humming noises of flies.
350	281	432	Use of bright colours to Hemiptera (bugs).
351	282	433	Musical apparatus of Homoptera.
354	284, 285	437–439	Development of stridulating apparatus in Orthoptera.
359	288, note	443, note	
366	292, 293	449, 450	Hermann Müller on sexual differences of bees.
387	308	471	Sounds produced by moths.
397	315	482	Display of beauty by butterflies.
401	319	488, 489	Female butterflies, taking the more active part in courtship, brighter than their males.
412	324, 325	497, 498	Further cases of mimicry in butterflies and moths.
417	326	500, 501	Cause of bright and diversified colours of caterpillars.
VOL. II.		VOL. II.	
2	331	2	Brush-like scales of male Mallotus.
14	341	15–17	Further facts on courtship of fishes, and the spawning of Macropus.
23	347	25	Dufossé on the sounds made by fishes.
26	349	29	Belt on a frog protected by bright colouring.
30	352	34	Further facts on mental powers of snakes.
32	353	35	Sounds produced by snakes; the rattlesnake.
36	357	41	Combats of Chameleons.
72	383	79	Marshall on protuberances on birds' heads.
91	398	99–101	Further facts on display by the Argus pheasant.

1st Ed., 1871. In 2 Vols. VOL. II.	2nd Ed., 1874. In 1 Vol.	2nd Ed., 1888. In 2 Vols. VOL. II.	
Page	Page	Page	
108	411	120	Attachment between paired birds.
118	417	131	Female pigeon rejecting certain males.
120	419	133	Albino birds not finding partners, in a state of nature.
124	423	139	Direct action of climate on birds' colours.
147–50	438–441	161–166	Further facts on the ocelli in the Argus pheasant.
152	443	169	Display by humming-birds in courtship.
157	446	174	Cases with pigeons of colour transmitted to one sex alone.
232	495–496	249, 250	Taste for the beautiful permanent enough to allow of sexual selection with the lower animals.
247	505	265	Horns of sheep originally a masculine character.
248	506	266	Castration affecting horns of animals.
256	513, 514	277	Prong-horned variety of *Cervus virginianus*.
260	516	281	Relative sizes of male and female whales and seals.
266	521	288	Absence of tusks in male miocene pigs.
286	534	309	Dobson on sexual differences of bats.
299	542, 543	322, 323	Reeks on advantage from peculiar colouring.
316	556	341	Difference of complexion in men and women of an African tribe.
337	572	365	Speech subsequent to singing.
356	586	387	Schopenhauer on importance of courtship to mankind.
359 *et seq.*	588 *et seq.*	391 *et seq.*	Revision of discussion on communal marriages and promiscuity.
373	598, 599	406–409	Power of choice of woman in marriage, amongst savages.
380	603	414	Long-continued habit of plucking out hairs may produce an inherited effect.

CONTENTS.

PART I.

THE DESCENT OR ORIGIN OF MAN.

CHAPTER I.

THE EVIDENCE OF THE DESCENT OF MAN FROM SOME LOWER FORM.

PAGE

CHAPTER II.

ON THE MANNER OF DEVELOPMENT OF MAN FROM SOME LOWER FORM.

CHAPTER VI.

ON THE AFFINITIES AND GENEALOGY OF MAN.

CHAPTER VII.

ON THE RACES OF MAN.

PART II.

SEXUAL SELECTION.

CHAPTER VIII.

PRINCIPLES OF SEXUAL SELECTION.

CHAPTER IX.

SECONDARY SEXUAL CHARACTERS IN THE LOWER
CLASSES OF THE ANIMAL KINGDOM.

CHAPTER X.

SECONDARY SEXUAL CHARACTERS OF INSECTS.

CHAPTER XI.

INSECTS, *continued*.—ORDER LEPIDOPTERA.

(BUTTERFLIES AND MOTHS.)

THE DESCENT OF MAN;

AND

SELECTION IN RELATION TO SEX.

———•———

INTRODUCTION.

The nature of the following work will be best understood by a brief account of how it came to be written.
During many years I collected notes on the origin or
descent of man, without any intention of publishing
on the subject, but rather with the determination not
to publish, as I thought that I should thus only add to
the prejudices against my views. It seemed to me
sufficient to indicate, in the first edition of my 'Origin
of Species,' that by this work "light would be thrown
"on the origin of man and his history;" and this
implies that man must be included with other organic
beings in any general conclusion respecting his manner
of appearance on this earth. Now the case wears a
wholly different aspect. When a naturalist like Carl
Vogt ventures to say in his address as President of the
National Institution of Geneva (1869), "personne, en
"Europe au moins, n'ose plus soutenir la création

" indépendante et de toutes pièces, des espèces," it is manifest that at least a large number of naturalists must admit that species are the modified descendants of other species; and this especially holds good with the younger and rising naturalists. The greater number accept the agency of natural selection; though some urge, whether with justice the future must decide, that I have greatly overrated its importance. Of the older and honoured chiefs in natural science, many unfortunately are still opposed to evolution in every form.

In consequence of the views now adopted by most naturalists, and which will ultimately, as in every other case, be followed by others who are not scientific, I have been led to put together my notes, so as to see how far the general conclusions arrived at in my former works were applicable to man. This seemed all the more desirable, as I had never deliberately applied these views to a species taken singly. When we confine our attention to any one form, we are deprived of the weighty arguments derived from the nature of the affinities which connect together whole groups of organisms—their geographical distribution in past and present times, and their geological succession. The homological structure, embryological development, and rudimentary organs of a species remain to be considered, whether it be man or any other animal, to which our attention may be directed; but these great classes of facts afford, as it appears to me, ample and conclusive evidence in favour of the principle of gradual evolution. The strong support derived from the other arguments should, however, always be kept before the mind.

The sole object of this work is to consider, firstly, whether man, like every other species, is descended from some pre-existing form; secondly, the manner of his development; and thirdly, the value of the differences between the so-called races of man. As I shall confine myself to these points, it will not be necessary to describe in detail the differences between the several races—an enormous subject which has been fully discussed in many valuable works. The high antiquity of man has recently been demonstrated by the labours of a host of eminent men, beginning with M. Boucher de Perthes; and this is the indispensable basis for understanding his origin. I shall, therefore, take this conclusion for granted, and may refer my readers to the admirable treatises of Sir Charles Lyell, Sir John Lubbock, and others. Nor shall I have occasion to do more than to allude to the amount of difference between man and the anthropomorphous apes; for Prof. Huxley, in the opinion of most competent judges, has conclusively shewn that in every visible character man differs less from the higher apes, than these do from the lower members of the same order of Primates.

This work contains hardly any original facts in regard to man; but as the conclusions at which I arrived, after drawing up a rough draft, appeared to me interesting, I thought that they might interest others. It has often and confidently been asserted, that man's origin can never be known: but ignorance more frequently begets confidence than does knowledge: it is those who know little, and not those who know much, who so positively assert that this or that problem will never be solved by science. The conclusion that man is the co-descendant with other species of some ancient, lower, and extinct form, is not in any degree new. Lamarck long ago came to this conclusion, which has lately been maintained by several eminent naturalists and philosophers; for instance, by Wallace, Huxley, Lyell, Vogt, Lubbock, Büchner, Rolle, &c.,[1] and especially by Häckel. This last naturalist, besides his great work, 'Generelle Morphologie' (1866), has recently (1868, with a second edit. in 1870), published his 'Natürliche Schöpfungsgeschichte,' in which he fully discusses the genealogy of man. If this work had appeared before my essay had been written, I should probably never have completed it. Almost all the conclusions at which I have arrived I find confirmed by this naturalist, whose knowledge on many points is much fuller than mine. Wherever I have added any fact or view from Prof. Häckel's writings, I give his authority in the text; other statements I leave as they originally stood in my manuscript, occasionally giving in the foot-notes references to his works, as a confirmation of the more doubtful or interesting points.

[1] As the works of the first-named authors are so well known, I need not give the titles; but as those of the latter are less well known in England, I will give them:—'Sechs Vorlesungen über die Darwin'sche Theorie:' zweite Auflage, 1868, von Dr. L. Büchner; translated into French under the title 'Conférences sur la Théorie Darwinienne,' 1869. 'Der Mensch, im Lichte der Darwin'sche Lehre,' 1865, von Dr. F. Rolle. I will not attempt to give references to all the authors who have taken the same side of the question. Thus G. Canestrini has published ('Annuario della Soc. d. Nat.,' Modena, 1867, p. 81) a very curious paper on rudimentary characters, as bearing on the origin of man. Another work has (1869) been published by Dr. Francesco Barrago, bearing in Italian the title of "Man, made in the "image of God, was also made "in the image of the ape."

During many years it has seemed to me highly probable that sexual selection has played an important part in differentiating the races of man; but in my 'Origin of Species' (first edition, p. 199) I contented myself by merely alluding to this belief. When I came to apply this view to man, I found it indispensable to treat the whole subject in full detail.[2] Consequently the second part of the present work, treating of sexual selection, has extended to an inordinate length, compared with the first part; but this could not be avoided.

I had intended adding to the present volumes an essay on the expression of the various emotions by man and the lower animals. My attention was called to this subject many years ago by Sir Charles Bell's admirable work. This illustrious anatomist maintains that man is endowed with certain muscles solely for the sake of expressing his emotions. As this view is obviously opposed to the belief that man is descended from some other and lower form, it was necessary for me to consider it. I likewise wished to ascertain how far the emotions are expressed in the same manner by the different races of man. But owing to the length of the present work, I have thought it better to reserve my essay for separate publication.

[2] Prof. Häckel was the only author who, at the time when this work first appeared, had discussed the subject of sexual selection, and had seen its full importance, since the publication of the 'Origin'; and this he did in a very able manner in his various works.

PART I.

THE DESCENT OR ORIGIN OF MAN.

———————

CHAPTER I.

THE EVIDENCE OF THE DESCENT OF MAN FROM SOME LOWER FORM.

Nature of the evidence bearing on the origin of man—Homologous structures in man and the lower animals—Miscellaneous points of correspondence — Development — Rudimentary structures, muscles, sense-organs, hair, bones, reproductive organs, &c.— The bearing of these three great classes of facts on the origin of man.

HE who wishes to decide whether man is the modified descendant of some pre-existing form, would probably first enquire whether man varies, however slightly, in bodily structure and in mental faculties; and if so, whether the variations are transmitted to his offspring in accordance with the laws which prevail with the lower animals. Again, are the variations the result, as far as our ignorance permits us to judge, of the same general causes, and are they governed by the same general laws, as in the case of other organisms; for instance, by correlation, the inherited effects of use and disuse, &c.? Is man subject to similar malconformations, the result of arrested development, of reduplication of parts, &c., and does he display in any of his anomalies reversion to some former and ancient type of structure? It might also naturally be enquired whether man, like so many other animals, has given rise to varieties and sub-races, differing but slightly from each other, or to races differing so much that they must be classed as doubtful species? How are such races distributed over the world; and how, when crossed, do they react on each other in the first and succeeding generations? And so with many other points.

The enquirer would next come to the important point, whether man tends to increase at so rapid a rate, as to lead to occasional severe struggles for existence; and consequently to beneficial variations, whether in body or mind, being preserved, and injurious ones eliminated. Do the races or species of men, whichever term may be applied, encroach on and replace one another, so that some finally become extinct? We shall see that all these questions, as indeed is obvious in respect to most of them, must be answered in the affirmative, in the same manner as with the lower animals. But the several considerations just referred to may be conveniently deferred for a time: and we will first see how far the bodily structure of man shows traces, more or less plain, of his descent from some lower form. In succeeding chapters the mental powers of man, in comparison with those of the lower animals, will be considered.

The Bodily Structure of Man.—It is notorious that man is constructed on the same general type or model as other mammals. All the bones in his skeleton can be compared with corresponding bones in a monkey, bat, or seal. So it is with his muscles, nerves, blood-vessels and internal viscera. The brain, the most important of all the organs, follows the same law, as shewn by Huxley and other anatomists. Bischoff,[1] who is a hostile witness, admits that every chief fissure and fold in the brain of man has its analogy in that of the orang; but he adds that at no period of development do their brains perfectly agree; nor could perfect agreement be expected, for otherwise their mental powers would have been the same. Vulpian[2] remarks: " Les différences réelles qui " existent entre l'encéphale de l'homme et celui des " singes supérieurs, sont bien minimes. Il ne faut pas " se faire d'illusions à cet égard. L'homme est bien " plus près des singes anthropomorphes par les " caractères anatomiques de son cerveau que ceux-ci ne " le sont non seulement des autres mammifères, mais " même de certains quadrumanes, des guenons et des " macaques." But it would be superfluous here to give further details on the correspondence between man and the higher mammals in the structure of the brain and all other parts of the body.

It may, however, be worth while to specify a few points, not directly or obviously connected with structure, by which this correspondence or relation-ship is well shewn.

Man is liable to receive from the lower animals, and

[1] ' Grosshirnwindungen des Menschen,' 1868, s. 96. The conclusions of this author, as well as those of Gratiolet and Aeby, concerning the brain, will be discussed by Prof. Huxley in the Appendix alluded to in the Preface to this edition.

[2] ' Leç. sur la Phys.' 1866, p. 890, as quoted by M. Dally, ' L'Ordre des Primates et le Transformisme,' 1868, p. 29.

to communicate to them, certain diseases, as hydro-
phobia, variola, the glanders, syphilis, cholera, herpes,
&c.; [3] and this fact proves the close similarity [4] of
their tissues and blood, both in minute structure and
composition, far more plainly than does their comparison under the best microscope, or by the aid of
the best chemical analysis. Monkeys are liable to
many of the same non-contagious diseases as we are;
thus Rengger,[5] who carefully observed for a long time
the *Cebus Azaræ* in its native land, found it liable to
catarrh, with the usual symptoms, and which, when
often recurrent, led to consumption. These monkeys
suffered also from apoplexy, inflammation of the
bowels, and cataract in the eye. The younger ones
when shedding their milk-teeth often died from fever.
Medicines produced the same effect on them as on us.
Many kinds of monkeys have a strong taste for tea,
coffee, and spirituous liquors : they will also, as I have
myself seen, smoke tobacco with pleasure.[6] Brehm
asserts that the natives of north-eastern Africa catch

[3] Dr. W. Lauder Lindsay has
treated this subject at some
length in the ' Journal of Mental
Science,' July 1871 ; and 'n the
' Edinburgh Veterinary Review,'
July 1858.

[4] A Reviewer has criticised
(' British Quarterly Review,'
Oct. 1st, 1871, p. 472) what I
have here said with much se-
verity and contempt; but as I
do not use the term identity, I
cannot see that I am greatly in
error. There appears to me a
strong analogy between the
same infection or contagion producing the same result, or one

closely similar, in two distinct
animals, and the testing of two
distinct fluids by the same
chemical reagent.

[5] 'Naturgeschichte der Säugethiere von Paraguay,' 1830, s.
50.

[6] The same tastes are common
to some animals much lower in
the scale. Mr. A. Nicols informs me that he kept in
Queensland, in Australia, three
individuals of the *Phaseolarctus
cinereus*; and that, without
having been taught in any way,
they acquired a strong taste for
rum, and for smoking tobacco.

the wild baboons by exposing vessels with strong beer, by which they are made drunk. He has seen some of these animals, which he kept in confinement, in this state; and he gives a laughable account of their behaviour and strange grimaces. On the following morning they were very cross and dismal; they held their aching heads with both hands, and wore a most pitiable expression: when beer or wine was offered them, they turned away with disgust, but relished the juice of lemons.[7] An American monkey, an Ateles, after getting drunk on brandy, would never touch it again, and thus was wiser than many men. These trifling facts prove how similar the nerves of taste must be in monkeys and man, and how similarly their whole nervous system is affected.

Man is infested with internal parasites, sometimes causing fatal effects; and is plagued by external parasites, all of which belong to the same genera or families as those infesting other mammals, and in the case of scabies to the same species.[8] Man is subject, like other mammals, birds, and even insects,[9] to that mysterious law, which causes certain normal processes, such as gestation, as well as the maturation and duration of various diseases, to follow lunar periods. His wounds are repaired by the same process of healing; and the stumps left after the amputation of

[7] Brehm, 'Thierleben,' B. i. 1864, s. 75, 86. On the Ateles, s. 105. For other analogous statements, see s. 25, 107.

[8] Dr. W. Lauder Lindsay, 'Edinburgh Vet. Review,' July 1858, p. 13.

[9] With respect to insects see Dr. Laycock, "On a General Law of Vital Periodicity," 'British Association,' 1842. Dr. Macculloch, 'Silliman's North American Journal of Science,' vol. xvii. p. 305, has seen a dog suffering from tertian ague. Hereafter I shall return to this subject.

his limbs, especially during an early embryonic period, occasionally possess some power of regeneration, as in the lowest animals.[10]

The whole process of that most important function, the reproduction cf the species, is strikingly the same in all mammals, from the first act of courtship by the male,[11] to the birth and nurturing of the young. Monkeys are born in almost as helpless a condition as our own infants; and in certain genera the young differ fully as much in appearance from the adults, as do our children from their full-grown parents.[12] It has been urged by some writers, as an important distinction, that with man the young arrive at maturity at a much later age than with any other animal : but if we look to the races of mankind which inhabit tropical countries the difference is not great, for the orang is believed not to be adult till the age of from ten to fifteen years.[13] Man differs from woman

[10] I have given the evidence on this head in my ' Variation of Animals and Plants under Domestication,' vol. ii. p. 15, and more could be added.

[11] Mares e diversis generibus Quadrumanorum sine dubio dignoscunt feminas humanas a maribus. Primum, credo, odoratu, postea aspectu. Mr. Youatt, qui diu in Hortis Zoologicis (Bestiariis) medicus animalium erat, vir in rebus observandis cautus et sagax, hoc mihi certissime probavit, et curatores ejusdem loci et alii e ministris confirmaverunt. Sir Andrew Smith et Brehm notabant idem in Cynocephalo. Illustrissimus Cuvier etiam narrat multa de hâc re, quâ ut opinor, nihil turpius potest indicari inter omnia hominibus et Quadrumanis communia. Narrat enim Cynocephalum quendam in furorem incidere aspectu feminarum aliquarum, sed nequaquam accendi tanto furore ab omnibus. Semper eligebat juniores, et dignoscebat in turbâ, et advocabat voce gestûque.

[12] This remark is made with respect to Cynocephalus and the anthropomorphous apes by Geoffroy Saint-Hilaire and F. Cuvier, ' Hist. Nat. des Mammifères,' tom. i. 1824.

[13] Huxley, ' Man's Place in Nature,' 1863, p. 34.

in size, bodily strength, hairiness, &c , as well as in mind, in the same manner as do the two sexes of many mammals. So that the correspondence in general structure, in the minute structure of the tissues, in chemical composition and in constitution, between man and the higher animals, especially the anthropomorphous apes, is extremely close.

Embryonic Development.—Man is developed from an ovule, about the 125th of an inch in diameter, which differs in no respect from the ovules of other animals. The embryo itself at a very early period can hardly be distinguished from that of other members of the vertebrate kingdom. At this period the arteries run in arch-like branches, as if to carry the blood to branchiæ which are not present in the higher vertebrata, though the slits on the sides of the neck still remain (*f*, *g*, fig. 1), marking their former position. At a somewhat later period, when the extremities are developed, " the feet of lizards and mammals," as the illustrious Von Baer remarks, " the wings and feet of " birds, no less than the hands and feet of man, all " arise from the same fundamental form." It is, says Prof. Huxley,[14] " quite in the later stages of develop- " ment that the young human being presents marked " differences from the young ape, while the latter " departs as much from the dog in its developments, as " the man does. Startling as this last assertion may " appear to be, it is demonstrably true."

As some of my readers may never have seen a drawing of an embryo, I have given one of man and another of a dog, at about the same early stage of develop-

[14] ' Man's Place in Nature,' 1863, p. 67.

ment, carefully copied from two works of undoubted accuracy.[15]

After the foregoing statements made by such high authorities, it would be superfluous on my part to give a number of borrowed details, shewing that the embryo of man closely resembles that of other mammals. It may, however, be added, that the human embryo likewise resembles certain low forms when adult in various points of structure. For instance, the heart at first exists as a simple pulsating vessel; the excreta are voided through a cloacal passage; and the os coccyx projects like a true tail, "extending considerably "beyond the rudimentary legs."[16] In the embryos of all air-breathing vertebrates, certain glands, called the corpora Wolffiana, correspond with, and act like the kidneys of mature fishes.[17] Even at a later embryonic period, some striking resemblances between man and the lower animals may be observed. Bischoff says that the convolutions of the brain in a human fœtus at the end of the seventh month reach about the same stage of development as in a baboon when adult."[18] The great toe, as Professor Owen remarks,[19] "which

[15] The human embryo (upper fig.) is from Ecker, 'Icones Phys.,' 1851–1859, tab. xxx. fig. 2. This embryo was ten lines in length, so that the drawing is much magnified. The embryo of the dog is from Bischoff, 'Entwicklungsge-schichte des Hunde-Eies,' 1845, tab. xi. fig. 42 B. This drawing is five times magnified, the embryo being twenty-five days old. The internal viscera have been omitted, and the uterine appendages in both drawings removed. I was directed to these figures by Prof. Huxley, from whose work, 'Man's Place in Nature,' the idea of giving them was taken. Häckel has also given analogous drawings in his 'Schöpfungsgeschichte.'

[16] Prof. Wyman in 'Proc. of American Acad. of Sciences,' vol. iv. 1860, p. 17.

[17] Owen, 'Anatomy of Verte-brates,' vol. i. p. 533.

[18] 'Die Grosshirnwindungen des Menschen,' 1868, s. 95.

[19] 'Anatomy of Vertebrates,' vol. ii. p. 553.

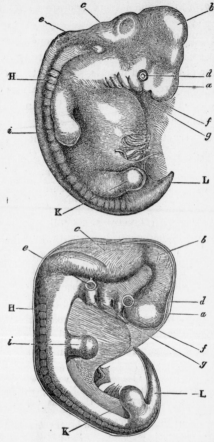

Fig. 1. Upper figure human embryo, from Ecker. Lower figure that of a dog, from Bischoff.

a. Fore-brain, cerebral hemispheres, &c.
b. Mid-brain, corpora quadrigemina.
c. Hind-brain, cerebellum, medulla oblongata.
d. Eye.
e. Ear.

f. First visceral arch.
g. Second visceral arch.
H. Vertebral columns and muscles in process of development.
i. Anterior }
K. Posterior } extremities.
L. Tail or os coccyx.

"forms the fulcrum when standing or walking, is "perhaps the most characteristic peculiarity in the "human structure;" but in an embryo, about an inch in length, Prof. Wyman[20] found "that the great toe "was shorter than the others; and, instead of being "parallel to them, projected at an angle from the side "of the foot, thus corresponding with the permanent "condition of this part in the quadrumana." I will conclude with a quotation from Huxley,[21] who after asking, does man originate in a different way from a dog, bird, frog or fish? says, "the reply is not doubt- "ful for a moment; without question, the mode of "origin, and the early stages of the development of man, "are identical with those of the animals immediately "below him in the scale: without a doubt in these "respects, he is far nearer to apes than the apes are to "the dog."

Rudiments.—This subject, though not intrinsically more important than the two last, will for several reasons be treated here more fully.[22] Not one of the higher animals can be named which does not bear some part in a rudimentary condition; and man forms no exception to the rule. Rudimentary organs must be distinguished from those that are nascent; though in some cases the distinction is not easy. The former are either absolutely useless, such as the mammæ of male

---

[20] 'Proc. Soc. Nat. Hist.' Boston, 1863, vol. ix. p. 185.

[21] 'Man's Place in Nature,' p. 65.

[22] I had written a rough copy of this chapter before reading a valuable paper, "Caratteri rudimentali in ordine all' origine dell' uomo" (' Annuario della Soc. d. Nat.,' Modena, 1867, p. 81), by G. Canestrini, to which paper I am considerably indebted. Häckel has given admirable discussions on this whole subject, under the title of Dysteleology, in his 'Generelle Morphologie' and 'Schöpfungsgeschichte.'

quadrupeds, or the incisor teeth of ruminants which never cut through the gums; or they are of such slight service to their present possessors, that we can hardly suppose that they were developed under the conditions which now exist. Organs in this latter state are not strictly rudimentary, but they are tending in this direction. Nascent organs, on the other hand, though not fully developed, are of high service to their possessors, and are capable of further development. Rudimentary organs are eminently variable; and this is partly intelligible, as they are useless, or nearly useless, and consequently are no longer subjected to natural selection. They often become wholly suppressed. When this occurs, they are nevertheless liable to occasional reappearance through reversion— a circumstance well worthy of attention.

The chief agents in causing organs to become rudimentary seem to have been disuse at that period of life when the organ is chiefly used (and this is generally during maturity), and also inheritance at a corresponding period of life. The term "disuse" does not relate merely to the lessened action of muscles, but includes a diminished flow of blood to a part or organ, from being subjected to fewer alternations of pressure, or from becoming in any way less habitually active. Rudiments, however, may occur in one sex of those parts which are normally present in the other sex; and such rudiments, as we shall hereafter see, have often originated in a way distinct from those here referred to. In some cases, organs have been reduced by means of natural selection, from having become injurious to the species under changed habits of life. The process of reduction is probably often aided through the two principles of compensation and economy of growth; but the later stages of reduction, after disuse has done all that can fairly be attributed to it, and when the saving to be effected by the economy of growth would be very small,[23] are difficult to understand. The final and complete suppression of a part, already useless and much reduced in size, in which case neither compensation nor economy can come into play, is perhaps intelligible by the aid of the hypothesis of pangenesis. But as the whole subject of rudimentary organs has been discussed and illustrated in my former works,[24] I need here say no more on this head.

Rudiments of various muscles have been observed in many parts of the human body;[25] and not a few muscles, which are regularly present in some of the lower animals can occasionally be detected in man in a greatly reduced condition. Every one must have noticed the power which many animals, especially horses, possess of moving or twitching their skin; and this is effected by the *panniculus carnosus*. Remnants of this muscle in an efficient state are found in various parts of our bodies; for instance, the muscle on the forehead, by which the eyebrows are raised. The *platysma myoides*, which is well developed on the neck, belongs

[23] Some good criticisms on this subject have been given by Messrs. Murie and Mivart, in 'Transact. Zoolog. Soc.' 1869, vol. vii. p. 92.

[24] 'Variation of Animals and Plants under Domestication,' vol. ii. pp. 317 and 397. See also 'Origin of Species,' 5th edit. p. 535.

[25] For instance M. Richard ('Annales des Sciences Nat. 3rd series, Zoolog. 1852, tom. xviii. p. 13) describes and figures rudiments of what he calls the "muscle pédieux de la main," which he says is sometimes "infiniment petit." Another muscle, called "le tibial postérieur," is generally quite absent in the hand, but appears from time to time in a more or less rudimentary condition.

to this system. Prof. Turner, of Edinburgh, has occasionally detected, as he informs me, muscular fasciculi in five different situations, namely in the axillæ, near the scapulæ, &c., all of which must be referred to the system of the *panniculus*. He has also shewn[26] that the *musculus sternalis* or *sternalis brutorum*, which is not an extension of the *rectus abdominalis*, but is closely allied to the *panniculus*, occurred in the proportion of about three per cent. in upwards of 600 bodies: he adds, that this muscle affords " an excellent illustration of the statement " that occasional and rudimentary structures are " especially liable to variation in arrangement."

Some few persons have the power of contracting the superficial muscles on their scalps ; and these muscles are in a variable and partially rudimentary condition. M. A. de Candolle has communicated to me a curious instance of the long-continued persistence or inheritance of this power, as well as of its unusual development. He knows a family, in which one member, the present head of the family, could, when a youth, pitch several heavy books from his head by the movement of the scalp alone ; and he won wagers by performing this feat. His father, uncle, grandfather, and his three children possess the same power to the same unusual degree. This family became divided eight generations ago into two branches ; so that the head of the above-mentioned branch is cousin in the seventh degree to the head of the other branch. This distant cousin resides in another part of France ; and on being asked whether he possessed the same faculty, immediately exhibited his power. This case offers a good illustra-

[26] Prof. W. Turner, 'Proc. Royal Soc. Edinburgh,' 1866–67, p. 65.

tion how persistent may be the transmission of an absolutely useless faculty, probably derived from our remote semi-human progenitors; since many monkeys have, and frequently use the power, of largely moving their scalps up and down.[27]

The extrinsic muscles which serve to move the external ear, and the intrinsic muscles which move the different parts, are in a rudimentary condition in man, and they all belong to the system of the *panniculus;* they are also variable in development, or at least in function. I have seen one man who could draw the whole ear forwards; other men can draw it upwards; another who could draw it backwards;[28] and from what one of these persons told me, it is probable that most of us, by often touching our ears, and thus directing our attention towards them, could recover some power of movement by repeated trials. The power of erecting and directing the shell of the ears to the various points of the compass, is no doubt of the highest service to many animals, as they thus perceive the direction of danger; but I have never heard, on sufficient evidence, of a man who possessed this power, the one which might be of use to him. The whole external shell may be considered a rudiment, together with the various folds and prominences (helix and anti-helix, tragus and anti-tragus, &c.) which in the lower animals strengthen and support the ear when erect, without adding much to its weight. Some authors, however, suppose that the cartilage of the shell serves to transmit vibrations to the acoustic

[27] See my 'Expression of the Emotions in Man and Animals,' 1872, p. 144.
[28] Canestrini quotes Hyrtl. ('Annuario della Soc. dei Naturalisti, Modena, 1867, p. 97) to the same effect.

nerve; but Mr. Toynbee,[29] after collecting all the known evidence on this head, concludes that the external shell is of no distinct use. The ears of the chimpanzee and orang are curiously like those of man, and the proper muscles are likewise but very slightly developed.[30] I am also assured by the keepers in the Zoological Gardens that these animals never move or erect their ears; so that they are in an equally rudimentary condition with those of man, as far as function is concerned. Why these animals, as well as the progenitors of man, should have lost the power of erecting their ears, we cannot say. It may be, though I am not satisfied with this view, that owing to their arboreal habits and great strength they were but little exposed to danger, and so during a lengthened period moved their ears but little, and thus gradually lost the power of moving them. This would be a parallel case with that of those large and heavy birds, which, from inhabiting oceanic islands, have not been exposed to the attacks of beasts of prey, and have consequently lost the power of using their wings for flight. The inability to move the ears in man and several apes is, however, partly compensated by the freedom with which they can move the head in a horizontal plane, so as to catch sounds from all directions. It has been asserted that the ear of man alone possesses a lobule; but "a rudiment of it is found in the gorilla;"[31] and, as

[29] 'The Diseases of the Ear,' by J. Toynbee, F.R.S., 1860, p. 12. A distinguished physiologist, Prof. Preyer, informs me that he had lately been experimenting on the function of the shell of the ear, and has come to nearly the same conclusion as that given here.

[30] Prof. A. Macalister, 'Annals and Mag. of Nat. History,' vol. vii., 1871, p. 342.

[31] Mr. St. George Mivart, 'Elementary Anatomy,' 1873, p. 396.

I hear from Prof. Preyer, it is not rarely absent in the negro.

The celebrated sculptor, Mr. Woolner, informs me of one little peculiarity in the external ear, which he has often observed both in men and women, and of which he perceived the full significance. His attention was first called to the subject whilst at work on his figure of Puck, to which he had given pointed ears. He was thus led to examine the ears of various monkeys, and subsequently more carefully those of man. The peculiarity consists in a little blunt point, projecting from the inwardly folded margin, or helix. When present, it is developed at birth, and, according to Prof. Ludwig Meyer, more frequently in man than in woman. Mr. Woolner made an exact model of one such case, and sent me the accompanying drawing. (Fig. 2.) These points not only project

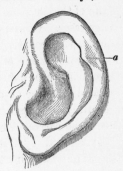

Fig. 2. Human Ear, modelled and drawn by Mr. Woolner.
a. The projecting point.

inwards towards the centre of the ear, but often a little outwards from its plane, so as to be visible when the head is viewed from directly in front or behind. They are variable in size, and somewhat in position, standing either a little higher or lower; and they sometimes occur on one ear and not on the other. They are not confined to mankind, for I observed a case in one of the spider-monkeys (*Ateles beelzebuth*) in our Zoological Gardens; and Mr. E. Ray Lankester informs me of another case in a chimpanzee in the gardens at Hamburg. The helix obviously consists of the extreme margin of the ear folded inwards; and this folding appears to be in some manner connected with the whole external ear being permanently pressed backwards. In many monkeys, which do not stand high in the order, as baboons and some species of macacus,[32] the upper portion of the ear is slightly pointed, and the margin is not at all folded inwards ; but if the margin were to be thus folded, a slight point would necessarily project inwards towards the centre, and probably a little outwards from the plane of the ear ; and this I believe to be their origin in many cases. On the other hand, Prof. L. Meyer, in an able paper recently published,[33] maintains that the whole case is one of mere variability; and that the projections are not real ones, but are due to the internal cartilage on each side of the points not having been fully developed. I am quite ready to admit that this is the correct explanation in many instances, as in those figured by Prof. Meyer, in which there are several minute points, or the whole margin is sinuous. I have myself seen, through the kindness of Dr. L. Down, the ear of a microcephalous idiot, on which there is a projection on the outside of the helix, and not on the inward folded edge, so that this point can have no relation to a former apex of the ear. Nevertheless in some cases, my original view, that the points are vestiges of the tips of formerly erect and pointed ears, still seems to me probable. I think so from the frequency of their occurrence, and from the general correspondence in position with that of the tip of a

[32] See also some remarks, and the drawings of the ears of the Lemuroidea, in Messrs. Murie and Mivart's excellent paper in 'Transact. Zoolog. Soc.' vol. vii.

1869, pp. 6 and 90.
[33] Ueber das Darwin'sche Spitzohr, Archiv für Path. Anat. und Phys. 1871, p. 485.

pointed ear. In one case, of which a photograph has been sent me, the projection is so large, that supposing, in accordance with Prof. Meyer's view, the ear to be made perfect by the equal development of the cartilage throughout the whole extent of the margin, it would have covered fully one-third of the whole ear. Two cases have been communicated to me, one in North America, and the other in England, in which the upper margin is not at all folded inwards, but is pointed, so that it closely resembles the pointed ear of an ordinary quadruped in outline. In one of these cases, which was that of a young child, the father compared the ear with the drawing which I have given[34] of the ear of a monkey, the *Cynopithecus niger*, and says that their outlines are closely similar. If, in these two cases, the margin had been folded inwards in the normal manner, an inward projection must have been formed. I may add that in two other cases the outline still remains somewhat pointed, although the margin of the upper part of the ear is normally folded inwards—in one of them, however, very narrowly. The following woodcut (No. 3) is an accurate copy of a photograph of the fœtus of an orang (kindly sent me by Dr. Nitsche), in which it may be seen how different the pointed outline of the ear is at this period from its adult condition, when it bears a close general resemblance to that of man. It is evident that the folding over of the tip of such an ear, unless it changed greatly during its further development, would give rise to a point projecting inwards. On the whole, it still seems to me probable that the points in question are in some cases, both in man and apes, vestiges of a former condition.

[34] 'The Expression of the Emotions,' p. 136.

The nictitating membrane, or third eyelid, with its accessory muscles and other structures, is especially well developed in birds, and is of much functional importance to them, as it can be rapidly drawn across the whole eye-ball. It is found in some reptiles and amphibians, and in certain fishes, as in sharks. It is fairly well developed in the two lower divisions of the

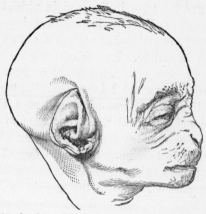

Fig. 3. Fœtus of an Orang. Exact copy of a photograph, shewing the form of the ear at this early age.

mammalian series, namely, in the monotremata and marsupials, and in some few of the higher mammals, as in the walrus. But in man, the quadrumana, and most other mammals, it exists, as is admitted by all anatomists, as a mere rudiment, called the semilunar fold.[35]

The sense of smell is of the highest importance to

[35] Müller's 'Elements of Physiology,' Eng. translat., 1842, vol. ii. p. 1117. Owen, 'Anatomy of Vertebrates,' vol. iii. p. 260; ibid. on the Walrus, 'Proc. Zoolog. Soc.' November 8th, 1854. See also R. Knox, 'Great Artists and Anatomists,' p. 106. This rudiment apparently is somewhat larger in Negroes and Australians than in Europeans, see Carl Vogt, 'Lectures on Man,' Eng. translat. p. 129.

the greater number of mammals—to some, as the ruminants, in warning them of danger; to others, as the carnivora, in finding their prey; to others, again, as the wild boar, for both purposes combined. But the sense of smell is of extremely slight service, if any, even to the dark coloured races of men, in whom it is much more highly developed than in the white and civilised races.[36] Nevertheless it does not warn them of danger, nor guide them to their food; nor does it prevent the Esquimaux from sleeping in the most fetid atmosphere, nor many savages from eating half-putrid meat. In Europeans the power differs greatly in different individuals, as I am assured by an eminent naturalist who possesses this sense highly developed, and who has attended to the subject. Those who believe in the principle of gradual evolution, will not readily admit that the sense of smell in its present state was originally acquired by man, as he now exists. He inherits the power in an enfeebled and so far rudimentary condition, from some early progenitor, to whom it was highly serviceable, and by whom it was continually used. In those animals which have this sense highly developed, such as dogs and horses, the recollection of persons and of places is strongly

[36] The account given by Humboldt of the power of smell possessed by the natives of South America is well known, and has been confirmed by others. M. Houzeau ('Études sur les Facultés Mentales,' &c., tom. i. 1872, p. 91) asserts that he repeatedly made experiments, and proved that Negroes and Indians could recognise persons in the dark by their odour. Dr. W. Ogle has made some curious observations on the connection between the power of smell and the colouring matter of the mucous membrane of the olfactory region, as well as of the skin of the body. I have, therefore, spoken in the text of the dark-coloured races having a finer sense of smell than the white races. See his paper, 'Medico - Chirurgical Transactions,' London, vol. liii., 1870, p. 276.

associated with their odour; and we can thus perhaps understand how it is, as Dr. Maudsley has truly remarked,[37] that the sense of smell in man "is "singularly effective in recalling vividly the ideas and "images of forgotten scenes and places."

Man differs conspicuously from all the other Primates in being almost naked. But a few short straggling hairs are found over the greater part of the body in the man, and fine down on that of the woman. The different races differ much in hairiness; and in the individuals of the same race the hairs are highly variable, not only in abundance, but likewise in position: thus in some Europeans the shoulders are quite naked, whilst in others they bear thick tufts of hair.[38] There can be little doubt that the hairs thus scattered over the body are the rudiments of the uniform hairy coat of the lower animals. This view is rendered all the more probable, as it is known that fine, short, and pale-coloured hairs on the limbs and other parts of the body, occasionally become developed into "thickset, long, and rather coarse dark hairs," when abnormally nourished near old-standing inflamed surfaces.[39]

I am informed by Sir James Paget that often several members of a family have a few hairs in their eyebrows much longer than the others; so that even this slight peculiarity seems to be inherited. These hairs, too, seem to have their representatives; for in the chimpanzee, and in certain species of Macacus, there are

[37] 'The Physiology and Pathology of Mind,' 2nd edit. 1868, p. 134.

[38] Eschricht, Ueber die Richtung der Haare am menschlichen Körper, ' Müller's Archiv für Anat. und Phys.' 1837, s. 47. I shall often have to refer to this very curious paper.

[39] Paget, ' Lectures on Surgical Pathology,' 1853, vol. i. p. 71.

scattered hairs of considerable length rising from the naked skin above the eyes, and corresponding to our eyebrows; similar long hairs project from the hairy covering of the superciliary ridges in some baboons.

The fine wool-like hair, or so-called lanugo, with which the human fœtus during the sixth month is thickly covered, offers a more curious case. It is first developed, during the fifth month, on the eyebrows and face, and especially round the mouth, where it is much longer than that on the head. A moustache of this kind was observed by Eschricht[40] on a female fœtus; but this is not so surprising a circumstance as it may at first appear, for the two sexes generally resemble each other in all external characters during an early period of growth. The direction and arrangement of the hairs on all parts of the fœtal body are the same as in the adult, but are subject to much variability. The whole surface, including even the forehead and ears, is thus thickly clothed; but it is a significant fact that the palms of the hands and the soles of the feet are quite naked, like the inferior surfaces of all four extremities in most of the lower animals. As this can hardly be an accidental coincidence, the woolly covering of the fœtus probably represents the first permanent coat of hair in those mammals which are born hairy. Three or four cases have been recorded of persons born with their whole bodies and faces thickly covered with fine long hairs; and this strange condition is strongly inherited, and is correlated with an abnormal condition of the teeth.[41]

[40] Eschricht, ibid. s. 40, 47.
[41] See my ' Variation of Animals and Plants under Domesti-
cation,' vol. ii. p. 327. Prof. Alex. Brandt has recently sent me an additional case of a father

Prof. Alex. Brandt informs me that he has compared the hair from the face of a man thus characterised, aged thirty-five, with the lanugo of a fœtus, and finds it quite similar in texture; therefore, as he remarks, the case may be attributed to an arrest of development in the hair, together with its continued growth. Many delicate children, as I have been assured by a surgeon to a hospital for children, have their backs covered by rather long silky hairs; and such cases probably come under the same head.

It appears as if the posterior molar or wisdom-teeth were tending to become rudimentary in the more civilised races of man. These teeth are rather smaller than the other molars, as is likewise the case with the corresponding teeth in the chimpanzee and orang; and they have only two separate fangs. They do not cut through the gums till about the seventeenth year, and I have been assured that they are much more liable to decay, and are earlier lost than the other teeth; but this is denied by some eminent dentists. They are also much more liable to vary, both in structure and in the period of their development, than the other teeth.[42] In the Melanian races, on the other hand, the wisdom-teeth are usually furnished with three separate fangs, and are generally sound; they also differ from the other molars in size, less than in the Caucasian races.[43] Prof. Schaaffhausen accounts

---

and son, born in Russia, with these peculiarities. I have received drawings of both from Paris.

[42] Dr. Webb, 'Teeth in Man and the Anthropoid Apes,' as quoted by Dr. C. Carter Blake in 'Anthropological Review,' July 1867, p. 299.

[43] Owen, 'Anatomy of Vertebrates,' vol. iii. pp. 320, 321, and 325.

for this difference between the races by "the posterior "dental portion of the jaw being always shortened" in those that are civilised,[44] and this shortening may, I presume, be attributed to civilised men habitually feeding on soft, cooked food, and thus using their jaws less. I am informed by Mr. Brace that it is becoming quite a common practice in the United States to remove some of the molar teeth of children, as the jaw does not grow large enough for the perfect development of the normal number.[45]

With respect to the alimentary canal, I have met with an account of only a single rudiment, namely the vermiform appendage of the cæcum. The cæcum is a branch or diverticulum of the intestine, ending in a cul-de-sac, and is extremely long in many of the lower vegetable-feeding mammals. In the marsupial koala it is actually more than thrice as long as the whole body.[46] It is sometimes produced into a long gradually-tapering point, and is sometimes constricted in parts. It appears as if, in consequence of changed diet or habits, the cæcum had become much shortened in various animals, the vermiform appendage being left as a rudiment of the shortened part. That this appendage is a rudiment, we may infer from its small size, and from the evidence which Prof. Canestrini[47] has collected of its variability in man. It is occasion-

---

[44] 'On the Primitive Form of the Skull,' Eng. translat. in 'Anthropological Review,' Oct. 1868, p. 426.

[45] Prof. Montegazza writes to me from Florence, that he has lately been studying the last molar teeth in the different races of man, and has come to the same conclusion as that given in my text, viz., that in the higher or civilised races they are on the road towards atrophy or elimination.

[46] Owen, 'Anatomy of Vertebrates,' vol. iii. pp. 416, 434, 441.

[47] 'Annuario della Soc. d. Nat.' Modena, 1867, p. 94.

ally quite absent, or again is largely developed. The passage is sometimes completely closed for half or two-thirds of its length, with the terminal part consisting of a flattened solid expansion. In the orang this appendage is long and convoluted: in man it arises from the end of the short cæcum, and is commonly from four to five inches in length, being only about the third of an inch in diameter. Not only is it useless, but it is sometimes the cause of death, of which fact I have lately heard two instances : this is due to small hard bodies, such as seeds, entering the passage, and causing inflammation.[48]

In some of the lower Quadrumana, in the Lemuridæ and Carnivora, as well as in many marsupials, there is a passage near the lower end of the humerus, called the supra-condyloid foramen, through which the great nerve of the fore limb and often the great artery pass. Now in the humerus of man, there is generally a trace of this passage, which is sometimes fairly well developed, being formed by a depending hook-like process of bone, completed by a band of ligament. Dr. Struthers,[49] who has closely attended to the subject, has now shewn that this peculiarity is sometimes inherited, as it has occurred in a father, and in no less

[48] M. C. Martins ("De l'Unité Organique," in 'Revue des Deux Mondes,' June 15, 1862, p. 16), and Häckel ('Generelle Morphologie,' B. ii. s. 278), have both remarked on the singular fact of this rudiment sometimes causing death.

[49] With respect to inheritance, see Dr. Struthers in the 'Lancet,' Feb. 15, 1873, and another important paper, ibid.,

Jan. 24, 1863, p. 83. Dr. Knox, as I am informed, was the first anatomist who drew attention to this peculiar structure in man; see his 'Great Artists and Anatomists,' p. 63. See also an important memoir on this process by Dr. Gruber, in the 'Bulletin de l'Acad. Imp. de St. Pétersbourg,' tom. xii. 1867, p. 448.

than four out of his seven children. When present, the great nerve invariably passes through it; and this clearly indicates that it is the homologue and rudiment of the supra-condyloid foramen of the lower animals. Prof. Turner estimates, as he informs me, that it occurs in about one per cent. of recent skeletons. But if the occasional development of this structure in man is, as seems probable, due to reversion, it is a return to a very ancient state of things, because in the higher Quadrumana it is absent.

There is another foramen or perforation in the humerus, occasionally present in man, which may be called the inter-condyloid. This occurs, but not constantly, in various anthropoid and other apes,[50] and likewise in many of the lower animals. It is remarkable that this perforation seems to have been present in man much more frequently during ancient times than recently. Mr. Busk[51] has collected the following evidence on this head: Prof. Broca " noticed "the perforation in four and a half per cent. of the "arm-bones collected in the 'Cimetière du Sud,' at "Paris; and in the Grotto of Orrony, the contents of "which are referred to the Bronze period, as many as "eight humeri out of thirty-two were perforated; but "this extraordinary proportion, he thinks, might be "due to the cavern having been a sort of 'family "vault.' Again, M. Dupont found thirty per cent.

[50] Mr. St. George Mivart, 'Transact. Phil. Soc.' 1867, p. 310.

[51] "On the Caves of Gibraltar," 'Tansact. Internat. Congress of Prehist. Arch.' Third Session, 1869, p. 159. Prof. Wyman has lately shewn (Fourth Annual Report, Peabody Museum, 1871, p. 20), that this perforation is present in thirty-one per cent. of some human remains from ancient mounds in the Western United States, and in Florida. It frequently occurs in the negro.

"of perforated bones in the caves of the Valley of
"the Lesse, belonging to the Reindeer period; whilst
"M. Leguay, in a sort of *dolmen* at Argenteuil, observed
"twenty-five per cent. to be perforated; and M.
"Pruner-Bey found twenty-six per cent. in the same
"condition in bones from Vauréal. Nor should it
"be left unnoticed that M. Pruner-Bey states that
"this condition is common in Guanche skeletons."
It is an interesting fact that ancient races, in
this and several other cases, more frequently present
structures which resemble those of the lower animals
than do the modern. One chief cause seems to be
that the ancient races stand somewhat nearer in
the long line of descent to their remote animal-like
progenitors.

In man, the os coccyx, together with certain other
vertebræ hereafter to be described, though functionless as a tail, plainly represent this part in other
vertebrate animals. At an early embryonic period it
is free, and projects beyond the lower extremities; as
may be seen in the drawing (Fig. 1.) of a human
embryo. Even after birth it has been known, in
certain rare and anomalous cases,[52] to form a small
external rudiment of a tail. The os coccyx is short,
usually including only four vertebræ, all anchylosed
together: and these are in a rudimentary condition,
for they consist, with the exception of the basal one,

[52] Quatrefages has lately collected the evidence on this
subject. 'Revue des Cours
Scientifiques,' 1867–1868, p.
625. In 1840 Fleischmann exhibited a human fœtus bearing a
free tail, which, as is not always
the case, included vertebral
bodies; and this tail was criti-
cally examined by the many
anatomists present at the meeting of naturalists at Erlangen
(see Marshall in Niederländi-
schen Archiv für Zoologie,
December 1871).

of the centrum alone.[53]　They are furnished with some
small muscles ; one of which, as I am informed by Prof.
Turner, has been expressly described by Theile as a
rudimentary repetition of the extensor of the tail, a
muscle which is so largely developed in many mammals.

The spinal cord in man extends only as far downwards as the last dorsal or first lumbar vertebra ; but
a thread-like structure (the *filum terminale*) runs down
the axis of the sacral part of the spinal canal, and even
along the back of the coccygeal bones. The upper
part of this filament, as Prof. Turner informs me, is
undoubtedly homologous with the spinal cord ; but the
lower part apparently consists merely of the *pia mater*,
or vascular investing membrane. Even in this case
the os coccyx may be said to possess a vestige of so
important a structure as the spinal cord, though no
longer enclosed within a bony canal. The following
fact, for which I am also indebted to Prof. Turner,
shews how closely the os coccyx corresponds with the
true tail in the lower animals : Luschka has recently
discovered at the extremity of the coccygeal bones a
very peculiar convoluted body, which is continuous
with the middle sacral artery ; and this discovery led
Krause and Meyer to examine the tail of a monkey
(Macacus), and of a cat, in both of which they found
a similarly convoluted body, though not at the extremity.

The reproductive system offers various rudimentary
structures ; but these differ in one important respect
from the foregoing cases. Here we are not concerned
with the vestige of a part which does not belong to
the species in an efficient state, but with a part

[53] Owen, 'On the Nature of Limbs,' 1849, p. 114.

efficient in the one sex, and represented in the other by a mere rudiment. Nevertheless, the occurrence of such rudiments is as difficult to explain, on the belief of the separate creation of each species, as in the foregoing cases. Hereafter I shall have to recur to these rudiments, and shall shew that their presence generally depends merely on inheritance, that is, on parts acquired by one sex having been partially transmitted to the other. I will in this place only give some instances of such rudiments. It is well known that in the males of all mammals, including man, rudimentary mammæ exist. These in several instances have become well developed, and have yielded a copious supply of milk. Their essential identity in the two sexes is likewise shewn by their occasional sympathetic enlargement in both during an attack of the measles. The *vesicula prostatica*, which has been observed in many male mammals, is now universally acknowledged to be the homologue of the female uterus, together with the connected passage. It is impossible to read Leuckart's able description of this organ, and his reasoning, without admitting the justness of his conclusion. This is especially clear in the case of those mammals in which the true female uterus bifurcates, for in the males of these the vesicula likewise bifurcates.[54] Some other rudimentary structures belonging to the reproductive system might have been here adduced.[55]

[54] Leuckart, in Todd's 'Cyclop. of Anat.' 1849–52, vol. iv. p. 1415. In man this organ is only from three to six lines in length, but, like so many other rudimentary parts, it is variable in development as well as in other characters.

[55] See, on this subject, Owen, 'Anatomy of Vertebrates,' vol. iii. pp. 675, 676, 706.

The bearing of the three great classes of facts now given is unmistakeable. But it would be superfluous fully to recapitulate the line of argument given in detail in my 'Origin of Species.' The homological construction of the whole frame in the members of the same class is intelligible, if we admit their descent from a common progenitor, together with their subsequent adaptation to diversified conditions. On any other view, the similarity of pattern between the hand of a man or monkey, the foot of a horse, the flipper of a seal, the wing of a bat, &c., is utterly inexplicable.[56] It is no scientific explanation to assert that they have all been formed on the same ideal plan. With respect to development, we can clearly understand, on the principle of variations supervening at a rather late

[56] Prof. Bianconi, in a recently published work, illustrated by admirable engravings (' La Théorie Darwinienne et la création dite indépendante.' 1874), endeavours to show that homological structures, in the above and other cases, can be fully explained on mechanical principles, in accordance with their uses. No one has shewn so well, how admirably such structures are adapted for their final purpose; and this adaptation can, as I believe, be explained through natural selection. In considering the wing of a bat, he brings forward (p. 218) what appears to me (to use Auguste Comte's words) a mere metaphysical principle, namely, the preservation " in its integrity of " the mammalian nature of the " animal." In only a few cases does he discuss rudiments, and then only those parts which are partially rudimentary, such as the little hoofs of the pig and ox, which do not touch the ground ; these he shews clearly to be of service to the animal. It is unfortunate that he did not consider such cases as the minute teeth, which never cut through the jaw in the ox, or the mammæ of male quadrupeds, or the wings of certain beetles, existing under the soldered wing-covers, or the vestiges of the pistil and stamens in various flowers, and many other such cases. Although I greatly admire Prof. Bianconi's work, yet the belief now held by most naturalists seems to me left unshaken, that homological structures are inexplicable on the principle of mere aptation.

embryonic period, and being inherited at a corresponding period, how it is that the embryos of wonderfully different forms should still retain, more or less perfectly, the structure of their common progenitor. No other explanation has ever been given of the marvellous fact that the embryos of a man, dog, seal, bat, reptile, &c., can at first hardly be distinguished from each other. In order to understand the existence of rudimentary organs, we have only to suppose that a former progenitor possessed the parts in question in a perfect state, and that under changed habits of life they became greatly reduced, either from simple disuse, or through the natural selection of those individuals which were least encumbered with a superfluous part, aided by the other means previously indicated.

Thus we can understand how it has come to pass that man and all other vertebrate animals have been constructed on the same general model, why they pass through the same early stages of development, and why they retain certain rudiments in common. Consequently we ought frankly to admit their community of descent; to take any other view, is to admit that our own structure, and that of all the animals around us, is a mere snare laid to entrap our judgment. This conclusion is greatly strengthened, if we look to the members of the whole animal series, and consider the evidence derived from their affinities or classification, their geographical distribution and geological succession. It is only our natural prejudice, and that arrogance which made our forefathers declare that they were descended from demi-gods, which leads us to demur to this conclusion. But the time will before long come, when it will be thought wonderful that naturalists, who were well acquainted with the comparative structure and development of man, and other mammals, should have believed that each was the work of a separate act of creation.

CHAPTER II.

ON THE MANNER OF DEVELOPMENT OF MAN FROM SOME LOWER FORM.

Variability of body and mind in man—Inheritance—Causes of variability—Laws of variation the same in man as in the lower animals—Direct action of the conditions of life—Effects of the increased use and disuse of parts—Arrested development—Reversion—Correlated variation—Rate of increase—Checks to increase—Natural selection—Man the most dominant animal in the world—Importance of his coporeal structure—The causes which have led to his becoming erect—Consequent changes of structure—Decrease in size of the canine teeth—Increased size and altered shape of the skull—Nakedness—Absence of a tail—Defenceless condition of man.

IT is manifest that man is now subject to much variability. No two individuals of the same race are quite alike. We may compare millions of faces, and each will be distinct. There is an equally great amount of diversity in the proportions and dimensions of the various parts of the body; the length of the legs being one of the most variable points.[1] Although in some quarters of the world an elongated skull, and in other quarters a short skull prevails, yet there is great diversity of shape even within the limits of the same race, as with the aborigines of America and South Australia—the latter a race " probably as pure " and homogeneous in blood, customs, and language as

[1] 'Investigations in Military and Anthropolog. Statistics of American Soldiers,' by B. A Gould, 1869, p. 256.

"any in existence"—and even with the inhabitants of so confined an area as the Sandwich Islands.[2] An eminent dentist assures me that there is nearly as much diversity in the teeth as in the features. The chief arteries so frequently run in abnormal courses, that it has been found useful for surgical purposes to calculate from 1040 corpses how often each course prevails.[3] The muscles are eminently variable : thus those of the foot were found by Prof. Turner[4] not to be strictly alike in any two out of fifty bodies; and in some the deviations were considerable. He adds, that the power of performing the appropriate movements must have been modified in accordance with the several deviations. Mr. J. Wood has recorded[5] the occurrence of 295 muscular variations in thirty-six subjects, and in another set of the same number no less than 558 variations, those occurring on both sides of the body being only reckoned as one. In the last set, not one body out of the thirty-six was "found "totally wanting in departures from the standard "descriptions of the muscular system given in ana- "tomical text books." A single body presented the extraordinary number of twenty-five distinct ab- normalities. The same muscle sometimes varies in many ways: thus Prof. Macalister describes[6] no less

[2] With respect to the "Cranial forms of the American abori- gines," see Dr. Aitken Meigs in 'Proc. Acad. Nat. Sci. Phila- delphia, May, 1868. On the Australians, see Huxley, in Lyell's 'Antiquity of Man,' 1863, p. 87. On the Sandwich Islanders, Prof. J. Wyman, 'Observations on Crania,' Boston, 1868, p. 18.

[3] 'Anatomy of the Arteries,' by R. Quain. Preface, vol. i. 1844.

[4] 'Transact. Royal Soc. Edin- burgh,' vol. xxiv. pp. 175, 189.

[5] 'Proc. Royal Soc.' 1867, p. 544; also 1868, pp. 483, 524. There is a previous paper, 1866, p. 229.

[6] 'Proc. R. Irish Academy,' vol. x. 1868, p. 141.

than twenty distinct variations in the *palmaris accessorius.*

The famous old anatomist, Wolff,[7] insists that the internal viscera are more variable than the external parts: *Nulla particula est quæ non aliter et aliter in aliis se habeat hominibus.* He has even written a treatise on the choice of typical examples of the viscera for representation. A discussion on the beau-ideal of the liver, lungs, kidneys, &c., as of the human face divine, sounds strange in our ears.

The variability or diversity of the mental faculties in men of the same race, not to mention the greater differences between the men of distinct races, is so notorious that not a word need here be said. So it is with the lower animals. All who have had charge of menageries admit this fact, and we see it plainly in our dogs and other domestic animals. Brehm especially insists that each individual monkey of those which he kept tame in Africa had its own peculiar disposition and temper: he mentions one baboon remarkable for its high intelligence; and the keepers in the Zoological Gardens pointed out to me a monkey, belonging to the New World division, equally remarkable for intelligence. Rengger, also, insists on the diversity in the various mental characters of the monkeys of the same species which he kept in Paraguay; and this diversity, as he adds, is partly innate, and partly the result of the manner in which they have been treated or educated.[8]

I have elsewhere [9] so fully discussed the subject of

[7] 'Act. Acad. St. Petersburg,' 1778, part ii. p. 217.

[8] Brehm, 'Thierleben,' B. i. s. 58, 87. Rengger, 'Säugethiere von Paraguay,' s. 57.

[9] 'Variation of Animals and Plants under Domestication,' vol. ii. chap. xii.

Inheritance, that I need here add hardly anything. A greater number of facts have been collected with respect to the transmission of the most trifling, as well as of the most important characters in man, than in any of the lower animals; though the facts are copious enough with respect to the latter. So in regard to mental qualities, their transmission is manifest in our dogs, horses, and other domestic animals. Besides special tastes and habits, general intelligence, courage, bad and good temper, &c., are certainly transmitted. With man we see similar facts in almost every family; and we now know, through the admirable labours of Mr. Galton,[10] that genius which implies a wonderfully complex combination of high faculties, tends to be inherited; and, on the other hand, it is too certain that insanity and deteriorated mental powers likewise run in families.

With respect to the causes of variability, we are in all cases very ignorant; but we can see that in man as in the lower animals, they stand in some relation to the conditions to which each species has been exposed, during several generations. Domesticated animals vary more than those in a state of nature; and this is apparently due to the diversified and changing nature of the conditions to which they have been subjected. In this respect the different races of man resemble domesticated animals, and so do the individuals of the same race, when inhabiting a very wide area, like that of America. We see the influence of diversified conditions in the more civilised nations; for the members belonging to different grades of rank,

[10] 'Hereditary Genius: an Inquiry into its Laws and Consequences,' 1869.

and following different occupations, present a greater range of character than do the members of barbarous nations. But the uniformity of savages has often been exaggerated, and in some cases can hardly be said to exist.[11] It is, nevertheless, an error to speak of man, even if we look only to the conditions to which he has been exposed, as "far more domesti-"cated "[12] than any other animal. Some savage races, such as the Australians, are not exposed to more diversified conditions than are many species which have a wide range. In another and much more important respect, man differs widely from any strictly domesticated animal; for his breeding has never long been controlled, either by methodical or unconscious selection. No race or body of men has been so completely subjugated by other men, as that certain individuals should be preserved, and thus unconsciously selected, from somehow excelling in utility to their masters. Nor have certain male and female individuals been intentionally picked out and matched, except in the well-known case of the Prussian grenadiers; and in this case man obeyed, as might have been expected, the law of methodical selection; for it is asserted that many tall men were reared in the villages inhabited by the grenadiers and their tall wives. In Sparta, also, a form of selection was followed, for it was enacted that all children should be examined shortly

[11] Mr. Bates remarks ('The Naturalist on the Amazons,' 1863, vol. ii. p. 159), with respect to the Indians of the same South American tribe, "no two "of them were at all similar in "the shape of the head; one "man had an oval visage with "fine features, and another was "quite Mongolian in breadth "and prominence of cheek, "spread of nostrils, and obli-"quity of eyes."

[12] Blumenbach, 'Treatises on A thropolog.' Eng. translat., 1865, p. 205.

after birth; the well-formed and vigorous being preserved, the others left to perish.[13]

If we consider all the races of man as forming a single species, his range is enormous; but some separate races, as the Americans and Polynesians, have very wide ranges. It is a well-known law that widely-ranging species are much more variable than species with restricted ranges; and the variability of man may with more truth be compared with that of widely-ranging species, than with that of domesticated animals.

Not only does variability appear to be induced in man and the lower animals by the same general causes, but in both the same parts of the body are affected in a closely analogous manner. This has been proved in

[13] Mitford's ' History of Greece,' vol. i. p. 282. It appears also from a passage in Xenophon's 'Memorabilia,' B. ii. 4 (to which my attention has been called by the Rev. J. N. Hoare), that it was a well recognised principle with the Greeks, that men ought to select their wives with a view to the health and vigour of their children. The Grecian poet, Theognis, who lived 550 B.C., clearly saw how important selection, if carefully applied, would be for the improvement of mankind. He saw, likewise, that wealth often checks the proper action of sexual selection. He thus writes:

" With kine and horses, Kurnus! we proceed
By reasonable rules, and choose a breed
For profit and increase, at any price;
Of a sound stock, without defect or vice.
But, in the daily matches that we make,
The price is everything : for money's sake,
Men marry : women are in marriage given
The churl or ruffian, that in wealth has thriven,
May match his offspring with the proudest race :
Thus everything is mix'd, noble and base !
If then in outward manner, form, and mind,
You find us a degraded, motley kind,
Wonder no more, my friend ! the cause is plain,
And to lament the consequence is vain."
(The works of J. Hookham Frere, vol. ii. 1872, p. 334.)

such full detail by Godron and Quatrefages, that I
need here only refer to their works.[14] Monstrosities,
which graduate into slight variations, are likewise so
similar in man and the lower animals, that the same
classification and the same terms can be used for both,
as has been shewn by Isidore Geoffroy St.-Hilaire.[15]
In my work on the variation of domestic animals, I
have attempted to arrange in a rude fashion the laws
of variation under the following heads:—The direct
and definite action of changed conditions, as exhibited
by all or nearly all the individuals of the same species,
varying in the same manner under the same circumstances. The effects of the long-continued use or
disuse of parts. The cohesion of homologous parts.
The variability of multiple parts. Compensation of
growth; but of this law I have found no good instance
in the case of man. The effects of the mechanical
pressure of one part on another; as of the pelvis on
the cranium of the infant in the womb. Arrests of
development, leading to the diminution or suppression
of parts. The reappearance of long-lost characters
through reversion. And lastly, correlated variation.
All these so-called laws apply equally to man and the
lower animals; and most of them even to plants. It
would be superfluous here to discuss all of them;[16] but

[14] Godron, 'De l'Espèce,' 1859,
tom. ii. livre 3. Quatrefages,
'Unité de l'Espèce Humaine,'
1861. Also Lectures on Anthropology, given in the 'Revue
des Cours Scientifiques,' 1866–
1868.
[15] 'Hist. Gén. et Part. des Anomalies de l'Organisation,' in three
volumes, tom. i. 1832.

[16] I have fully discussed these
laws in my 'Variation of Animals and Plants under Domestication,' vol. ii. chap. xxii. and
xxiii. M. J. P. Durand has
lately (1868) published a valuable essay 'De l'Influence des
Milieux,' &c. He lays much
stress, in the case of plants, on
the nature of the soil.

several are so important, that they must be treated at considerable length.

The direct and definite action of changed conditions.— This is a most perplexing subject. It cannot be denied that changed conditions produce some, and occasionally a considerable effect, on organisms of all kinds; and it seems at first probable that if sufficient time were allowed this would be the invariable result. But I have failed to obtain clear evidence in favour of this conclusion; and valid reasons may be urged on the other side, at least as far as the innumerable structures are concerned, which are adapted for special ends. There can, however, be no doubt that changed conditions induce an almost indefinite amount of fluctuating variability, by which the whole organisation is rendered in some degree plastic.

In the United States, above 1,000,000 soldiers, who served in the late war, were measured, and the States in which they were born and reared were recorded.[17] From this astonishing number of observations it is proved that local influences of some kind act directly on stature; and we further learn that " the State " where the physical growth has in great measure " taken place, and the State of birth, which indicates " the ancestry, seem to exert a marked influence on " the stature." For instance, it is established, " that " residence in the Western States, during the years of " growth, tends to produce increase of stature." On the other hand, it is certain that with sailors, their life delays growth, as shewn " by the great difference " between the statures of soldiers and sailors at the

[17] 'Investigations in Military   1869, by B. A. Gould, p. 93, 107, and Anthrop. Statistics,' &c.   126, 131, 134.

"ages of seventeen and eighteen years." Mr. B. A. Gould endeavoured to ascertain the nature of the influences which thus act on stature; but he arrived only at negative results, namely, that they did not relate to climate, the elevation of the land, soil, nor even "in any controlling degree" to the abundance or the need of the comforts of life. This latter conclusion is directly opposed to that arrived at by Villermé, from the statistics of the height of the conscripts in different parts of France. When we compare the differences in stature between the Polynesian chiefs and the lower orders within the same islands, or between the inhabitants of the fertile volcanic and low barren coral islands of the same ocean,[18] or again between the Fuegians on the eastern and western shores of their country, where the means of subsistence are very different, it is scarcely possible to avoid the conclusion that better food and greater comfort do influence stature. But the preceding statements shew how difficult it is to arrive at any precise result. Dr. Beddoe has lately proved that, with the inhabitants of Britain, residence in towns and certain occupations have a deteriorating influence on height; and he infers that the result is to a certain extent inherited, as is likewise the case in the United States. Dr. Beddoe further believes that wherever a "race attains its "maximum of physical development, it rises highest in "energy and moral vigour."[19]

[18] For the Polynesians, see Prichard's 'Physical Hist. of Mankind,' vol. v. 1847, p. 145, 283. Also Godron, 'De l'Espèce,' tom. ii. p. 289. There is also a remarkable difference in appearance between the closely-allied Hindoos inhabiting the Upper Ganges and Bengal; see Elphinstone's 'History of India,' vol. i. p. 324.

[19] 'Memoirs, Anthropolog. Soc.' vol. iii. 1867–69, pp. 561, 565, 567.

Whether external conditions produce any other direct effect on man is not known. It might have been expected that differences of climate would have had a marked influence, inasmuch as the lungs and kidneys are brought into activity under a low temperature, and the liver and skin under a high one.[20] It was formerly thought that the colour of the skin and the character of the hair were determined by light or heat; and although it can hardly be denied that some effect is thus produced, almost all observers now agree that the effect has been very small, even after exposure during many ages. But this subject will be more properly discussed when we treat of the different races of mankind. With our domestic animals there are grounds for believing that cold and damp directly affect the growth of the hair; but I have not met with any evidence on this head in the case of man.

Effects of the increased Use and Disuse of Parts.— It is well known that use strengthens the muscles in the individual, and complete disuse, or the destruction of the proper nerve, weakens them. When the eye is destroyed, the optic nerve often becomes atrophied. When an artery is tied, the lateral channels increase not only in diameter, but in the thickness and strength of their coats. When one kidney ceases to act from disease, the other increases in size, and does double work. Bones increase not only in thickness, but in length, from carrying a greater weight.[21] Different

[20] Dr. Brakenridge, 'Theory of Diathesis,' 'Medical Times,' June 19 and July 17, 1869.

[21] I have given authorities for these several statements in my 'Variation of Animals under Domestication,' vol. ii. pp. 297–300. Dr. Jaeger, "Ueber das Längenwachsthum der Knochen," 'Jenaischen Zeitschrift,' B. v. Heft. i.

occupations, habitually followed, lead to changed proportions in various parts of the body. Thus it was ascertained by the United States Commission [22] that the legs of the sailors employed in the late war were longer by 0·217 of an inch than those of the soldiers, though the sailors were on an average shorter men; whilst their arms were shorter by 1·09 of an inch, and therefore, out of proportion, shorter in relation to their lesser height. This shortness of the arms is apparently due to their greater use, and is an unexpected result: but sailors chiefly use their arms in pulling, and not in supporting weights. With sailors, the girth of the neck and the depth of the instep are greater, whilst the circumference of the chest, waist, and hips is less, than in soldiers.

Whether the several foregoing modifications would become hereditary, if the same habits of life were followed during many generations, is not known, but it is probable. Rengger [23] attributes the thin legs and thick arms of the Payaguas Indians to successive generations having passed nearly their whole lives in canoes, with their lower extremities motionless. Other writers have come to a similar conclusion in analogous cases. According to Cranz,[24] who lived for a long time with the Esquimaux, "the natives believe that ingenuity and "dexterity in seal-catching (their highest art and "virtue) is hereditary; there is really something in it, "for the son of a celebrated seal-catcher will distinguish "himself, though he lost his father in childhood." But in this case it is mental aptitude, quite as much as

---

[22] 'Investigations,' &c. By B. A. Gould, 1869, p. 288.

[23] 'Säugethiere von Paraguay,' 1830, s. 4.

[24] 'History of Greenland,' Eng. translat. 1767, vol. i. p. 230.

bodily structure, which appears to be inherited. It is asserted that the hands of English labourers are at birth larger than those of the gentry.[25] From the correlation which exists, at least in some cases,[26] between the development of the extremities and of the jaws, it is possible that in those classes which do not labour much with their hands and feet, the jaws would be reduced in size from this cause. That they are generally smaller in refined and civilised men than in hard-working men or savages, is certain. But with savages, as Mr. Herbert Spencer[27] has remarked, the greater use of the jaws in chewing coarse, uncooked food, would act in a direct manner on the masticatory muscles, and on the bones to which they are attached. In infants, long before birth, the skin on the soles of the feet is thicker than on any other part of the body;[28] and it can hardly be doubted that this is due to the inherited effects of pressure during a long series of generations.

It is familiar to every one that watchmakers and engravers are liable to be short-sighted, whilst men living much out of doors, and especially savages, are generally long-sighted.[29] Short-sight and long-sight certainly tend to be inherited.[30] The inferiority of

[25] 'Intermarriage.' By Alex. Walker, 1838, p. 377.

[26] 'The Variation of Animals under Domestication,' vol. i. p. 173.

[27] 'Principles of Biology,' vol. i. p. 455.

[28] Paget, 'Lectures on Surgical Pathology,' vol. ii. 1853, p. 209.

[29] It is a singular and unexpected fact that sailors are inferior to landsmen in their mean distance of distinct vision. Dr. B. A. Gould ('Sanitary Memoirs of the War of the Rebellion,' 1869, p. 530), has proved this to be the case; and he accounts for it by the ordinary range of vision in sailors being "restricted "to the length of the vessel and "the height of the masts."

[30] 'The Variation of Animals under Domestication,' vol. i. p. 8.

Europeans, in comparison with savages, in eyesight and in the other senses, is no doubt the accumulated and transmitted effect of lessened use during many generations; for Rengger [31] states that he has repeatedly observed Europeans, who had been brought up and spent their whole lives with the wild Indians, who nevertheless did not equal them in the sharpness of their senses. The same naturalist observes that the cavities in the skull for the reception of the several sense-organs are larger in the American aborigines than in Europeans; and this probably indicates a corresponding difference in the dimensions of the organs themselves. Blumenbach has also remarked on the large size of the nasal cavities in the skulls of the American aborigines, and connects this fact with their remarkably acute power of smell. The Mongolians of the plains of Northern Asia, according to Pallas, have wonderfully perfect senses; and Prichard believes that the great breadth of their skulls across the zygomas follows from their highly-developed sense-organs. [32]

The Quechua Indians inhabit the lofty plateaux of Peru; and Alcide d'Orbigny states [33] that, from continually breathing a highly rarefied atmosphere, they have acquired chests and lungs of extraordinary dimensions. The cells, also, of the lungs are larger

[31] 'Säugethiere von Paraguay,' s. 8, 10. I have had good opportunities for observing the extraordinary power of eyesight in the Fuegians. See also Lawrence ('Lectures on Physiology,' &c., 1822, p. 404) on this same subject. M. Giraud-Teulon has recently collected ('Revue des Cours Scientifiques,' 1870, p. 625) a large and valuable body of evidence proving that the cause of short-sight, "*C'est le travail assidu, de près.*"

[32] Prichard, 'Phys. Hist. of Mankind,' on the authority of Blumenbach, vol. i. 1851, p. 311; for the statement by Pallas, vol. iv. 1844, p. 407.

[33] Quoted by Prichard, 'Researches into the Phys. Hist. of Mankind,' vol. v. p. 463.

and more numerous than in Europeans. These observations have been doubted; but Mr. D. Forbes carefully measured many Aymaras, an allied race, living at the height of between 10,000 and 15,000 feet; and he informs me [34] that they differ conspicuously from the men of all other races seen by him in the circumference and length of their bodies. In his table of measurements, the stature of each man is taken at 1000, and the other measurements are reduced to this standard. It is here seen that the extended arms of the Aymaras are shorter than those of Europeans, and much shorter than those of Negroes. The legs are likewise shorter; and they present this remarkable peculiarity, that in every Aymara measured, the femur is actually shorter than the tibia. On an average, the length of the femur to that of the tibia is as 211 to 252; whilst in two Europeans, measured at the same time, the femora to the tibiæ were as 244 to 230; and in three Negroes as 258 to 241. The humerus is likewise shorter relatively to the forearm. This shortening of that part of the limb which is nearest to the body, appears to be, as suggested to me by Mr. Forbes, a case of compensation in relation with the greatly increased length of the trunk. The Aymaras present some other singular points of structure, for instance, the very small projection of the heel.

These men are so thoroughly acclimatised to their cold and lofty abode, that when formerly carried down by the Spaniards to the low eastern plains, and when now tempted down by high wages to the gold-washings,

[34] Mr. Forbes' valuable paper is now published in the 'Journal of the Ethnological Soc. of London,' new series, vol. ii. 1870, p. 193.

they suffer a frightful rate of mortality. Nevertheless Mr. Forbes found a few pure families which had survived during two generations : and he observed that they still inherited their characteristic peculiarities. But it was manifest, even without measurement, that these peculiarities had all decreased ; and on measurement, their bodies were found not to be so much elongated as those of the men on the high plateau ; whilst their femora had become somewhat lengthened, as had their tibiæ, although in a less degree. The actual measurements may be seen by consulting Mr. Forbes's memoir. From these observations, there can, I think, be no doubt that residence during many generations at a great elevation tends, both directly and indirectly, to induce inherited modifications in the proportions of the body.[35]

Although man may not have been much modified during the latter stages of his existence through the increased or decreased use of parts, the facts now given shew that his liability in this respect has not been lost ; and we positively know that the same law holds good with the lower animals. Consequently we may infer that when at a remote epoch the progenitors of man were in a transitional state, and were changing from quadrupeds into bipeds, natural selection would probably have been greatly aided by the inherited effects of the increased or diminished use of the different parts of the body.

Arrests of Development.—There is a difference between

[35] Dr. Wilckens ('Landwirth-schaft. Wochenblatt,' No. 10, 1869) has lately published an interesting Essay shewing how domestic animals, which live in mountainous regions, have their frames modified.

arrested development and arrested growth, for parts in
the former state continue to grow whilst still retaining
their early condition. Various monstrosities come under
this head; and some, as a cleft-palate, are known
to be occasionally inherited. It will suffice for our
purpose to refer to the arrested brain-development of
microcephalous idiots, as described in Vogt's memoir.[36]
Their skulls are smaller, and the convolutions of the
brain are less complex than in normal men. The
frontal sinus, or the projection over the eye-brows, is
largely developed, and the jaws are prognathous to an
"*effrayant*" degree; so that these idiots somewhat
resemble the lower types of mankind. Their intelligence, and most of their mental faculties, are
extremely feeble. They cannot acquire the power of
speech, and are wholly incapable of prolonged attention, but are much given to imitation. They are
strong and remarkably active, continually gambolling
and jumping about, and making grimaces. They often
ascend stairs on all-fours; and are curiously fond of
climbing up furniture or trees. We are thus reminded
of the delight shewn by almost all boys in climbing
trees; and this again reminds us how lambs and kids,
originally alpine animals, delight to frisk on any
hillock, however small. Idiots also resemble the
lower animals in some other respects; thus several
cases are recorded of their carefully smelling every
mouthful of food before eating it. One idiot is described as often using his mouth in aid of his hands,
whilst hunting for lice. They are often filthy in their
habits, and have no sense of decency; and several cases

[36] 'Mémoire sur les Microcéphales,' 1867, pp. 50, 125, 169, 171,
184-198.

have been published of their bodies being remarkably hairy.[37]

Reversion.—Many of the cases to be here given, might have been introduced under the last heading. When a structure is arrested in its development, but still continues growing, until it closely resembles a corresponding structure in some lower and adult member of the same group, it may in one sense be considered as a case of reversion. The lower members in a group give us some idea how the common progenitor was probably constructed; and it is hardly credible that a complex part, arrested at an early phase of embryonic development, should go on growing so as ultimately to perform its proper function, unless it had acquired such power during some earlier state of existence, when the present exceptional or arrested structure was normal. The simple brain of a microcephalous idiot, in as far as it resembles that of an ape, may in this sense be said to offer a case of reversion.[38] There are other cases which come more

[37] Prof. Laycock sums up the character of brute-like idiots by calling them *theroid;* 'Journal of Mental Science,' July, 1863. Dr. Scott ('The Deaf and Dumb,' 2nd edit., 1870, p. 10) has often observed the imbecile smelling their food. See, on this same subject, and on the hairiness of idiots, Dr. Maudsley, 'Body and Mind,' 1870, pp. 46–51. Pinel has also given a striking case of hairiness in an idiot.

[38] In my 'Variation of Animals under Domestication' (vol. ii. p. 57), I attributed the not very rare cases of supernumerary mammæ in women to reversion. I was led to this as a probable conclusion, by the additional mammæ being generally placed symmetrically on the breast; and more especially from one case, in which a single efficient mamma occurred in the inguinal region of a woman, the daughter of another woman with supernumerary mammæ. But I now find (see, for instance, Prof. Preyer, 'Der Kampf um das Dasein,' 1869, s. 45) that *mammæ erraticæ* occur in other situations, as on the back, in the armpit, and on the thigh;

strictly under our present head of reversion.   Certain
structures, regularly occurring in the lower members

the mammæ in this latter instance having given so much
milk that the child was thus
nourished. The probability that
the additional mammæ are due
to reversion is thus much weakened; nevertheless, it still seems
to me probable, because two pairs
are often found symmetrically on
the breast; and of this I myself
have received information in
several cases. It is well known
that some Lemurs normally have
two pairs of mammæ on the
breast.   Five cases have been
recorded of the presence of more
than a pair of mammæ (of course
rudimentary) in the male sex of
mankind; see ' Journal of Anat.
and Physiology,' 1872, p. 56, for
a case given by Dr. Handyside,
in which two brothers exhibited
this peculiarity; see also a paper
by Dr. Bartels, in ' Reichert's
and du Bois-Reymond's Archiv.,'
1872, p. 304. In one of the cases
alluded to by Dr. Bartels, a man
bore five mammæ, one being
medial and placed above the
navel; Meckel von Hemsbach
thinks that this latter case is
illustrated by a medial mamma
occurring in certain Cheiroptera.
On the whole, we may well doubt
if additional mammæ would ever
have been developed in both sexes
of mankind, had not his early
progenitors been provided with
more than a single pair.

In the above work (vol. ii. p.
12), I also attributed, though
with much hesitation, the frequent cases of polydactylism in
men and various animals to re-

version. I was partly led to
this through Prof. Owen's statement, that some of the Ichthy-
opterygia possess more than five
digits, and therefore, as I supposed, had retained a primordial
condition; but Prof. Gegenbaur
(' Jenaischen Zeitschrift,' B. v.
Heft 3, s. 341), disputes Owen's
conclusion. On the other hand,
according to the opinion lately
advanced by Dr. Günther, on
the paddle of Ceratodus, which
is provided with articulated bony
rays on both sides of a central
chain of bones, there seems no
great difficulty in admitting that
six or more digits on one side,
or on both sides, might reappear
through reversion. I am informed by Dr. Zouteveen that
there is a case on record of a
man having twenty-four fingers
and twenty-four toes! I was
chiefly led to the conclusion that
the presence of supernumerary
digits might be due to reversion
from the fact that such digits,
not only are strongly inherited,
but, as I then believed, had the
power of regrowth after amputation, like the normal digits of
the lower vertebrata.   But I
have explained in the Second
Edition of my Variation under
Domestication why I now place
little reliance on the recorded
cases of such regrowth. Nevertheless it deserves notice, inasmuch as arrested development
and reversion are intimately related processes; that various
structures in an embryonic or
arrested condition, such as a

of the group to which man belongs, occasionally make their appearance in him, though not found in the normal human embryo; or, if normally present in the human embryo, they become abnormally developed, although in a manner which is normal in the lower members of the group. These remarks will be rendered clearer by the following illustrations.

In various mammals the uterus graduates from a double organ with two distinct orifices and two passages, as in the marsupials, into a single organ, which is in no way double except from having a slight internal fold, as in the higher apes and man. The rodents exhibit a perfect series of gradations between these two extreme states. In all mammals the uterus is developed from two simple primitive tubes, the inferior portions of which form the cornua; and it is in the words of Dr. Farre, " by the coalescence of the " two cornua at their lower extremities that the body " of the uterus is formed in man; while in those " animals in which no middle portion or body exists, " the cornua remain ununited. As the development of " the uterus proceeds, the two cornua become gradually " shorter, until at length they are lost, or, as it were, " absorbed into the body of the uterus." The angles of the uterus are still produced into cornua, even in animals as high up in the scale as the lower apes and lemurs.

Now in women, anomalous cases are not very infre-

---

cleft palate, bifid uterus, &c., are frequently accompanied by polydactylism. This has been strongly insisted on by Meckel and Isidore Geoffroy St.-Hilaire. But at present it is the safest course to give up altogether the idea that there is any relation between the development of supernumerary digits and reversion to some lowly organised progenitor of man.

quent, in which the mature uterus is furnished with
cornua, or is partially divided into two organs ; and
such cases, according to Owen, repeat " the grade
" of concentrative development," attained by certain
rodents. Here perhaps we have an instance of a simple
arrest of embryonic development, with subsequent
growth and perfect functional development; for either
side of the partially double uterus is capable of performing the proper office of gestation. In other and
rarer cases, two distinct uterine cavities are formed,
each having its proper orifice and passage.[39] No such
stage is passed through during the ordinary development of the embryo; and it is difficult to believe,
though perhaps not impossible, that the two simple,
minute, primitive tubes should know how (if such an
expression may be used) to grow into two distinct
uteri, each with a well-constructed orifice and passage,
and each furnished with numerous muscles, nerves,
glands and vessels, if they had not formerly passed
through a similar course of development, as in the case
of existing marsupials. No one will pretend that so
perfect a structure as the abnormal double uterus in
woman could be the result of mere chance. But the
principle of reversion, by which a long-lost structure is
called back into existence, might serve as the guide for
its full development, even after the lapse of an enormous interval of time.

Professor Canestrini, after discussing the foregoing
and various analogous cases, arrives at the same conclusion as that just given. He adduces another

[39] See Dr. A Farre's well-
known article in the ' Cyclopædia
of Anatomy and Physiology,'
vol. v. 1859, p. 642. Owen,
' Anatomy of Vertebrates,' vol.
iii., 1868, p. 687. Professor
Turner in ' Edinburgh Medical
Journal,' February 1865.

instance, in the case of the malar bone,[40] which, in some of the Quadrumana and other mammals, normally consists of two portions. This is its condition in the human fœtus when two months old; and through arrested development, it sometimes remains thus in man when adult, more especially in the lower prognathous races. Hence Canestrini concludes that some ancient progenitor of man must have had this bone normally divided into two portions, which afterwards became fused together. In man the frontal bone consists of a single piece, but in the embryo, and in children, and in almost all the lower mammals, it consists of two pieces separated by a distinct suture. This suture occasionally persists more or less distinctly in man after maturity; and more frequently in ancient than in recent crania, especially, as Canestrini has observed, in those exhumed from the Drift, and belonging to the brachycephalic type. Here again he comes to the same conclusion as in the analogous case of the malar bones. In this, and other instances presently to

---

[40] 'Annuario della Soc. dei Naturalisti in Modena,' 1867, p. 83. Prof. Canestrini gives extracts on this subject from various authorities. Laurillard remarks, that as he has found a complete similarity in the form, proportions, and connection of the two malar bones in several human subjects and in certain apes, he cannot consider this disposition of the parts as simply accidental. Another paper on this same anomaly has been published by Dr. Saviotti in the 'Gazzetta delle Cliniche,' Turin, 1871, where he says that traces of the division may be detected in about two per cent. of adult skulls; he also remarks that it more frequently occurs in prognathous skulls, not of the Aryan race, than in others. See also G. Delorenzi on the same subject; 'Tre nuovi casi d' anomalia dell' osso malare,' Torino, 1872. Also, E. Morselli, 'Sopra una rara anomalia dell' osso malare,' Modena, 1872. Still more recently Gruber has written a pamphlet on the division of this bone. I give these references because a reviewer, without any grounds or scruples, has thrown doubts on my statements.

be given, the cause of ancient races approaching the lower animals in certain characters more frequently than do the modern races, appears to be, that the latter stand at a somewhat greater distance in the long line of descent from their early semi-human progenitors.

Various other anomalies in man, more or less analogous to the foregoing, have been advanced by different authors, as cases of reversion; but these seem not a little doubtful, for we have to descend extremely low in the mammalian series, before we find such structures normally present.[41]

In man, the canine teeth are perfectly efficient instruments for mastication. But their true canine character, as Owen[42] remarks, " is indicated by the " conical form of the crown, which terminates in an " obtuse point, is convex outward and flat or sub-con- " cave within, at the base of which surface there is a " feeble prominence. The conical form is best expressed " in the Melanian races, especially the Australian.

---

[41] A whole series of cases is given by Isid. Geoffroy St.-Hilaire, 'Hist. des Anomalies,' tom. iii. p. 437.   A reviewer ('Journal of Anat. and Physiology,' 1871, p. 366) blames me much for not having discussed the numerous cases, which have been recorded, of various parts arrested in their development. He says that, according to my theory, " every transient con- " dition of an organ, during its " development, is not only a " means to an end, but once was " an end in itself." This does not seem to me necessarily to hold good.   Why should not variations occur during an early period of development, having no relation to reversion; yet such variations might be preserved and accumulated, if in any way serviceable, for instance, in shortening and simplifying the course of development ? And again, why should not injurious abnormalities, such as atrophied or hypertrophied parts, which have no relation to a former state of existence, occur at an early period, as well as during maturity ?

[42] 'Anatomy of Vertebrates,' vol. iii. 1868, p. 323.

"The canine is more deeply implanted, and by a "stronger fang than the incisors." Nevertheless, this tooth no longer serves man as a special weapon for tearing his enemies or prey; it may, therefore, as far as its proper function is concerned, be considered as rudimentary. In every large collection of human skulls some may be found, as Häckel[43] observes, with the canine teeth projecting considerably beyond the others in the same manner as in the anthropomorphous apes, but in a less degree. In these cases, open spaces between the teeth in the one jaw are left for the reception of the canines of the opposite jaw. An interspace of this kind in a Kaffir skull, figured by Wagner, is surprisingly wide.[44] Considering how few are the ancient skulls which have been examined, compared to recent skulls, it is an interesting fact that in at least three cases the canines project largely; and in the Naulette jaw they are spoken of as enormous.[45]

Of the anthropomorphous apes the males alone have their canines fully developed; but in the female gorilla, and in a less degree in the female orang, these teeth project considerably beyond the others; therefore the fact, of which I have been assured, that women sometimes have considerably projecting canines, is no serious objection to the belief that their occasional great development in man is a case of reversion to an ape-like progenitor. He who rejects with scorn the belief that the shape of his own canines, and their occasional great development in other men, are due to

[43] 'Generelle Morphologie,' 1866, B. ii. s. clv.

[44] Carl Vogt's 'Lectures on Man,' Eng. translat. 1864, p. 151.

[45] C. Carter Blake, on a jaw from La Naulette, 'Anthropolog. Review,' 1867, p. 295. Schaaffhausen, ibid. 1868, p, 426.

our early forefathers having been provided with these
formidable weapons, will probably reveal, by sneering,
the line of his descent.   For though he no longer
intends, nor has the power, to use these teeth as weapons, he will unconsciously retract his "snarling
muscles" (thus named by Sir C. Bell),[46] so as to expose
them ready for action, like a dog prepared to fight.

Many muscles are occasionally developed in man,
which are proper to the Quadrumana or other mammals.
Professor Vlacovich [47] examined forty male subjects,
and found a muscle, called by him the ischio-pubic, in
nineteen of them; in three others there was a ligament which represented this muscle; and in the
remaining eighteen no trace of it.   In only two out of
thirty female subjects was this muscle developed on
both sides, but in three others the rudimentary ligament was present.   This muscle, therefore, appears to
be much more common in the male than in the female
sex; and on the belief in the descent of man from some
lower form, the fact is intelligible; for it has been
detected in several of the lower animals, and in all of
these it serves exclusively to aid the male in the act of
reproduction.

Mr. J. Wood, in his valuable series of papers,[48] has

[46] 'The Anatomy of Expression,' 1844, pp. 110, 131.

[47] Quoted by Prof. Canestrini
in the 'Annuario,' &c., 1867,
p. 90.

[48] These papers deserve careful study by any one who
desires to learn how frequently
our muscles vary, and in varying
come to resemble those of the
Quadrumana.   The following
references relate to the few points

touched on in my text: 'Proc.
Royal Soc.' vol. xiv. 1865, pp.
379–384; vol. xv. 1866, pp,
241, 242; vol. xv. 1867, p. 544;
vol. xvi 1868, p. 524.   I may
here add that Dr. Murie and
Mr. St. George Mivart have
shewn in their Memoir on the
Lemuroidea ('Transact. Zoolog.
Soc.' vol. vii. 1869, p. 96), how
extraordinarily variable some of
the muscles are in these animals,

minutely described a vast number of muscular variations in man, which resemble normal structures in the lower animals. The muscles which closely resemble those regularly present in our nearest allies, the Quadrumana, are too numerous to be here even specified. In a single male subject, having a strong bodily frame, and well-formed skull, no less than seven muscular variations were observed, all of which plainly represented muscles proper to various kinds of apes. This man, for instance, had on both sides of his neck a true and powerful "*levator claviculæ,*" such as is found in all kinds of apes, and which is said to occur in about one out of sixty human subjects.[49] Again, this man had "a special abductor of the metatarsal bone of the "fifth digit, such as Professor Huxley and Mr. Flower "have shewn to exist uniformly in the higher and "lower apes." I will give only two additional cases; the *acromio-basilar* muscle is found in all mammals below man, and seems to be correlated with a quadrupedal gait,[50] and it occurs in about one out of sixty human subjects. In the lower extremities Mr. Bradley [51] found an *abductor ossis metatarsi quinti* in both feet of man; this muscle had not up to that time been recorded in mankind, but is always present in the anthropomorphous apes. The muscles of the hands and arms—parts which are so eminently characteristic of man—are extremely liable to vary, so as to resemble

the lowest members of the Primates. Gradations, also, in the muscles leading to structures found in animals still lower in the scale, are numerous in the Lemuroidea.

[49] See also Prof. Macalister in 'Proc. R. Irish Academy,' vol. x. 1868, p. 124.

[50] Mr. Champneys in 'Journal of Anat. and Phys.' Nov., 1871, p. 178.

[51] 'Journal of Anat. and Phys.' May, 1872, p. 421.

the corresponding muscles in the lower animals.[52]
Such resemblances are either perfect or imperfect; yet
in the latter case they are manifestly of a transitional
nature.   Certain variations are more common in man,
and others in woman, without our being able to assign
any reason.   Mr. Wood, after describing numerous
variations, makes the following pregnant remark:
"Notable departures from the ordinary type of the
"muscular structures run in grooves or directions,
"which must be taken to indicate some unknown
"factor, of much importance to a comprehensive know-
"ledge of general and scientific anatomy."[53]

That this unknown factor is reversion to a former
state of existence may be admitted as in the highest
degree probable.[54]   It is quite incredible that a man

[52] Prof. Macalister (ibid. p. 121) has tabulated his observations, and finds that muscular abnormalities are most frequent in the fore-arms, secondly, in the face, thirdly, in the foot, &c.

[53] The Rev. Dr. Haughton, after giving ('Proc. R. Irish Academy,' June 27, 1864, p. 715) a remarkable case of variation in the human *flexor pollicis longus*, adds, "This remarkable " example shows that man may " sometimes possess the arrange- " ment of tendons of thumb and " fingers characteristic of the " macaque; but whether such a " case should be regarded as a " macaque passing upwards into " a man, or a man passing " downwards into a macaque, or " as a congenital freak of nature, " I cannot undertake to say." It is satisfactory to hear so capable an anatomist, and so embittered an opponent of

evolutionism, admitting even the possibility of either of his first propositions.   Prof. Macalister has also described ('Proc. R. Irish Acad.' vol. x. 1864, p. 138) variations in the *flexor pollicis longus*, remarkable from their relations to the same muscle in the Quadrumana.

[54] Since the first edition of this book appeared, Mr. Wood has published another memoir in the 'Phil. Transactions,' 1870, p. 83, on the varieties of the muscles of the human neck, shoulder, and chest.   He here shows how extremely variable these muscles are, and how often and how closely the variations resemble the normal muscles of the lower animals.   He sums up by remarking, "It will be " enough for my purpose if I " have succeeded in shewing the " more important forms which, " when occurring as varieties in

should through mere accident abnormally resemble certain apes in no less than seven of his muscles, if there had been no genetic connection between them. On the other hand, if man is descended from some ape-like creature, no valid reason can be assigned why certain muscles should not suddenly reappear after an interval of many thousand generations, in the same manner as with horses, asses, and mules, dark-coloured stripes suddenly reappear on the legs, and shoulders, after an interval of hundreds, or more probably of thousands of generations.

These various cases of reversion are so closely related to those of rudimentary organs given in the first chapter, that many of them might have been indifferently introduced either there or here. Thus a human uterus furnished with cornua may be said to represent, in a rudimentary condition, the same organ in its normal state in certain mammals. Some parts which are rudimentary in man, as the os coccyx in both sexes, and the mammæ in the male sex, are always present; whilst others, such as the supracondyloid foramen, only occasionally appear, and therefore might have been introduced under the head of reversion. These several reversionary structures, as well as the strictly rudimentary ones, reveal the descent of man from some lower form in an unmistakable manner.

Correlated Variation.—In man, as in the lower animals, many structures are so intimately related,

---

"the human subject, tend to "exhibit in a sufficiently marked "manner what may be considered "as proofs and examples of the "Darwinian principle of rever-"sion, or law of inheritance, in "this department of anatomical "science."

that when one part varies so does another, without our
being able, in most cases, to assign any reason. We
cannot say whether the one part governs the other, or
whether both are governed by some earlier developed
part. Various monstrosities, as I. Geoffroy repeatedly
insists, are thus intimately connected. Homologous
structures are particularly liable to change together,
as we see on the opposite sides of the body, and in
the upper and lower extremities. Meckel long ago
remarked, that when the muscles of the arm depart
from their proper type, they almost always imitate
those of the leg; and so, conversely, with the muscles
of the legs. The organs of sight and hearing, the teeth
and hair, the colour of the skin and of the hair, colour
and constitution, are more or less correlated.[55] Professor Schaaffhausen first drew attention to the relation
apparently existing between a muscular frame and the
strongly-pronounced supra-orbital ridges, which are so
characteristic of the lower races of man.

Besides the variations which can be grouped with
more or less probability under the foregoing heads,
there is a large class of variations which may be
provisionally called spontaneous, for to our ignorance
they appear to arise without any exciting cause. It
can, however, be shewn that such variations, whether
consisting of slight individual differences, or of
strongly-marked and abrupt deviations of structure,
depend much more on the constitution of the organism
than on the nature of the conditions to which it has
been subjected.[56]

[55] The authorities for these
several statements are given in
my 'Variation of Animals under
Domestication,' vol. ii. pp. 320–
335.

[56] This whole subject has been

Rate of Increase.—Civilised populations have been known under favourable conditions, as in the United States, to double their numbers in twenty-five years; and, according to a calculation, by Euler, this might occur in a little over twelve years.[57] At the former rate, the present population of the United States (thirty millions), would in 657 years cover the whole terraqueous globe so thickly, that four men would have to stand on each square yard of surface. The primary or fundamental check to the continued increase of man is the difficulty of gaining subsistence, and of living in comfort. We may infer that this is the case from what we see, for instance, in the United States, where subsistence is easy, and there is plenty of room. If such means were suddenly doubled in Great Britain, our number would be quickly doubled. With civilised nations this primary check acts chiefly by restraining marriages. The greater death-rate of infants in the poorest classes is also very important; as well as the greater mortality, from various diseases, of the inhabitants of crowded and miserable houses, at all ages. The effects of severe epidemics and wars are soon counterbalanced, and more than counterbalanced, in nations placed under favourable conditions. Emigration also comes in aid as a temporary check, but, with the extremely poor classes, not to any great extent.

There is reason to suspect, as Malthus has remarked, that the reproductive power is actually less in barbarous, than in civilised races. We know nothing

---

discussed in chap. xxiii. vol. ii. of my 'Variation of Animals and Plants under Domestication.'
[57] See the ever memorable

'Essay on the Principle of Population,' by the Rev. T. Malthus, vol. i. 1826, p. 6, 517.

positively on this head, for with savages no census has been taken; but from the concurrent testimony of missionaries, and of others who have long resided with such people, it appears that their families are usually small, and large ones rare. This may be partly accounted for, as it is believed, by the women suckling their infants during a long time; but it is highly probable that savages, who often suffer much hardship, and who do not obtain so much nutritious food as civilised men, would be actually less prolific. I have shewn in a former work,[58] that all our domesticated quadrupeds and birds, and all our cultivated plants, are more fertile than the corresponding species in a state of nature. It is no valid objection to this conclusion that animals suddenly supplied with an excess of food, or when grown very fat; and that most plants on sudden removal from very poor to very rich soil, are rendered more or less sterile. We might, therefore, expect that civilised men, who in one sense are highly domesticated, would be more prolific than wild men. It is also probable that the increased fertility of civilised nations would become, as with our domestic animals, an inherited character : it is at least known that with mankind a tendency to produce twins runs in families.[59]

Notwithstanding that savages appear to be less prolific than civilised people, they would no doubt rapidly increase if their numbers were not by some means rigidly kept down. The Santali, or hill-tribes of India, have recently afforded a good illustration of

[58] ‘Variation of Animals and Plants under Domestication,’ vol. ii. pp. 111–113, 163.

[59] Mr. Sedgwick, ‘British and Foreign Medico-Chirurg. Review,’ July, 1863, p. 170.

this fact; for, as shewn by Mr. Hunter,[60] they have increased at an extraordinary rate since vaccination has been introduced, other pestilences mitigated, and war sternly repressed. This increase, however, would not have been possible had not these rude people spread into the adjoining districts, and worked for hire. Savages almost always marry; yet there is some prudential restraint, for they do not commonly marry at the earliest possible age. The young men are often required to shew that they can support a wife; and they generally have first to earn the price with which to purchase her from her parents. With savages the difficulty of obtaining subsistence occasionally limits their number in a much more direct manner than with civilised people, for all tribes periodically suffer from severe famines. At such times savages are forced to devour much bad food, and their health can hardly fail to be injured. Many accounts have been published of their protruding stomachs and emaciated limbs after and during famines. They are then, also, compelled to wander much, and, as I was assured in Australia, their infants perish in large numbers. As famines are periodical, depending chiefly on extreme seasons, all tribes must fluctuate in number. They cannot steadily and regularly increase, as there is no artificial increase in the supply of food. Savages, when hard pressed, encroach on each other's territories, and war is the result; but they are indeed almost always at war with their neighbours. They are liable to many accidents on land and water in their search for food; and in some countries they suffer much from the larger beasts

[60] 'The Annals of Rural Bengal,' by W. W. Hunter, 1868, p. 259.

of prey. Even in India, districts have been depopulated by the ravages of tigers.

Malthus has discussed these several checks, but he does not lay stress enough on what is probably the most important of all, namely infanticide, especially of female infants, and the habit of procuring abortion. These practices now prevail in many quarters of the world; and infanticide seems formerly to have prevailed, as Mr. M'Lennan [61] has shewn, on a still more extensive scale. These practices appear to have originated in savages recognising the difficulty, or rather the impossibility of supporting all the infants that are born. Licentiousness may also be added to the foregoing checks; but this does not follow from failing means of subsistence; though there is reason to believe that in some cases (as in Japan) it has been intentionally encouraged as a means of keeping down the population.

If we look back to an extremely remote epoch, before man had arrived at the dignity of manhood, he would have been guided more by instinct and less by reason than are the lowest savages at the present time. Our early semi-human progenitors would not have practised infanticide or polyandry; for the instincts of the lower animals are never so perverted [62] as to lead them re-

---

[61] 'Primitive Marriage,' 1865.

[62] A writer in the 'Spectator' (March 12th, 1871, p. 320) comments as follows on this passage:—" Mr. Darwin finds himself compelled to reintroduce a " new doctrine of the fall of man. " He shews that the instincts of " the higher animals are far " nobler than the habits of " savage races of men, and he

" finds himself, therefore, com- " pelled to re-introduce,—in a " form of the substantial ortho- " doxy of which he appears to " be quite unconscious,—and to " introduce as a scientific hypo- " thesis the doctrine that man's " gain of *knowledge* was the " cause of a temporary but long- " enduring moral deterioration, " as indicated by the many foul

gularly to destroy their own offspring, or to be quite
devoid of jealousy. There would have been no prudential restraint from marriage, and the sexes would
have freely united at an early age. Hence the progenitors of man would have tended to increase rapidly;
but checks of some kind, either periodical or constant,
must have kept down their numbers, even more severely
than with existing savages. What the precise nature
of these checks were, we cannot say, any more than
with most other animals. We know that horses and
cattle, which are not extremely prolific animals, when
first turned loose in South America, increased at an
enormous rate. The elephant, the slowest breeder of
all known animals, would in a few thousand years stock
the whole world. The increase of every species of
monkey must be checked by some means; but not, as
Brehm remarks, by the attacks of beasts of prey. No
one will assume that the actual power of reproduction
in the wild horses and cattle of America, was at first in
any sensible degree increased; or that, as each district
became fully stocked, this same power was diminished.
No doubt in this case, and in all others, many checks
concur, and different checks under different circumstances; periodical dearths, depending on unfavourable
seasons, being probably the most important of all. So
it will have been with the early progenitors of man.

Natural Selection.—We have now seen that man is
variable in body and mind; and that the variations are

" customs, especially as to mar-
" riage, of savage tribes. What
" does the Jewish tradition of
" the moral degeneration of man
" through his snatching at a
" knowledge forbidden him by
" his highest instinct assert
" beyond this?"

induced, either directly or indirectly, by the same general causes, and obey the same general laws, as with the lower animals. Man has spread widely over the face of the earth, and must have been exposed, during his incessant migrations,[63] to the most diversified conditions. The inhabitants of Tierra del Fuego, the Cape of Good Hope, and Tasmania in the one hemisphere, and of the Arctic regions in the other, must have passed through many climates, and changed their habits many times, before they reached their present homes.[64] The early progenitors of man must also have tended, like all other animals, to have increased beyond their means of subsistence; they must, therefore, occasionally have been exposed to a struggle for existence, and consequently to the rigid law of natural selection. Beneficial variations of all kinds will thus, either occasionally or habitually, have been preserved and injurious ones eliminated. I do not refer to strongly-marked deviations of structure, which occur only at long intervals of time, but to mere individual differences. We know, for instance, that the muscles of our hands and feet, which determine our powers of movement, are liable, like those of the lower animals,[65] to incessant variability. If then the progenitors of man inhabiting any district, especially one undergoing some change in its conditions, were divided into two

[63] See some good remarks to this effect by W. Stanley Jevons, "A Deduction from Darwin's "Theory," 'Nature,' 1869, p. 231.

[64] Latham, 'Man and his Migrations,' 1851, p. 135.

[65] Messrs. Murie and Mivart in their 'Anatomy of the Lemuroidea' ('Transact. Zoolog. Soc.' vol. vii. 1869, pp. 96–98) say, "some muscles are so irregular "in their distribution that they "cannot be well classed in any "of the above groups." These muscles differ even on the opposite sides of the same individual.

equal bodies, the one half which included all the individuals best adapted by their powers of movement for gaining subsistence, or for defending themselves, would on an average survive in greater numbers, and procreate more offspring than the other and less well endowed half.

Man in the rudest state in which he now exists is the most dominant animal that has ever appeared on this earth. He has spread more widely than any other highly organised form : and all others have yielded before him. He manifestly owes this immense superiority to his intellectual faculties, to his social habits, which lead him to aid and defend his fellows, and to his corporeal structure. The supreme importance of these characters has been proved by the final arbitrament of the battle for life. Through his powers of intellect, articulate language has been evolved; and on this his wonderful advancement has mainly depended. As Mr. Chauncey Wright remarks :[66] " a psychological " analysis of the faculty of language shews, that even " the smallest proficiency in it might require more " brain power than the greatest proficiency in any " other direction." He has invented and is able to use various weapons, tools, traps, &c., with which he defends himself, kills or catches prey, and otherwise obtains food. He has made rafts or canoes for fishing or crossing over to neighbouring fertile islands. He has discovered the art of making fire, by which hard and stringy roots can be rendered digestible, and poisonous roots or herbs innocuous. This discovery of fire, probably the greatest ever made by man, excepting

[66] Limits of Natural Selection, 'North American Review,' Oct. 1870, p. 295.

language, dates from before the dawn of history. These several inventions, by which man in the rudest state has become so pre-eminent, are the direct results of the development of his powers of observation, memory, curiosity, imagination, and reason. I cannot, therefore, understand how it is that Mr. Wallace [67] maintains, that "natural selection could only have "endowed the savage with a brain a little superior to "that of an ape."

Although the intellectual powers and social habits of man are of paramount importance to him, we must not underrate the importance of his bodily structure, to which subject the remainder of this chapter will be devoted; the development of the intellectual and social or moral faculties being discussed in a later chapter.

Even to hammer with precision is no easy matter, as every one who has tried to learn carpentry will admit. To throw a stone with as true an aim as a Fuegian in defending himself, or in killing birds, requires the most consummate perfection in the correlated action of the

[67] 'Quarterly Review,' April 1869, p. 392. This subject is more fully discussed in Mr. Wallace's 'Contributions to the Theory of Natural Selection,' 1870, in which all the essays referred to in this work are republished. The 'Essay on Man,' has been ably criticised by Prof. Claparède, one of the most distinguished zoologists in Europe, in an article published in the 'Bibliothèque Universelle,' June 1870. The remark quoted in my text will surprise every one who has read Mr. Wallace's celebrated paper on 'The Origin of Human Races deduced from the Theory of Natural Selection,' originally published in the 'Anthropological Review,' May 1864, p. clviii. I cannot here resist quoting a most just remark by Sir J. Lubbock ('Prehistoric Times,' 1865, p. 479) in reference to this paper, namely, that Mr. Wallace, "with characteristic unselfish-"ness, ascribes it (i.e. the idea "of natural selection) unreserv-"edly to Mr. Darwin, although, "as is well known, he struck "out the idea independently, "and published it, though not "with the same elaboration, at "the same time."

muscles of the hand, arm, and shoulder, and, further, a
fine sense of touch. In throwing a stone or spear, and
in many other actions, a man must stand firmly on his
feet; and this again demands the perfect co-adaptation
of numerous muscles. To chip a flint into the rudest
tool, or to form a barbed spear or hook from a bone,
demands the use of a perfect hand; for, as a most
capable judge, Mr. Schoolcraft,[68] remarks, the shaping
fragments of stone into knives, lances, or arrow-heads,
shews " extraordinary ability and long practice." This
is to a great extent proved by the fact that primeval
men practised a division of labour; each man did not
manufacture his own flint tools or rude pottery, but
certain individuals appear to have devoted themselves
to such work, no doubt receiving in exchange the
produce of the chase. Archæologists are convinced
that an enormous interval of time elapsed before our
ancestors thought of grinding chipped flints into
smooth tools. One can hardly doubt, that a man-like
animal who possessed a hand and arm sufficiently
perfect to throw a stone with precision, or to form a
flint into a rude tool, could, with sufficient practice, as
far as mechanical skill alone is concerned, make almost
anything which a civilised man can make. The
structure of the hand in this respect may be compared
with that of the vocal organs, which in the apes are used
for uttering various signal-cries, or, as in one genus,
musical cadences; but in man the closely similar vocal
organs have become adapted through the inherited
effects of use for the utterance of articulate language.

---

[68] Quoted by Mr. Lawson
Tait in his 'Law of Natural
Selection,'—' Dublin Quarterly
Journal of Medical Science,'
Feb. 1869. Dr. Keller is like-
wise quoted to the same effect.

Turning now to the nearest allies of men, and therefore to the best representatives of our early progenitors, we find that the hands of the Quadrumana are constructed on the same general pattern as our own, but are far less perfectly adapted for diversified uses. Their hands do not serve for locomotion so well as the feet of a dog; as may be seen in such monkeys as the chimpanzee and orang, which walk on the outer margins of the palms, or on the knuckles.[69] Their hands, however, are admirably adapted for climbing trees. Monkeys seize thin branches or ropes, with the thumb on one side and the fingers and palm on the other, in the same manner as we do. They can thus also lift rather large objects, such as the neck of a bottle, to their mouths. Baboons turn over stones, and scratch up roots with their hands. They seize nuts, insects, or other small objects with the thumb in opposition to the fingers, and no doubt they thus extract eggs and the young from the nests of birds. American monkeys beat the wild oranges on the branches until the rind is cracked, and then tear it off with the fingers of the two hands. In a wild state they break open hard fruits with stones. Other monkeys open mussel-shells with the two thumbs. With their fingers they pull out thorns and burs, and hunt for each other's parasites. They roll down stones, or throw them at their enemies: nevertheless, they are clumsy in these various actions, and, as I have myself seen, are quite unable to throw a stone with precision.

It seems to me far from true that because "objects "are grasped clumsily" by monkeys, "a much less "specialised organ of prehension" would have served

[69] Owen, 'Anatomy of Vertebrates,' vol. iii. p. 71.

them [70] equally well with their present hands. On the contrary, I see no reason to doubt that more perfectly constructed hands would have been an advantage to them, provided that they were not thus rendered less fitted for climbing trees. We may suspect that a hand as perfect as that of man would have been disadvantageous for climbing; for the most arboreal monkeys in the world, namely, Ateles in America, Colobus in Africa, and Hylobates in Asia, are either thumbless, or their toes partially cohere, so that their limbs are converted into mere grasping hooks. [71]

As soon as some ancient member in the great series of the Primates came to be less arboreal, owing to a change in its manner of procuring subsistence, or to some change in the surrounding conditions, its habitual manner of progression would have been modified: and thus it would have been rendered more strictly quadrupedal or bipedal. Baboons frequent hilly and rocky districts, and only from necessity climb high trees; [72] and they have acquired almost the gait of a dog. Man alone has become a biped; and we can, I think, partly see how he has come to assume his erect attitude, which forms one of his most conspicuous characters. Man could not have attained his present dominant position in the world without the use of his hands,

[70] 'Quarterly Review,' April 1869, p. 392.

[71] In *Hylobates syndactylus*, as the name expresses, two of the toes regularly cohere; and this, as Mr. Blyth informs me, is occasionally the case with the toes of *H. agilis, lar*, and *leuciscus.* Colobus is strictly arboreal and extraordinarily active (Brehm, 'Thierleben,' B. i. s. 50), but whether a better climber than the species of the allied genera, I do not know. It deserves notice that the feet of the sloths, the most arboreal animals in the world, are wonderfully hook-like.

[72] Brehm, 'Thierleben,' B. i. s. 80.

which are so admirably adapted to act in obedience to
his will. Sir C. Bell[73] insists that " the hand supplies
" all instruments, and by its correspondence with the
" intellect gives him universal dominion." But the
hands and arms could hardly have become perfect
enough to have manufactured weapons, or to have
hurled stones and spears with a true aim, as long as
they were habitually used for locomotion and for
supporting the whole weight of the body, or, as before
remarked, so long as they were especially fitted for
climbing trees. Such rough treatment would also
have blunted the sense of touch, on which their
delicate use largely depends. From these causes alone
it would have been an advantage to man to become a
biped; but for many actions it is indispensable that
the arms and whole upper part of the body should be
free; and he must for this end stand firmly on his
feet. To gain this great advantage, the feet have been
rendered flat; and the great toe has been peculiarly
modified, though this has entailed the almost complete
loss of its power of prehension. It accords with the
principle of the division of physiological labour, prevailing throughout the animal kingdom, that as the
hands became perfected for prehension, the feet should
have become perfected for support and locomotion.
With some savages, however, the foot has not
altogether lost its prehensile power, as shewn by
their manner of climbing trees, and of using them in
other ways.[74]

[73] " The Hand," &c. ' Bridgewater Treatise,' 1833, p. 38.

[74] Häckel has an excellent
discussion on the steps by which
man became a biped : ' Na-

türliche Schöpfungsgeschichte,'
1868 s. 507. Dr. Büchner
(' Conférences sur la Théorie
Darwinienne,' 1869, p. 135) has
given good cases of the use of

If it be an advantage to man to stand firmly on his feet and to have his hands and arms free, of which, from his pre-eminent success in the battle of life there can be no doubt, then I can see no reason why it should not have been advantageous to the progenitors of man to have become more and more erect or bipedal. They would thus have been better able to defend themselves with stones or clubs, to attack their prey, or otherwise to obtain food. The best built individuals would in the long run have succeeded best, and have survived in larger numbers. If the gorilla and a few allied forms had become extinct, it might have been argued, with great force and apparent truth, that an animal could not have been gradually converted from a quadruped into a biped, as all the individuals in an intermediate condition would have been miserably ill-fitted for progression. But we know (and this is well worthy of reflection) that the anthropomorphous apes are now actually in an intermediate condition; and no one doubts that they are on the whole well adapted for their conditions of life. Thus the gorilla runs with a sidelong shambling gait, but more commonly progresses by resting on its bent hands. The long-armed apes occasionally use their arms like crutches, swinging their bodies forward between them, and some kinds of Hylobates, without having been taught, can walk or run upright with tolerable quickness; yet they move awkwardly, and much less securely than man. We see, in short, in existing

---

the foot as a prehensile organ by man; and has also written on the manner of progression of the higher apes, to which I allude in the following paragraph: see also Owen ('Anatomy of Vertebrates,' vol. iii. p. 71) on this latter subject.

monkeys a manner of progression intermediate between
that of a quadruped and a biped; but, as an un-
prejudiced judge[75] insists, the anthropomorphous apes
approach in structure more nearly to the bipedal than
to the quadrupedal type.

As the progenitors of man became more and more
erect, with their hands and arms more and more
modified for prehension and other purposes, with their
feet and legs at the same time transformed for firm
support and progression, endless other changes of
structure would have become necessary. The pelvis
would have to be broadened, the spine peculiarly
curved, and the head fixed in an altered position, all
which changes have been attained by man. Prof.
Schaaffhausen[76] maintains that " the powerful mastoid
" processes of the human skull are the result of his
" erect position;" and these processes are absent in
the orang, chimpanzee, &c., and are smaller in the
gorilla than in man. Various other structures, which
appear connected with man's erect position, might
here have been added. It is very difficult to decide
how far these correlated modifications are the result of
natural selection, and how far of the inherited effects
of the increased use of certain parts, or of the action
of one part on another. No doubt these means of
change often co-operate : thus when certain muscles,
and the crests of bone to which they are attached,
become enlarged by habitual use, this shews that

[75] Prof. Broca, La Constitution des Vertèbres caudales;
' La Revue d'Anthropologie,'
1872, p. 26, (separate copy).
[76] ' On the Primitive Form
of the Skull,' translated in ' Anthropological Review,' Oct. 1868,
p. 428. Owen (' Anatomy of
Vertebrates,' vol. ii. 1866, p.
551) on the mastoid processes
in the higher apes.

certain actions are habitually performed and must be serviceable. Hence the individuals which performed them best, would tend to survive in greater numbers.

The free use of the arms and hands, partly the cause and partly the result of man's erect position, appears to have led in an indirect manner to other modifications of structure. The early male forefathers of man were, as previously stated, probably furnished with great canine teeth; but as they gradually acquired the habit of using stones, clubs, or other weapons, for fighting with their enemies or rivals, they would use their jaws and teeth less and less. In this case, the jaws, together with the teeth, would become reduced in size, as we may feel almost sure from innumerable analogous cases. In a future chapter we shall meet with a closely parallel case, in the reduction or complete disappearance of the canine teeth in male ruminants, apparently in relation with the development of their horns; and in horses, in relation to their habit of fighting with their incisor teeth and hoofs.

In the adult male anthropomorphous apes, as Rütimeyer,[77] and others, have insisted, it is the effect on the skull of the great development of the jaw-muscles that causes it to differ so greatly in many respects from that of man, and has given to these animals " a truly frightful physiognomy." Therefore, as the jaws and teeth in man's progenitors gradually become reduced in size, the adult skull would have come to resemble more and more that of existing man. As we shall hereafter see, a great reduction of the

[77] 'Die Grenzen der Thierwelt, eine Betrachtung zu Darwin's Lehre,' 1868, s. 51.

canine teeth in the males would almost certainly affect the teeth of the females through inheritance.

As the various mental faculties gradually developed themselves the brain would almost certainly become larger. No one, I presume, doubts that the large proportion which the size of man's brain bears to his body, compared to the same proportion in the gorilla or orang, is closely connected with his higher mental powers. We meet with closely analogous facts with insects, for in ants the cerebral ganglia are of extraordinary dimensions, and in all the Hymenoptera these ganglia are many times larger than in the less intelligent orders, such as beetles.[78] On the other hand, no one supposes that the intellect of any two animals or of any two men can be accurately gauged by the cubic contents of their skulls. It is certain that there may be extraordinary mental activity with an extremely small absolute mass of nervous matter: thus the wonderfully diversified instincts, mental powers, and affections of ants are notorious, yet their cerebral ganglia are not so large as the quarter of a small pin's head. Under this point of view, the brain of an ant is one of the most marvellous atoms of matter in the world, perhaps more so than the brain of a man.

The belief that there exists in man some close relation between the size of the brain and the development of the intellectual faculties is supported by the comparison of the skulls of savage and civilised races,

[78] Dujardin, 'Annales des Sc. Nat.' 3rd series Zoolog. tom. xiv. 1850, p. 203. See also Mr. Lowne, 'Anatomy and Phys. of the *Musca vomitoria*,' 1870, p. 14. My son, Mr. F. Darwin, dissected for me the cerebral ganglia of the *Formica rufa*.

of ancient and modern people, and by the analogy of the whole vertebrate series. Dr. J. Barnard Davis has proved,[79] by many careful measurements, that the mean internal capacity of the skull in Europeans is 92·3 cubic inches; in Americans 87·5; in Asiatics 87·1; and in Australians only 81·9 cubic inches. Professor Broca[80] found that the nineteenth century skulls from graves in Paris were larger than those from vaults of the twelfth century, in the proportion of 1484 to 1426; and that the increased size, as ascertained by measurements, was exclusively in the frontal part of the skull—the seat of the intellectual faculties. Prichard is persuaded that the present inhabitants of Britain have "much more capacious brain-cases" than the ancient inhabitants. Nevertheless, it must be admitted that some skulls of very high antiquity, such as the famous one of Neanderthal, are well developed and capacious.[81] With respect to the lower animals, M. E. Lartet,[82] by comparing the crania of tertiary and recent mammals belonging to the same groups, has come to the remarkable conclusion that the brain

[79] 'Philosophical Transactions,' 1869, p. 513.

[80] 'Les Sélections,' M. P. Broca, 'Revue d'Anthropologies,' 1873; see also, as quoted in C. Vogt's 'Lectures on Man,' Eng. translat. 1864, pp. 88, 90. Prichard, 'Phys. Hist. of Mankind,' vol. i. 1838, p. 305.

[81] In the interesting article just referred to, Prof. Broca has well remarked, that in civilised nations, the average capacity of the skull must be lowered by the preservation of a considerable number of individuals, weak in mind and body, who would have been promptly eliminated in the savage state. On the other hand, with savages, the average includes only the more capable individuals, who have been able to survive under extremely hard conditions of life. Broca thus explains the otherwise inexplicable fact, that the mean capacity of the skull of the ancient Troglodytes of Lozère is greater than that of modern Frenchmen.

[82] 'Comptes-rendus des Sciences,' &c., June 1, 1868.

is generally larger and the convolutions are more complex in the more recent forms. On the other hand, I have shewn[83] that the brains of domestic rabbits are considerably reduced in bulk, in comparison with those of the wild rabbit or hare; and this may be attributed to their having been closely confined during many generations, so that they have exerted their intellect, instincts, senses and voluntary movements but little.

The gradually increasing weight of the brain and skull in man must have influenced the development of the supporting spinal column, more especially whilst he was becoming erect. As this change of position was being brought about, the internal pressure of the brain will also have influenced the form of the skull; for many facts shew how easily the skull is thus affected. Ethnologists believe that it is modified by the kind of cradle in which infants sleep. Habitual spasms of the muscles, and a cicatrix from a severe burn, have permanently modified the facial bones. In young persons whose heads have become fixed either sideways or backwards, owing to disease, one of the two eyes has changed its position, and the shape of the skull has been altered apparently by the pressure of the brain in a new direction.[84] I have shewn that

[83] ' The Variation of Animals and Plants under Domestication,' vol. i. pp. 124–129.

[84] Schaaffhausen gives from Blumenbach and Busch, the cases of the spasms and cicatrix, in ' Anthropolog. Review,' Oct. 1868, p. 420. Dr. Jarrold ('Anthropologia,' 1808, pp. 115, 116) adduces from Camper and from his own observations, cases of the modification of the skull from the head being fixed in an unnatural position. He believes that in certain trades, such as that of a shoemaker, where the head is habitually held forward, the forehead becomes more rounded and prominent.

with long-eared rabbits even so trifling a cause as the lopping forward of one ear drags forward almost every bone of the skull on that side; so that the bones on the opposite side no longer strictly correspond. Lastly, if any animal were to increase or diminish much in general size, without any change in its mental powers, or if the mental powers were to be much increased or diminished, without any great change in the size of the body, the shape of the skull would almost certainly be altered. I infer this from my observations on domestic rabbits, some kinds of which have become very much larger than the wild animal, whilst others have retained nearly the same size, but in both cases the brain has been much reduced relatively to the size of the body. Now I was at first much surprised on finding that in all these rabbits the skull had become elongated or dolichoce-phalic; for instance, of two skulls of nearly equal breadth, the one from a wild rabbit and the other from a large domestic kind, the former was 3·15 and the latter 4·3 inches in length.[85] One of the most marked distinctions in different races of men is that the skull in some is elongated, and in others rounded; and here the explanation suggested by the case of the rabbits may hold good; for Welcker finds that short " men incline more to brachycephaly, and tall men to " dolichocephaly;"[86] and tall men may be compared with the larger and longer-bodied rabbits, all of which have elongated skulls, or are dolichocephalic.

[85] 'Variation of Animals,' &c., vol. i. p. 117, on the elongation of the skull; p. 119, on the effect of the lopping of one ear.

[86] Quoted by Schaaffhausen, in 'Anthropolog. Review,' Oct. 1868, p. 419.

From these several facts we can understand, to a certain extent, the means by which the great size and more or less rounded form of the skull have been acquired by man; and these are characters eminently distinctive of him in comparison with the lower animals.

Another most conspicuous difference between man and the lower animals is the nakedness of his skin. Whales and porpoises (Cetacea), dugongs (Sirenia) and the hippopotamus are naked; and this may be advantageous to them for gliding through the water; nor would it be injurious to them from the loss of warmth, as the species, which inhabit the colder regions, are protected by a thick layer of blubber, serving the same purpose as the fur of seals and otters.   Elephants and rhinoceroses are almost hairless; and as certain extinct species, which formerly lived under an Arctic climate, were covered with long wool or hair, it would almost appear as if the existing species of both genera had lost their hairy covering from exposure to heat. This appears the more probable, as the elephants in India which live on elevated and cool districts are more hairy [87] than those on the lowlands.   May we then infer that man became divested of hair from having aboriginally inhabited some tropical land ?   That the hair is chiefly retained in the male sex on the chest and face, and in both sexes at the junction of all four limbs with the trunk, favours this inference — on the assumption that the hair was lost before man became erect; for the parts which now retain most hair would then have been most protected from the heat of the sun.   The crown of the head, however, offers a curious

[87] Owen, 'Anatomy of Vertebrates,' vol. iii. p. 619.

exception, for at all times it must have been one of the
most exposed parts, yet it is thickly clothed with hair.
The fact, however, that the other members of the order
of Primates, to which man belongs, although inhabiting
various hot regions, are well clothed with hair, generally
thickest on the upper surface,[88] is opposed to the supposition that man became naked through the action of
the sun.   Mr. Belt believes [89] that within the tropics it
is an advantage to man to be destitute of hair, as he is
thus enabled to free himself of the multitude of ticks
(acari) and other parasites, with which he is often
infested, and which sometimes cause ulceration.   But
whether this evil is of sufficient magnitude to have led
to the denudation of his body through natural selection,
may be doubted, since none of the many quadrupeds
inhabiting the tropics have, as far as I know, acquired
any specialised means of relief.   The view which seems
to me the most probable is that man, or rather
primarily woman, became divested of hair for ornamental purposes, as we shall see under Sexual Selection ;
and, according to this belief, it is not surprising that
man should differ so greatly in hairiness from all other
Primates, for characters, gained through sexual selec-

[88] Isidore Geoffroy St.-Hilaire
remarks ('Hist. Nat. Générale,'
tom. ii. 1859, pp. 215–217) on
the head of man being covered
with long hair; also on the
upper surfaces of monkeys and
of other mammals being more
thickly clothed than the lower
surfaces. This has likewise been
observed by various authors.
Prof. P. Gervais ('Hist. Nat. des
Mammifères,' tom. i. 1854, p.
28), however, states that in the

Gorilla the hair is thinner on the
back, where it is partly rubbed
off, than on the lower surface.
[89] The 'Naturalist in Nicaragua,' 1874, p. 209. As some
confirmation of Mr. Belt's view,
I may quote the following passage from Sir W. Denison ('Varieties of Vice-Regal Life,' vol. i.
1870, p. 440) : "It is said to be
"a practice with the Australians,
"when the vermin get trouble-
"some, to singe themselves."

tion, often differ to an extraordinary degree in closely
related forms.

According to a popular impression, the absence of a
tail is eminently distinctive of man; but as those apes
which come nearest to him are destitute of this organ,
its disappearance does not relate exclusively to man.
The tail often differs remarkably in length within the
same genus: thus in some species of Macacus it is
longer than the whole body, and is formed of twenty-
four vertebræ; in others it consists of a scarcely visible
stump, containing only three or four vertebræ.   In
some kinds of baboons there are twenty-five, whilst in
the mandrill there are ten very small stunted caudal
vertebræ, or, according to Cuvier,[90] sometimes only
five.   The tail, whether it be long or short, almost
always tapers towards the end; and this, I presume,
results from the atrophy of the terminal muscles,
together with their arteries and nerves, through disuse,
leading to the atrophy of the terminal bones.   But no
explanation can at present be given of the great
diversity which often occurs in its length.   Here,
however, we are more specially concerned with the
complete external disappearance of the tail.   Professor
Broca has recently shewn[91] that the tail in all quadrupeds consists of two portions, generally separated
abruptly from each other; the basal portion consists
of vertebræ, more or less perfectly channelled and
furnished with apophyses like ordinary vertebræ;
whereas those of the terminal portion are not chan-

[90] Mr. St. George Mivart,
'Proc. Zoolog. Soc.' 1865, pp.
562, 583. Dr. J. E. Gray, 'Cat.
Brit. Mus.: Skeletons.' Owen,
'Anatomy of Vertebrates,' vol.
ii. p. 517.   Isidore Geoffroy,
'Hist. Nat. Gén.' tom. ii. p. 244.
[91] 'Revue d'Anthropologie,'
1872; 'La Constitution des
Vertèbres caudales.'

nelled, are almost smooth, and scarcely resemble true
vertebræ.   A tail, though not externally visible, is
really present in man and the anthropomorphous apes,
and is constructed on exactly the same pattern in both.
In the terminal portion the vertebræ, constituting the
os coccyx, are quite rudimentary, being much reduced in
size and number.   In the basal portion, the vertebræ
are likewise few, are united firmly together, and are
arrested in development; but they have been rendered
much broader and flatter than the corresponding vertebræ in the tails of other animals: they constitute
what Broca calls the accessory sacral vertebræ.   These
are of functional importance by supporting certain
internal parts and in other ways; and their modification is directly connected with the erect or semi-erect
attitude of man and the anthropomorphous apes.   This
conclusion is the more trustworthy, as Broca formerly
held a different·view, which he has now abandoned.
The modification, therefore, of the basal caudal vertebræ in man and the higher apes may have been
effected, directly or indirectly, through natural selection.

But what are we to say about the rudimentary and
variable vertebræ of the terminal portion of the tail,
forming the *os coccyx?*   A notion which has often been,
and will no doubt again be ridiculed, namely, that
friction has had something to do with the disappearance of the external portion of the tail, is not so
ridiculous as it at first appears.   Dr. Anderson[92] states
that the extremely short tail of *Macacus brunneus* is
formed of eleven vertebræ, including the imbedded
basal ones.   The extremity is tendinous and contains

[92] 'Proc. Zoolog. Soc.,' 1872, p. 210.

no vertebræ; this is succeeded by five rudimentary
ones, so minute that together they are only one line
and a half in length, and these are permanently bent
to one side in the shape of a hook. The free part of
the tail, only a little above an inch in length, includes
only four more small vertebræ. This short tail is
carried erect; but about a quarter of its total length is
doubled on to itself to the left; and this terminal part,
which includes the hook-like portion, serves "to fill up
"the interspace between the upper divergent portion
"of the calosities;" so that the animal sits on it, and
thus renders it rough and callous. Dr. Anderson thus
sums up his observations: "These facts seem to me to
"have only one explanation; this tail, from its short
"size, is in the monkey's way when it sits down, and
"frequently becomes placed under the animal while it
"is in this attitude; and from the circumstance that
"it does not extend beyond the extremity of the ischial
"tuberosities, it seems as if the tail originally had been
"bent round by the will of the animal, into the inter-
"space between the callosities, to escape being pressed
"between them and the ground, and that in time the
"curvature became permanent, fitting in of itself when
"the organ happens to be sat upon." Under these
circumstances it is not surprising that the surface of
the tail should have been roughened and rendered
callous, and Dr. Murie,[93] who carefully observed this
species in the Zoological Gardens, as well as three
other closely allied forms with slightly longer tails,
says that when the animal sits down, the tail "is
"necessarily thrust to one side of the buttocks; and
"whether long or short its root is consequently liable

[93] 'Proc. Zoolog. Soc.,' 1872, p. 786.

" to be rubbed or chafed." As we now have evidence
that mutilations occasionally produce an inherited
effect,[94] it is not very improbable that in short-tailed
monkeys, the projecting part of the tail, being functionally useless, should after many generations have
become rudimentary and distorted, from being continually rubbed and chafed. We see the projecting
part in this condition in the *Macacus brunneus*, and
absolutely aborted in the *M. ecaudatus* and in several
of the higher apes. Finally, then, as far as we can
judge, the tail has disappeared in man and the anthropomorphous apes, owing to the terminal portion having
been injured by friction during a long lapse of time ;
the basal and embedded portion having been reduced
and modified, so as to become suitable to the erect or
semi-erect position.

I have now endeavoured to shew that some of the
most distinctive characters of man have in all probability been acquired, either directly, or more commonly
indirectly, through natural selection. We should bear
in mind that modifications in structure or constitution
which do not serve to adapt an organism to its habits
of life, to the food which it consumes, or passively to
the surrounding conditions, cannot have been thus
acquired. We must not, however, be too confident in
deciding what modifications are of service to each

[94] I allude to Dr. Brown-
Séquard's observations on the
transmitted effect of an operation causing epilepsy in guinea-
pigs, and likewise more recently
on the analogous effects of cutting the sympathetic nerve in
the neck. I shall hereafter
have occasion to refer to Mr.
Salvin's interesting case of the
apparently inherited effects of
mot-mots biting off the barbs of
their own tail-feathers. See also
on the general subject 'Variation
of Animals and Plants under Domestication,' vol. ii. pp. 22–24.

being : we should remember how little we know about
the use of many parts, or what changes in the blood
or tissues may serve to fit an organism for a new
climate or new kinds of food. Nor must we forget the
principle of correlation, by which, as Isidore Geoffroy
has shewn in the case of man, many strange deviations
of structure are tied together. Independently of
correlation, a change in one part often leads, through
the increased or decreased use of other parts, to other
changes of a quite unexpected nature. It is also well
to reflect on such facts, as the wonderful growth of
galls on plants caused by the poison of an insect, and
on the remarkable changes of colour in the plumage of
parrots when fed on certain fishes, or inoculated with
the poison of toads ;[95] for we can thus see that the
fluids of the system, if altered for some special purpose,
might induce other changes. We should especially
bear in mind that modifications acquired and continually
used during past ages for some useful purpose, would
probably become firmly fixed, and might be long
inherited.

Thus a large yet undefined extension may safely be
given to the direct and indirect results of natural
selection ; but I now admit, after reading the essay by
Nägeli on plants, and the remarks by various authors
with respect to animals, more especially those recently
made by Professor Broca, that in the earlier editions
of my 'Origin of Species' I perhaps attributed too
much to the action of natural selection or the survival
of the fittest. I have altered the fifth edition of the
'Origin' so as to confine my remarks to adaptive

[95] 'The Variation of Animals and Plants under Domestication,'
vol. ii. pp. 280, 282.

changes of structure; but I am convinced, from the light gained during even the last few years, that very many structures which now appear to us useless, will hereafter be proved to be useful, and will therefore come within the range of natural selection. Nevertheless, I did not formerly consider sufficiently the existence of structures, which, as far as we can at present judge, are neither beneficial nor injurious; and this I believe to be one of the greatest oversights as yet detected in my work. I may be permitted to say, as some excuse, that I had two distinct objects in view; firstly, to shew that species had not been separately created, and secondly, that natural selection had been the chief agent of change, though largely aided by the inherited effects of habit, and slightly by the direct action of the surrounding conditions. I was not, however, able to annul the influence of my former belief, then almost universal, that each species had been purposely created; and this led to my tacit assumption that every detail of structure, excepting rudiments, was of some special, though unrecognised, service. Any one with this assumption in his mind would naturally extend too far the action of natural selection, either during past or present times. Some of those who admit the principle of evolution, but reject natural selection, seem to forget, when criticising my book, that I had the above two objects in view; hence if I have erred in giving to natural selection great power, which I am very far from admitting, or in having exaggerated its power, which is in itself probable, I have at least, as I hope, done good service in aiding to overthrow the dogma of separate creations.

It is, as I can now see, probable that all organic

beings, including man, possess peculiarities of structure, which neither are now, nor were formerly of any service to them, and which, therefore, are of no physiological importance. We know not what produces the numberless slight differences between the individuals of each species, for reversion only carries the problem a few steps backwards, but each peculiarity must have had its efficient cause. If these causes, whatever they may be, were to act more uniformly and energetically during a lengthened period (and against this no reason can be assigned), the result would probably be not a mere slight individual difference, but a well-marked and constant modification, though one of no physiological importance. Changed structures, which are in no way beneficial, cannot be kept uniform through natural selection, though the injurious will be thus eliminated. Uniformity of character would, however, naturally follow from the assumed uniformity of the exciting causes, and likewise from the free intercrossing of many individuals. During successive periods, the same organism might in this manner acquire successive modifications, which would be transmitted in a nearly uniform state as long as the exciting causes remained the same and there was free intercrossing. With respect to the exciting causes we can only say, as when speaking of so-called spontaneous variations, that they relate much more closely to the constitution of the varying organism, than to the nature of the conditions to which it has been subjected.

Conclusion.—In this chapter we have seen that as man at the present day is liable, like every other animal, to multiform individual differences or slight

variations, so no doubt were the early progenitors of
man; the variations being formerly induced by the
same general causes, and governed by the same general
and complex laws as at present. As all animals tend
to multiply beyond their means of subsistence, so it
must have been with the progenitors of man; and this
would inevitably lead to a struggle for existence and
to natural selection. The latter process would be
greatly aided by the inherited effects of the increased
use of parts, and these two processes would incessantly
react on each other. It appears, also, as we shall
hereafter see, that various unimportant characters have
been acquired by man through sexual selection. An
unexplained residuum of change must be left to the
assumed uniform action of those unknown agencies,
which occasionally induce strongly marked and abrupt
deviations of structure in our domestic productions.

Judging from the habits of savages and of the
greater number of the Quadrumana, primeval men, and
even their ape-like progenitors, probably lived in
society. With strictly social animals, natural selection
sometimes acts on the individual, through the preservation of variations which are beneficial to the
community. A community which includes a large
number of well-endowed individuals increases in
number, and is victorious over other less favoured ones;
even although each separate member gains no advantage
over the others of the same community. Associated
insects have thus acquired many remarkable structures,
which are of little or no service to the individual, such
as the pollen-collecting apparatus, or the sting of the
worker-bee, or the great jaws of soldier-ants. With
the higher social animals, I am not aware that any

structure has been modified solely for the good of the community, though some are of secondary service to it. For instance, the horns of ruminants and the great canine teeth of baboons appear to have been acquired by the males as weapons for sexual strife, but they are used in defence of the herd or troop. In regard to certain mental powers the case, as we shall see in the fifth chapter, is wholly different; for these faculties have been chiefly, or even exclusively, gained for the benefit of the community, and the individuals thereof have at the same time gained an advantage indirectly.

It has often been objected to such views as the foregoing, that man is one of the most helpless and defenceless creatures in the world; and that during his early and less well-developed condition, he would have been still more helpless. The Duke of Argyll, for instance, insists [96] that " the human frame has diverged "from the structure of brutes, in the direction of "greater physical helplessness and weakness. That is "to say, it is a divergence which of all others it is "most impossible to ascribe to mere natural selection." He adduces the naked and unprotected state of the body, the absence of great teeth or claws for defence, the small strength and speed of man, and his slight power of discovering food or of avoiding danger by smell. To these deficiencies there might be added one still more serious, namely, that he cannot climb quickly, and so escape from enemies. The loss of hair would not have been a great injury to the inhabitants of a a warm country. For we know that the unclothed Fuegians can exist under a wretched climate. When

[96] ' Primeval Man,' 1869, p. 66.

we compare the defenceless state of man with that of apes, we must remember that the great canine teeth with which the latter are provided, are possessed in their full development by the males alone, and are chiefly used by them for fighting with their rivals; yet the females, which are not thus provided, manage to survive.

In regard to bodily size or strength, we do not know whether man is descended from some small species, like the chimpanzee, or from one as powerful as the gorilla; and, therefore, we cannot say whether man has become larger and stronger, or smaller and weaker, than his ancestors. We should, however, bear in mind than an animal possessing great size, strength, and ferocity, and which, like the gorilla, could defend itself from all enemies, would not perhaps have become social: and this would most effectually have checked the acquirement of the higher mental qualities, such as sympathy and the love of his fellows. Hence it might have been an immense advantage to man to have sprung from some comparatively weak creature.

The small strength and speed of man, his want of natural weapons, &c., are more than counterbalanced, firstly, by his intellectual powers, through which he has formed for himself weapons, tools, &c., though still remaining in a barbarous state, and, secondly, by his social qualities which lead him to give and receive aid from his fellow-men. No country in the world abounds in a greater degree with dangerous beasts than Southern Africa; no country presents more fearful physical hardships than the Arctic regions; yet one of the puniest of races, that of the Bushmen, maintains itself in Southern Africa, as do the dwarfed Esquimaux in the Arctic regions.   The ancestors of man were, no doubt, inferior in intellect, and probably in social disposition, to the lowest existing savages; but it is quite conceivable that they might have existed, or even flourished, if they had advanced in intellect, whilst gradually losing their brute-like powers, such as that of climbing trees, &c.   But these ancestors would not have been exposed to any special danger, even if far more helpless and defenceless than any existing savages, had they inhabited some warm continent or large island, such as Australia, New Guinea, or Borneo, which is now the home of the orang.   And natural selection arising from the competition of tribe with tribe, in some such large area as one of these, together with the inherited effects of habit, would, under favourable conditions, have sufficed to raise man to his present high position in the organic scale.

CHAPTER III.

Comparison of the Mental Powers of Man and the Lower Animals.

The difference in mental power between the highest ape and the lowest savage, immense—Certain instincts in common—The emotions—Curiosity—Imitation—Attention—Memory—Imagination—Reason—Progressive improvement—Tools and weapons used by animals—Abstraction, self-consciousness—Language—Sense of Beauty—Belief in God, spiritual agencies, superstitions.

WE have seen in the last two chapters that man bears in his bodily structure clear traces of his descent from some lower form; but it may be urged that, as man differs so greatly in his mental power from all other animals, there must be some error in this conclusion. No doubt the difference in this respect is enormous, even if we compare the mind of one of the lowest savages, who has no words to express any number higher than four, and who uses hardly any abstract terms for common objects or for the affections,[1] with that of the most highly organised ape. The difference would, no doubt, still remain immense, even if one of the higher apes had been improved or civilised as much as a dog has been in comparison with its parent-form, the wolf or jackal. The Fuegians rank amongst the lowest barbarians; but I was continually struck with

[1] See the evidence on those points, as given by Lubbock, 'Prehistoric Times,' p. 354, &c.

surprise how closely the three natives on board H.M.S. "Beagle," who had lived some years in England, and could talk a little English, resembled us in disposition and in most of our mental faculties. If no organic being excepting man had possessed any mental power, or if his powers had been of a wholly different nature from those of the lower animals, then we should never have been able to convince ourselves that our high faculties had been gradually developed. But it can be shewn that there is no fundamental difference of this kind. We must also admit that there is a much wider interval in mental power between one of the lowest fishes, as a lamprey or lancelet, and one of the higher apes, than between an ape and man; yet this interval is filled up by numberless gradations.

Nor is the difference slight in moral disposition between a barbarian, such as the man described by the old navigator Byron, who dashed his child on the rocks for dropping a basket of sea-urchins, and a Howard or Clarkson; and in intellect, between a savage who uses hardly any abstract terms, and a Newton or Shakspeare Differences of this kind between the highest men of the highest races and the lowest savages, are connected by the finest gradations. Therefore it is possible that they might pass and be developed into each other.

My object in this chapter is to shew that there is no fundamental difference between man and the higher mammals in their mental faculties. Each division of the subject might have been extended into a separate essay, but must here be treated briefly. As no classification of the mental powers has been universally accepted, I shall arrange my remarks in the order most convenient for my purpose; and will select those facts which have struck me most, with the hope that they may produce some effect on the reader.

With respect to animals very low in the scale, I shall give some additional facts under Sexual Selection, shewing that their mental powers are much higher than might have been expected. The variability of the faculties in the individuals of the same species is an important point for us, and some few illustrations will here be given. But it would be superfluous to enter into many details on this head, for I have found on frequent enquiry, that it is the unanimous opinion of all those who have long attended to animals of many kinds, including birds, that the individuals differ greatly in every mental characteristic. In what manner the mental powers were first developed in the lowest organisms, is as hopeless an enquiry as how life itself first originated. These are problems for the distant future, if they are ever to be solved by man.

As man possesses the same senses as the lower animals, his fundamental intuitions must be the same. Man has also some few instincts in common, as that of self-preservation, sexual love, the love of the mother for her new-born offspring, the desire possessed by the latter to suck, and so forth. But man, perhaps, has somewhat fewer instincts than those possessed by the animals which come next to him in the series. The orang in the Eastern islands, and the chimpanzee in Africa, build platforms on which they sleep; and, as both species follow the same habit, it might be argued that this was due to instinct, but we cannot feel sure that it is not the result of both animals having similar wants, and possessing similar powers of reasoning. These apes, as we may assume, avoid the many

poisonous fruits of the tropics, and man has no such
knowledge : but as our domestic animals, when taken
to foreign lands, and when first turned out in the
spring, often eat poisonous herbs, which they afterwards avoid, we cannot feel sure that the apes do not
learn from their own experience or from that of their
parents what fruits to select. It is, however, certain,
as we shall presently see, that apes have an instinctive
dread of serpents, and probably of other dangerous
animals.

The fewness and the comparative simplicity of the
instincts in the higher animals are remarkable in
contrast with those of the lower animals. Cuvier
maintained that instinct and intelligence stand in an
inverse ratio to each other ; and some have thought
that the intellectual faculties of the higher animals
have been gradually developed from their instincts.
But Pouchet, in an interesting essay,[2] has shewn that
no such inverse ratio really exists. Those insects
which possess the most wonderful instincts are certainly
the most intelligent. In the vertebrate series, the
least intelligent members, namely fishes and amphibians,
do not possess complex instincts ; and amongst mammals the animal most remarkable for its instincts,
namely the beaver, is highly intelligent, as will be
admitted by every one who has read Mr. Morgan's
excellent work.[3]

Although the first dawnings of intelligence, according to Mr. Herbert Spencer,[4] have been developed
through the multiplication and co-ordination of reflex

[2] 'L'Instinct chez les Insectes,'
'Revue des Deux Mondes,' Feb.
1870, p. 690.
[3] 'The American Beaver and

His Works,' 1868.
[4] 'The Principles of Psycho-
logy,' 2nd edit. 1870, pp. 418–
443.

actions, and although many of the simpler instincts graduate into reflex actions, and can hardly be distinguished from them, as in the case of young animals sucking, yet the more complex instincts seem to have originated independently of intelligence. I am, however, very far from wishing to deny that instinctive actions may lose their fixed and untaught character, and be replaced by others performed by the aid of the free will. On the other hand, some intelligent actions, after being performed during several generations, become converted into instincts and are inherited, as when birds on oceanic islands learn to avoid man. These actions may then be said to be degraded in character, for they are no longer performed through reason or from experience. But the greater number of the more complex instincts appear to have been gained in a wholly different manner, through the natural selection of variations of simpler instinctive actions. Such variations appear to arise from the same unknown causes acting on the cerebral organisation, which induce slight variations or individual differences in other parts of the body; and these variations, owing to our ignorance, are often said to arise spontaneously. We can, I think, come to no other conclusion with respect to the origin of the more complex instincts, when we reflect on the marvellous instincts of sterile worker-ants and bees, which leave no offspring to inherit the effects of experience and of modified habits.

Although, as we learn from the above-mentioned insects and the beaver, a high degree of intelligence is certainly compatible with complex instincts, and although actions, at first learnt voluntarily can soon through habit be performed with the quickness and certainty of a reflex action, yet it is not improbable that there is a certain amount of interference between the development of free intelligence and of instinct,— which latter implies some inherited modification of the brain. Little is known about the functions of the brain, but we can perceive that as the intellectual powers become highly developed, the various parts of the brain must be connected by very intricate channels of the freest intercommunication ; and as a consequence each separate part would perhaps tend to be less well fitted to answer to particular sensations or associations in a definite and inherited—that is instinctive—manner. There seems even to exist some relation between a low degree of intelligence and a strong tendency to the formation of fixed, though not inherited habits ; for as a sagacious physician remarked to me, persons who are slightly imbecile tend to act in everything by routine or habit ; and they are rendered much happier if this is encouraged.

I have thought this digression worth giving, because we may easily underrate the mental powers of the higher animals, and especially of man, when we compare their actions founded on the memory of past events, on foresight, reason, and imagination, with exactly similar actions instinctively performed by the lower animals ; in this latter case the capacity of performing such actions has been gained, step by step, through the variability of the mental organs and natural selection, without any conscious intelligence on the part of the animal during each successive generation. No doubt, as Mr. Wallace has argued,[5] much of

[5] 'Contributions to the Theory of Natural Selection,' 1870, p. 212.

the intelligent work done by man is due to imitation and not to reason; but there is this great difference between his actions and many of those performed by the lower animals, namely, that man cannot, on his first trial, make, for instance, a stone hatchet or a canoe, through his power of imitation. He has to learn his work by practice; a beaver, on the other hand, can make its dam or canal, and a bird its nest, as well, or nearly as well, and a spider its wonderful web, quite as well,[6] the first time it tries as when old and experienced.

To return to our immediate subject: the lower animals, like man, manifestly feel pleasure and pain, happiness and misery. Happiness is never better exhibited than by young animals, such as puppies, kittens, lambs, &c., when playing together, like our own children. Even insects play together, as has been described by that excellent observer, P. Huber,[7] who saw ants chasing and pretending to bite each other, like so many puppies.

The fact that the lower animals are excited by the same emotions as ourselves is so well established, that it will not be necessary to weary the reader by many details. Terror acts in the same manner on them as on us, causing the muscles to tremble, the heart to palpitate, the sphincters to be relaxed, and the hair to stand on end. Suspicion, the offspring of fear, is eminently characteristic of most wild animals. It is, I think, impossible to read the account given by Sir E.

[6] For the evidence on this head, see Mr. J. Traherne Moggridge's most interesting work, 'Harvesting Ants and Trap-door Spiders,' 1873, pd. 126, 128.

[7] 'Recherches sur les Mœurs des Fourmis,' 1810, p. 173.

Tennent, of the behaviour of the female elephants, used as decoys, without admitting that they intentionally practise deceit, and well know what they are about. Courage and timidity are extremely variable qualities in the individuals of the same species, as is plainly seen in our dogs. Some dogs and horses are ill-tempered, and easily turn sulky; others are good-tempered; and these qualities are certainly inherited. Every one knows how liable animals are to furious rage, and how plainly they shew it. Many, and probably true, anecdotes have been published on the long-delayed and artful revenge of various animals. The accurate Rengger, and Brehm [8] state that the American and African monkeys which they kept tame, certainly revenged themselves. Sir Andrew Smith, a zoologist whose scrupulous accuracy was known to many persons, told me the following story of which he was himself an eye-witness; at the Cape of Good Hope an officer had often plagued a certain baboon, and the animal, seeing him approaching one Sunday for parade, poured water into a hole and hastily made some thick mud, which he skilfully dashed over the officer as he passed by, to the amusement of many bystanders. For long afterwards the baboon rejoiced and triumphed whenever he saw his victim.

The love of a dog for his master is notorious; as an old writer quaintly says,[9] "A dog is the only thing on " this earth that luvs you more than he luvs himself."

[8] All the following statements, given on the authority of these two naturalists, are taken from Rengger's 'Naturgesch. der Säugethiere von Paraguay,' 1830, s. 41–57, and from Brehm's 'Thierleben,' B. i. s. 10–87.

[9] Quoted by Dr. Lauder Lindsay, in his ' Physiology of Mind in the Lower Animals;' ' Journal of Mental Science,' April 1871, p. 38.

In the agony of death a dog has been known to caress his master, and every one has heard of the dog suffering under vivisection, who licked the hand of the operator; this man, unless the operation was fully justified by an increase of our knowledge, or unless he had a heart of stone, must have felt remorse to the last hour of his life.

As Whewell [10] has well asked, "who that reads the "touching instances of maternal affection, related so "often of the women of all nations, and of the females "of all animals, can doubt that the principle of action "is the same in the two cases?" We see maternal affection exhibited in the most trifling details; thus Rengger observed an American monkey (a Cebus) carefully driving away the flies which plagued her infant; and Duvaucel saw a Hylobates washing the faces of her young ones in a stream. So intense is the grief of female monkeys for the loss of their young, that it invariably caused the death of certain kinds kept under confinement by Brehm in N. Africa. Orphan monkeys were always adopted and carefully guarded by the other monkeys, both males and females. One female baboon had so capacious a heart that she not only adopted young monkeys of other species, but stole young dogs and cats, which she continually carried about. Her kindness, however, did not go so far as to share her food with her adopted offspring, at which Brehm was surprised, as his monkeys always divided everything quite fairly with their own young ones. An adopted kitten scratched this affectionate baboon, who certainly had a fine intellect, for she was much astonished at being scratched, and immediately ex-

[10] 'Bridgewater Treatise,' p. 263.

amined the kitten's feet, and without more ado bit off the claws.[11] In the Zoological Gardens, I heard from the keeper that an old baboon (*C. chacma*) had adopted a Rhesus monkey; but when a young drill and mandrill were placed in the cage, she seemed to perceive that these monkeys, though distinct species, were her nearer relatives, for she at once rejected the Rhesus and adopted both of them. The young Rhesus, as I saw, was greatly discontented at being thus rejected, and it would, like a naughty child, annoy and attack the young drill and mandrill whenever it could do so with safety; this conduct exciting great indignation in the old baboon. Monkeys will also, according to Brehm, defend their master when attacked by any one, as well as dogs to whom they are attached, from the attacks of other dogs. But we here trench on the subjects of sympathy and fidelity, to which I shall recur. Some of Brehm's monkeys took much delight in teasing a certain old dog whom they disliked, as well as other animals, in various ingenious ways.

Most of the more complex emotions are common to the higher animals and ourselves. Every one has seen how jealous a dog is of his master's affection, if lavished on any other creature; and I have observed the same fact with monkeys. This shews that animals not only love, but have desire to be loved. Animals manifestly feel emulation. They love approbation or praise; and a dog carrying a basket for his master exhibits in a high degree self-complacency or pride. There can, I

[11] A critic, without any grounds ('Quarterly Review,' July, 1871, p. 72), disputes the possibility of this act as described by Brehm, for the sake of discrediting my work. Therefore I tried, and found that I could readily seize with my own teeth the sharp little claws of a kitten nearly five weeks old.

think, be no doubt that a dog feels shame, as distinct from fear, and something very like modesty when begging too often for food. A great dog scorns the snarling of a little dog, and this may be called magnanimity. Several observers have stated that monkeys certainly dislike being laughed at; and they sometimes invent imaginary offences. In the Zoological Gardens I saw a baboon who always got into a furious rage when his keeper took out a letter or book and read it aloud to him; and his rage was so violent that, as I witnessed on one occasion, he bit his own leg till the blood flowed. Dogs shew what may be fairly called a sense of humour, as distinct from mere play; if a bit of stick or other such object be thrown to one, he will often carry it away for a short distance; and then squatting down with it on the ground close before him, will wait until his master comes quite close to take it away. The dog will then seize it and rush away in triumph, repeating the same manoeuvre, and evidently enjoying the practical joke.

We will now turn to the more intellectual emotions and faculties, which are very important, as forming the basis for the development of the higher mental powers. Animals manifestly enjoy excitement, and suffer from ennui, as may be seen with dogs, and, according to Rengger, with monkeys. All animals feel *Wonder*, and many exhibit *Curiosity*. They sometimes suffer from this latter quality, as when the hunter plays antics and thus attracts them; I have witnessed this with deer, and so it is with the wary chamois, and with some kinds of wild-ducks. Brehm gives a curious account of the instinctive dread, which his monkeys exhibited, for snakes; but their curiosity was so great that they could not desist from occasionally satiating their horror in a most human fashion, by lifting up the lid of the box in which the snakes were kept. I was so much surprised at his account, that I took a stuffed and coiled-up snake into the monkey-house at the Zoological Gardens, and the excitement thus caused was one of the most curious spectacles which I ever beheld. Three species of Cercopithecus were the most alarmed; they dashed about their cages, and uttered sharp signal cries of danger, which were understood by the other monkeys. A few young monkeys and one old Anubis baboon alone took no notice of the snake. I then placed the stuffed specimen on the ground in one of the larger compartments. After a time all the monkeys collected round it in a large circle, and staring intently, presented a most ludicrous appearance. They became extremely nervous; so that when a wooden ball, with which they were familiar as a plaything, was accidentally moved in the straw, under which it was partly hidden, they all instantly started away. These monkeys behaved very differently when a dead fish, a mouse,[12] a living turtle, and other new objects were placed in their cages; for though at first frightened, they soon approached, handled and examined them. I then placed a live snake in a paper bag, with the mouth loosely closed, in one of the larger compartments. One of the monkeys immediately approached, cautiously opened the bag a little, peeped in, and instantly dashed away. Then I witnessed what Brehm has described, for monkey after monkey, with head raised high and turned on one side, could not resist taking a momentary

[12] I have given a short account of their behaviour on this occasion in my 'Expression of the Emotions,' p. 43.

peep into the upright bag, at the dreadful object lying quietly at the bottom. It would almost appear as if monkeys had some notion of zoological affinities, for those kept by Brehm exhibited a strange, though mistaken, instinctive dread of innocent lizards and frogs. An orang, also, has been known to be much alarmed at the first sight of a turtle.[13]

The principle of *Imitation* is strong in man, and especially, as I have myself observed, with savages. In certain morbid states of the brain this tendency is exaggerated to an extraordinary degree: some hemiplegic patients and others, at the commencement of inflammatory softening of the brain, unconsciously imitate every word which is uttered, whether in their own or in a foreign language, and every gesture or action which is performed near them.[14] Desor[15] has remarked that no animal voluntarily imitates an action performed by man, until in the ascending scale we come to monkeys, which are well known to be ridiculous mockers. Animals, however, sometimes imitate each other's actions: thus two species of wolves, which had been reared by dogs, learned to bark, as does sometimes the jackal,[16] but whether this can be called voluntary imitation is another question. Birds imitate the songs of their parents, and sometimes of other birds; and parrots are notorious imitators of any sound which they often hear. Dureau de la Malle gives an account[17] of

[13] W. C. L. Martin, 'Nat. Hist. of Mammalia,' 1841, p. 405.

[14] Dr. Bateman 'On Aphasia,' 1870, p. 110.

[15] Quoted by Vogt, 'Mémoire sur les Microcéphales,' 1867, p. 168.

[16] 'The Variation of Animals and Plants under Domestication,' vol. i. p. 27.

[17] 'Annales des Sc. Nat.' (1st Series), tom. xxii. p. 397.

a dog reared by a cat, who learnt to imitate the well-known action of a cat licking her paws, and thus washing her ears and face ; this was also witnessed by the celebrated naturalist Audouin. I have received several confirmatory accounts ; in one of these, a dog had not been suckled by a cat, but had been brought up with one, together with kittens, and had thus acquired the above habit, which he ever afterwards practised during his life of thirteen years. Dureau de la Malle's dog likewise learnt from the kittens to play with a ball by rolling it about with his fore paws, and springing on it. A correspondent assures me that a cat in his house used to put her paws into jugs of milk having too narrow a mouth for her head. A kitten of this cat soon learned the same trick, and practised it ever afterwards, whenever there was an opportunity.

The parents of many animals, trusting to the principle of imitation in their young, and more especially to their instinctive or inherited tendencies, may be said to educate them. We see this when a cat brings a live mouse to her kittens ; and Dureau de la Malle has given a curious account (in the paper above quoted) of his observations on hawks which taught their young dexterity, as well as judgment of distances, by first dropping through the air dead mice and sparrows, which the young generally failed to catch, and then bringing them live birds and letting them loose.

Hardly any faculty is more important for the intellectual progress of man than *Attention*. Animals clearly manifest this power, as when a cat watches by a hole and prepares to spring on its prey. Wild animals sometimes become so absorbed when thus engaged, that they may be easily approached. Mr. Bartlett has given me a curious proof how variable this faculty is in monkeys. A man who trains monkeys to act in plays, used to purchase common kinds from the Zoological Society at the price of five pounds for each; but he offered to give double the price, if he might keep three or four of them for a few days, in order to select one. When asked how he could possibly learn so soon, whether a particular monkey would turn out a good actor, he answered that it all depended on their power of attention. If when he was talking and explaining anything to a monkey, its attention was easily distracted, as by a fly on the wall or other trifling object, the case was hopeless. If he tried by punishment to make an inattentive monkey act, it turned sulky. On the other hand, a monkey which carefully attended to him could always be trained.

It is almost superfluous to state that animals have excellent *Memories* for persons and places. A baboon at the Cape of Good Hope, as I have been informed by Sir Andrew Smith, recognised him with joy after an absence of nine months. I had a dog who was savage and averse to all strangers, and I purposely tried his memory after an absence of five years and two days. I went near the stable where he lived, and shouted to him in my old manner; he shewed no joy, but instantly followed me out walking, and obeyed me, exactly as if I had parted with him only half an hour before. A train of old associations, dormant during five years, had thus been instantaneously awakened in his mind. Even ants, as P. Huber[18] has clearly

[18] 'Les Mœurs des Fourmis,' 1810, p. 150.

shewn, recognised their fellow-ants belonging to the same community after a separation of four months. Animals can certainly by some means judge of the intervals of time between recurrent events.

The *Imagination* is one of the highest prerogatives of man. By this faculty he unites former images and ideas, independently of the will, and thus creates brilliant and novel results. A poet, as Jean Paul Richter remarks,[19] " who must reflect whether he shall "make a character say yes or no—to the devil with "him; he is only a stupid corpse." Dreaming gives us the best notion of this power; as Jean Paul again says, " The dream is an involuntary art of poetry." The value of the products of our imagination depends of course on the number, accuracy, and clearness of our impressions, on our judgment and taste in selecting or rejecting the involuntary combinations, and to a certain extent on our power of voluntarily combining them. As dogs, cats, horses, and probably all the higher animals, even birds [20] have vivid dreams, and this is shewn by their movements and the sounds uttered, we must admit that they possess some power of imagination. There must be something special, which causes dogs to howl in the night, and especially during moonlight, in that remarkable and melancholy manner called baying. All dogs do not do so; and, according to Houzeau,[21] they do not then look at the moon, but at some fixed point near the horizon.

---

[19] Quoted in Dr. Maudsley's 'Physiology and Pathology of Mind,' 1868, pp. 19, 220.

[20] Dr. Jerdon, 'Birds of India,' vol. i. 1862, p. xxi. Houzeau says that his parokeets and canary-birds dreamt: ' Facultés Mentales,' tom. ii. p. 136.

[21] ' Facultés Mentales des Animaux,' 1872, tom. ii. p. 181.

Houzeau thinks that their imaginations are disturbed by the vague outlines of the surrounding objects, and conjure up before them fantastic images : if this be so, their feelings may almost be called superstitious.

Of all the faculties of the human mind, it will, I presume, be admitted that *Reason* stands at the summit. Only a few persons now dispute that animals possess some power of reasoning. Animals may constantly be seen to pause, deliberate, and resolve. It is a significant fact, that the more the habits of any particular animal are studied by a naturalist, the more he attributes to reason and the less to unlearnt instincts.[22] In future chapters we shall see that some animals extremely low in the scale apparently display a certain amount of reason. No doubt it is often difficult to distinguish between the power of reason and that of instinct. For instance, Dr. Hayes, in his work on 'The Open Polar Sea,' repeatedly remarks that his dogs, instead of continuing to draw the sledges in a compact body, diverged and separated when they came to thin ice, so that their weight might be more evenly distributed. This was often the first warning which the travellers received that the ice was becoming thin and dangerous. Now, did the dogs act thus from the experience of each individual, or from the example of the older and wiser dogs, or from an inherited habit, that is from instinct? This instinct, may possibly have arisen since the time, long ago, when dogs were first employed by the natives in drawing their sledges ; or the Arctic wolves, the

[22] Mr. L. H. Morgan's work on 'The American Beaver,' 1868, offers a good illustration of this remark. I cannot help thinking, however, that he goes too far in underrating the power of instinct.

parent-stock of the Esquimaux dog, may have acquired an instinct impelling them not to attack their prey in a close pack, when on thin ice.

We can only judge by the circumstances under which actions are performed, whether they are due to instinct, or to reason, or to the mere association of ideas: this latter principle, however, is intimately connected with reason. A curious case has been given by Prof. Möbius,[23] of a pike, separated by a plate of glass from an adjoining aquarium stocked with fish, and who often dashed himself with such violence against the glass in trying to catch the other fishes, that he was sometimes completely stunned. The pike went on thus for three months, but at last learnt caution, and ceased to do so. The plate of glass was then removed, but the pike would not attack these particular fishes, though he would devour others which were afterwards introduced; so strongly was the idea of a violent shock associated in his feeble mind with the attempt on his former neighbours. If a savage, who had never seen a large plate-glass window, were to dash himself even once against it, he would for a long time afterwards associate a shock with a window-frame; but very differently from the pike, he would probably reflect on the nature of the impediment, and be cautious under analogous circumstances. Now with monkeys, as we shall presently see, a painful or merely a disagreeable impression, from an action once performed, is sometimes sufficient to prevent the animal from repeating it. If we attribute this difference between the monkey and the pike solely to the association of ideas being so much stronger and more

[23] 'Die Bewegungen der Thiere,' &c., 1873, p. 11.

persistent in the one than the other, though the pike often received much the more severe injury, can we maintain in the case of man that a similar difference implies the possession of a fundamentally different mind?

Houzeau relates [24] that, whilst crossing a wide and arid plain in Texas, his two dogs suffered greatly from thirst, and that between thirty and forty times they rushed down the hollows to search for water. These hollows were not valleys, and there were no trees in them, or any other difference in the vegetation, and as they were absolutely dry there could have been no smell of damp earth. The dogs behaved as if they knew that a dip in the ground offered them the best chance of finding water, and Houzeau has often witnessed the same behaviour in other animals.

I have seen, as I daresay have others, that when a small object is thrown on the ground beyond the reach of one of the elephants in the Zoological Gardens, he blows through his trunk on the ground beyond the object, so that the current reflected on all sides may drive the object within his reach. Again a well-known ethnologist, Mr. Westropp, informs me that he observed in Vienna a bear deliberately making with his paw a current in some water, which was close to the bars of his cage, so as to draw a piece of floating bread within his reach. These actions of the elephant and bear can hardly be attributed to instinct or inherited habit, as they would be of little use to an animal in a state of nature. Now, what is the difference between such actions, when performed by an uncultivated man, and by one of the higher animals?

[24] 'Facultés Mentales des Animaux,' 1872, tom. ii. p. 265.

The savage and the dog have often found water at a low level, and the coincidence under such circumstances has become associated in their minds. A cultivated man would perhaps make some general proposition on the subject; but from all that we know of savages it is extremely doubtful whether they would do so, and a dog certainly would not. But a savage, as well as a dog, would search in the same way, though frequently disappointed; and in both it seems to be equally an act of reason, whether or not any general proposition on the subject is consciously placed before the mind.[25] The same would apply to the elephant and the bear making currents in the air or water. The savage would certainly neither know nor care by what law the desired movements were effected; yet his act would be guided by a rude process of reasoning, as surely as would a philosopher in his longest chain of deductions. There would no doubt be this difference between him and one of the higher animals, that he would take notice of much slighter circumstances and conditions, and would observe any connection between them after much less experience, and this would be of paramount importance. I kept a daily record of the actions of one of my infants, and when he was about eleven months old, and before he could speak a single word, I was continually struck with the greater quickness, with which all sorts of objects and sounds were associated to-

---

[25] Prof. Huxley has analysed with admirable clearness the mental steps by which a man, as well as a dog, arrives at a conclusion in a case analogous to that given in my text. See his article, 'Mr. Darwin's Critics,' in the ' Contemporary Review,' Nov. 1871, p. 462, and in his ' Critiques and Essays,' 1873, p. 279.

gether in his mind, compared with that of the most intelligent dogs I ever knew. But the higher animals differ in exactly the same way in this power of association from those low in the scale, such as the pike, as well as in that of drawing inferences and of observation.

The promptings of reason, after very short experience, are well shewn by the following actions of American monkeys, which stand low in their order. Rengger, a most careful observer, states that when he first gave eggs to his monkeys in Paraguay, they smashed them, and thus lost much of their contents; afterwards they gently hit one end against some hard body, and picked off the bits of shell with their fingers. After cutting themselves only *once* with any sharp tool, they would not touch it again, or would handle it with the greatest caution. Lumps of sugar were often given them wrapped up in paper; and Rengger sometimes put a live wasp in the paper, so that in hastily unfolding it they got stung; after this had *once* happened, they always first held the packet to their ears to detect any movement within.[26]

The following cases relate to dogs. Mr. Colquhoun[27] winged two wild-ducks, which fell on the further side of a stream; his retriever tried to bring over both at once, but could not succeed; she then, though never before known to ruffle a feather, deliberately killed one, brought over the other, and returned for the dead

[26] Mr. Belt, in his most interesting work, 'The Naturalist in Nicaragua,' 1874 (p. 119), likewise describes various actions of a tamed Cebus, which, I think, clearly shew that this animal possessed some reasoning power.

[27] 'The Moor and the Loch,' p. 45. Col. Hutchinson on 'Dog Breaking,' 1850, p. 46.

bird. Col. Hutchinson relates that two partridges were shot at once, one being killed, the other wounded; the latter ran away, and was caught by the retriever, who on her return came across the dead bird; "she "stopped, evidently greatly puzzled, and after one or "two trials, finding she could not take it up without "permitting the escape of the winged bird, she con- "sidered a moment, then deliberately murdered it by "giving it a severe crunch, and afterwards brought "away both together. This was the only known "instance of her ever having wilfully injured any "game." Here we have reason though not quite perfect, for the retriever might have brought the wounded bird first and then returned for the dead one, as in the case of the two wild-ducks. I give the above cases, as resting on the evidence of two inde- pendent witnesses, and because in both instances the retrievers, after deliberation, broke through a habit which is inherited by them (that of not killing the game retrieved), and because they shew how strong their reasoning faculty must have been to overcome a fixed habit.

I will conclude by quoting a remark by the il- lustrious Humboldt.[28] "The muleteers in S. America "say, 'I will not give you the mule whose step is "'easiest, but *la mas racional*,—the one that reasons "'best;'" and as he adds, "this popular expression, "dictated by long experience, combats the system of "animated machines, better perhaps than all the argu- "ments of speculative philosophy." Nevertheless some writers even yet deny that the higher animals possess a trace of reason; and they endeavour to

[28] 'Personal Narrative,' Eng. translat., vol. iii. p. 106.

explain away, by what appears to be mere verbiage,[29] all such facts as those above given.

It has, I think, now been shewn that man and the higher animals, especially the Primates, have some few instincts in common. All have the same senses, intuitions, and sensations,—similar passions, affections, and emotions, even the more complex ones, such as jealousy, suspicion, emulation, gratitude, and magnanimity; they practise deceit and are revengeful; they are sometimes susceptible to ridicule, and even have a sense of humour; they feel wonder and curiosity; they possess the same faculties of imitation, attention, deliberation, choice, memory, imagination, the association of ideas, and reason, though in very different degrees. The individuals of the same species graduate in intellect from absolute imbecility to high excellence. They are also liable to insanity, though far less often than in the case of man.[30] Nevertheless, many authors have insisted that man is divided by an insuperable barrier from all the lower animals in his mental faculties. I formerly made a collection of above a score of such aphorisms, but they

[29] I am glad to find that so acute a reasoner as Mr. Leslie Stephen ('Darwinism and Divinity, Essays on Free-thinking,' 1873, p. 80), in speaking of the supposed impassable barrier between the minds of man and the lower animals, says, "The distinctions, indeed, which have "been drawn, seem to us to rest "upon no better foundation "than a great many other "metaphysical distinctions; "that is, the assumption that "because you can give two "things different names, they "must therefore have different "natures. It is difficult to "understand how anybody who "has ever kept a dog, or seen "an elephant, can have any "doubts as to an animal's "power of performing the "essential processes of reasoning."

[30] See 'Madness in Animals,' by Dr. W. Lauder Lindsay, in 'Journal of Mental Science,' July 1871.

are almost worthless, as their wide difference and number prove the difficulty, if not the impossibility, of the attempt. It has been asserted that man alone is capable of progressive improvement; that he alone makes use of tools or fire, domesticates other animals, or possesses property; that no animal has the power of abstraction, or of forming general concepts, is self-conscious and comprehends itself; that no animal employs language; that man alone has a sense of beauty, is liable to caprice, has the feeling of gratitude, mystery, &c.; believes in God, or is endowed with a conscience. I will hazard a few remarks on the more important and interesting of these points.

Archbishop Sumner formerly maintained [31] that man alone is capable of progressive improvement. That he is capable of incomparably greater and more rapid improvement than is any other animal, admits of no dispute; and this is mainly due to his power of speaking and handing down his acquired knowledge. With animals, looking first to the individual, every one who has had any experience in setting traps, knows that young animals can be caught much more easily than old ones; and they can be much more easily approached by an enemy. Even with respect to old animals, it is impossible to catch many in the same place and in the same kind of trap, or to destroy them by the same kind of poison; yet it is improbable that all should have partaken of the poison, and impossible that all should have been caught in a trap. They must learn caution by seeing their brethren caught or poisoned. In North America, where the fur-bearing animals have long been pursued, they exhibit,

[31] Quoted by Sir C. Lyell, 'Antiquity of Man,' p. 497.

according to the unanimous testimony of all observers, an almost incredible amount of sagacity, caution and cunning; but trapping has been there so long carried on, that inheritance may possibly have come into play. I have received several accounts that when telegraphs are first set up in any district, many birds kill themselves by flying against the wires, but that in the course of a very few years they learn to avoid this danger, by seeing, as it would appear, their comrades killed.[32]

If we look to successive generations, or to the race, there is no doubt that birds and other animals gradually both acquire and lose caution in relation to man or other enemies;[33] and this caution is certainly in chief part an inherited habit or instinct, but in part the result of individual experience. A good observer, Leroy,[34] states, that in districts where foxes are much hunted, the young, on first leaving their burrows, are incontestably much more wary than the old ones in districts where they are not much disturbed.

Our domestic dogs are descended from wolves and jackals,[35] and though they may not have gained in cunning, and may have lost in wariness and suspicion, yet they have progressed in certain moral qualities, such as in affection, trust-worthiness, temper, and probably in general intelligence. The common rat has conquered and beaten several other species throughout

[32] For additional evidence, with details, see M. Houzeau, ' Les Facultés Mentales,' tom. ii. 1872, p. 147.

[33] See, with respect to birds on oceanic islands, my ' Journal of Researches during the voyage of the "Beagle,"' 1845, p. 398.

' Origin of Species,' 5th ed. p. 260.

[34] ' Lettres Phil. sur l'Intelligence des Animaux,' nouvelle édit. 1802, p. 86.

[35] See the evidence on this head in chap. i. vol. i. ' On the Variation of Animals and Plants under Domestication.'

Europe, in parts of North America, New Zealand, and recently in Formosa, as well as on the mainland of China. Mr. Swinhoe,[36] who describes these two latter cases, attributes the victory of the common rat over the large *Mus coninga* to its superior cunning; and this latter quality may probably be attributed to the habitual exercise of all its faculties in avoiding extirpation by man, as well as to nearly all the less cunning or weak-minded rats having been continuously destroyed by him. It is, however, possible that the success of the common rat may be due to its having possessed greater cunning than its fellow-species, before it became associated with man. To maintain, independently of any direct evidence, that no animal during the course of ages has progressed in intellect or other mental faculties, is to beg the question of the evolution of species. We have seen that, according to Lartet, existing mammals belonging to several orders have larger brains than their ancient tertiary prototypes.

It has often been said that no animal uses any tool; but the chimpanzee in a state of nature cracks a native fruit, somewhat like a walnut, with a stone.[37] Rengger[38] easily taught an American monkey thus to break open hard palm-nuts; and afterwards of its own accord, it used stones to open other kinds of nuts, as well as boxes. It thus also removed the soft rind of fruit that had a disagreeable flavour. Another monkey was taught to open the lid of a large box with a stick,

[36] 'Proc. Zoolog. Soc.' 1864, p. 186.

[37] Savage and Wyman in 'Boston Journal of Nat. Hist.' vol. iv. 1843–44, p. 383.

[38] 'Saugethiere von Paraguay,' 1830, s. 51–56.

and afterwards it used the stick as a lever to move heavy bodies; and I have myself seen a young orang put a stick into a crevice, slip his hand to the other end, and use it in the proper manner as a lever. The tamed elephants in India are well known to break off branches of trees and use them to drive away the flies; and this same act has been observed in an elephant in a state of nature.[39]   I have seen a young orang, when she thought she was going to be whipped, cover and protect herself with a blanket or straw. In these several cases stones and sticks were employed as implements; but they are likewise used as weapons. Brehm[40] states, on the authority of the well-known traveller Schimper, that in Abyssinia when the baboons belonging to one species (*C. gelada*) descend in troops from the mountains to plunder the fields, they sometimes encounter troops of another species (*C. hamadryas*), and then a fight ensues. The Geladas roll down great stones, which the Hamadryas try to avoid, and then both species, making a great uproar, rush furiously against each other. Brehm, when, accompanying the Duke of Coburg-Gotha, aided in an attack with fire-arms on a troop of baboons in the pass of Mensa in Abyssinia. The baboons in return rolled so many stones down the mountain, some as large as a man's head, that the attackers had to beat a hasty retreat; and the pass was actually closed for a time against the caravan. It deserves notice that these baboons thus acted in concert. Mr. Wallace[41] on three occasions saw female orangs, ac-

---

[39] The 'Indian Field,' March 4, 1871.

[40] 'Thierleben,' B. i. s. 79, 82.

[41] 'The Malay Archipelago,' vol. i. 1869, p. 87.

companied by their young, " breaking off branches and
" the great spiny fruit of the Durian tree, with every
" appearance of rage ; causing such a shower of
" missiles as effectually kept us from approaching too
" near the tree." As I have repeatedly seen, a
chimpanzee will throw any object at hand at a person
who offends him ; and the before-mentioned baboon at
the Cape of Good Hope prepared mud for the purpose.

In the Zoological Gardens, a monkey, which had
weak teeth, used to break open nuts with a stone ;
and I was assured by the keepers that after using the
stone, he hid it in the straw, and would not let any
other monkey touch it. Here, then, we have the idea
of property ; but this idea is common to every dog
with a bone, and to most or all birds with their nests.

The Duke of Argyll [42] remarks, that the fashioning
of an implement for a special purpose is absolutely
peculiar to man ; and he considers that this forms an
immeasurable gulf between him and the brutes. This
is no doubt a very important distinction ; but there
appears to me much truth in Sir J. Lubbock's suggestion,[43] that when primeval man first used flint-
stones for any purpose, he would have accidentally
splintered them, and would then have used the sharp
fragments. From this step it would be a small one to
break the flints on purpose, and not a very wide step
to fashion them rudely. This latter advance, however,
may have taken long ages, if we may judge by the
immense interval of time which elapsed before the men
of the neolithic period took to grinding and polishing
their stone tools. In breaking the flints, as Sir J.

[42] 'Primeval Man,' 1869, pp.   [43] 'Prehistoric Times,' 1865,
145, 147.   p. 473, &c.

Lubbock likewise remarks, sparks would have been emitted, and in grinding them heat would have been evolved: thus the two usual methods of "obtaining "fire may have originated." The nature of fire would have been known in the many volcanic regions where lava occasionally flows through forests. The anthropomorphous apes, guided probably by instinct, build for themselves temporary platforms; but as many instincts are largely controlled by reason, the simpler ones, such as this of building a platform, might readily pass into a voluntary and conscious act. The orang is known to cover itself at night with the leaves of the Pandanus; and Brehm states that one of his baboons used to protect itself from the heat of the sun by throwing a straw-mat over its head. In these several habits, we probably see the first steps towards some of the simpler arts, such as rude architecture and dress, as they arose amongst the early progenitors of man.

Abstraction, General Conceptions, Self-consciousness, Mental Individuality.—It would be very difficult for any one with even much more knowledge than I possess, to determine how far animals exhibit any traces of these high mental powers. This difficulty arises from the impossibility of judging what passes through the mind of an animal; and again, the fact that writers differ to a great extent in the meaning which they attribute to the above terms, causes a further difficulty. If one may judge from various articles which have been published lately, the greatest stress seems to be laid on the supposed entire absence in animals of the power of abstraction, or of forming general concepts. But when a dog sees another dog at a distance, it is often clear that he perceives that it is a dog in the abstract; for when he gets nearer his whole manner suddenly changes, if the other dog be a friend. A recent writer remarks, that in all such cases it is a pure assumption to assert that the mental act is not essentially of the same nature in the animal as in man. If either refers what he perceives with his senses to a mental concept, then so do both.[44] When I say to my terrier, in an eager voice (and I have made the trial many times), " Hi, hi, where is it?" she at once takes it as a sign that something is to be hunted, and generally first looks quickly all around, and then rushes into the nearest thicket, to scent for any game, but finding nothing, she looks up into any neighbouring tree for a squirrel. Now do not these actions clearly shew that she had in her mind a general idea or concept that some animal is to be discovered and hunted?

It may be freely admitted that no animal is self-conscious, if by this term it is implied, that he reflects on such points, as whence he comes or whither he will go, or what is life and death, and so forth. But how can we feel sure that an old dog with an excellent memory and some power of imagination, as shewn by his dreams, never reflects on his past pleasures or pains in the chase? And this would be a form of self-consciousness. On the other hand, as Büchner[45] has remarked, how little can the hard-worked wife of a degraded Australian savage, who uses very few abstract words, and cannot count above four, exert her self-consciousness, or reflect on the nature of her own

---

[44] Mr. Hookham, in a letter to Prof. Max Müller, in the 'Birmingham News,' May 1873.

[45] 'Conférences sur la Théorie Darwinienne,' French translat. 1869, p. 132.

existence. It is generally admitted, that the higher animals possess memory, attention, association, and even some imagination and reason. If these powers, which differ much in different animals, are capable of improvement, there seems no great improbability in more complex faculties, such as the higher forms of abstraction, and self-consciousness, &c., having been evolved through the development and combination of the simpler ones. It has been urged against the views here maintained that it is impossible to say at what point in the ascending scale animals become capable of abstraction, &c. ; but who can say at what age this occurs in our young children? We see at least that such powers are developed in children by imperceptible degrees.

That animals retain their mental individuality is unquestionable. When my voice awakened a train of old associations in the mind of the before-mentioned dog, he must have retained his mental individuality, although every atom of his brain had probably undergone change more than once during the interval of five years. This dog might have brought forward the argument lately advanced to crush all evolutionists, and said, "I abide amid all mental moods and all "material changes. . . . The teaching that atoms leave "their impressions as legacies to other atoms falling "into the places they have vacated is contradictory of "the utterance of consciousness, and is therefore false ; "but it is the teaching necessitated by evolutionism, "consequently the hypothesis is a false one." [46]

Language.—This faculty has justly been considered as one of the chief distinctions between man and the lower animals. But man, as a highly competent

[46] The Rev. Dr. J. M'Cann, 'Anti-Darwinism,' 1869, p. 13.

judge, Archbishop Whately remarks, " is not the " only animal that can make use of language to " express what is passing in his mind, and can under- " stand, more or less, what is so expressed by " another." [47] In Paraguay the *Cebus azaræ* when excited utters at least six distinct sounds, which excite in other monkeys similar emotions.[48] The movements of the features and gestures of monkeys are understood by us, and they partly understand ours, as Rengger and others declare. It is a more remarkable fact that the dog, since being domesticated, has learnt to bark[49] in at least four or five distinct tones. Although barking is a new art, no doubt the wild parent-species of the dog expressed their feelings by cries of various kinds. With the domesticated dog we have the bark of eagerness, as in the chase; that of anger, as well as growling; the yelp or howl of despair, as when shut up; the baying at night; the bark of joy, as when starting on a walk with his master; and the very distinct one of demand or supplication, as when wishing for a door or window to be opened. According to Houzeau, who paid particular attention to the subject, the domestic fowl utters at least a dozen significant sounds.[50]

The habitual use of articulate language is, however, peculiar to man; but he uses, in common with the lower animals, inarticulate cries to express his meaning, aided by gestures and the movements of the muscles of the face.[51] This especially holds good with the more

[47] Quoted in 'Anthropological Review,' 1864, p. 158.

[48] Rengger, ibid. s. 45.

[49] See my 'Variation of Animals and Plants under Domesti-cation,' vol. i. p. 27.

[50] 'Facultés Mentales des Animaux,' tom. ii. 1872, p. 346–349.

[51] See a discussion on this

simple and vivid feelings, which are but little connected with our higher intelligence. Our cries of pain,
fear, surprise, anger, together with the their appropriate actions, and the murmur of a mother to her
beloved child, are more expressive than any words.
That which distinguishes man from the lower animals
is not the understanding of articulate sounds, for, as
every one knows, dogs understand many words and
sentences. In this respect they are at the same stage
of development as infants, between the ages of ten and
twelve months, who understand many words and short
sentences, but cannot yet utter a single word. It is
not the mere articulation which is our distinguishing
character, for parrots and other birds possess this
power. Nor is it the mere capacity of connecting
definite sounds with definite ideas; for it is certain
that some parrots, which have been taught to speak,
connect unerringly words with things, and persons
with events.[52] The lower animals differ from man

subject in Mr. E. B. Tylor's
very interesting work, ' Researches into the Early History
of Mankind,' 1865, chaps. ii. to
iv.

[52] I have received several
detailed accounts to this effect.
Admiral Sir B. J. Sulivan, whom
I know to be a careful observer,
assures me that an African
parrot, long kept in his father's
house, invariably called certain
persons of the household, as
well as visitors, by their names.
He said "good morning" to
every one at breakfast, and
"good night" to each as they
left the room at night, and
never reversed these salutations.

To Sir B. J. Sulivan's father, he
used to add to the "good morning" a short sentence, which
was never once repeated after
his father's death. He scolded
violently a strange dog which
came into the room through the
open window; and he scolded
another parrot (saying "you
naughty polly") which had got
out of its cage, and was eating
apples on the kitchen table.
See also, to the same effect,
Houzeau on parrots, ' Facultés
Mentales,' tom. ii. p. 309. Dr.
A. Moschkau informs me that
he knew a starling which never
made a mistake in saying in
German "good morning" to

solely in his almost infinitely larger power of associating together the most diversified sounds and ideas; and this obviously depends on the high development of his mental powers.

As Horne Tooke, one of the founders of the noble science of philology, observes, language is an art, like brewing or baking; but writing would have been a better simile. It certainly is not a true instinct, for every language has to be learnt. It differs, however, widely from all ordinary arts, for man has an instinctive tendency to speak, as we see in the babble of our young children; whilst no child has an instinctive tendency to brew, bake, or write. Moreover, no philologist now supposes that any language has been deliberately invented; it has been slowly and unconsciously developed by many steps.[53] The sounds uttered by birds offer in several respects the nearest analogy to language, for all the members of the same species utter the same instinctive cries expressive of their emotions; and all the kinds which sing, exert their power instinctively; but the actual song, and even the call-notes, are learnt from their parents or foster-parents. These sounds, as Daines Barrington[54] has proved, "are no more innate than language is in man."

---

persons arriving, and "good bye, old fellow," to those departing. I could add several other such cases.

[53] See some good remarks on this head by Prof. Whitney, in his 'Oriental and Linguistic Studies,' 1873, p. 354. He observes that the desire of communication between man is the living force, which, in the development of language, "works both consciously and unconsciously; consciously as regards the immediate end to be attained; unconsciously as regards the further consequences of the act."

[54] Hon. Daines Barrington in 'Philosoph. Transactions,' 1773, p. 262. See also Dureau de la Malle, in 'Ann. des. Sc. Nat.' 3rd series, Zoolog. tom. x. p. 119.

The first attempts to sing " may be compared to the
" imperfect endeavour in a child to babble." The
young males continue practising, or as the bird-
catchers say, " recording," for ten or eleven months.
Their first essays show hardly a rudiment of the future
song; but as they grow older we can perceive what
they are aiming at; and at last they are said " to sing
" their song round." Nestlings which have learnt the
song of a distinct species, as with the canary-birds
educated in the Tyrol, teach and transmit their new
song to their offspring. The slight natural differences
of song in the same species inhabiting different
districts may be appositely compared, as Barrington
remarks, " to provincial dialects; " and the songs of
allied, though distinct species may be compared with
the languages of distinct races of man. I have given
the foregoing details to shew that an instinctive
tendency to acquire an art is not peculiar to man.

With respect to the origin of articulate language,
after having read on the one side the highly interesting works of Mr. Hensleigh Wedgwood, the Rev. F.
Farrar, and Prof. Schleicher,[55] and the celebrated
lectures of Prof. Max Müller on the other side, I cannot doubt that language owes its origin to the imitation
and modification of various natural sounds, the voices
of other animals, and man's own instinctive cries, aided
by signs and gestures. When we treat of sexual

[55] 'On the Origin of
Language,' by H. Wedgwood,
1866. ' Chapters on Language,'
by the Rev. F. W. Farrar, 1865.
These works are most interesting. See also 'De la Phys. et
de Parole,' par Albert Lemoine,
1865, p. 190. The work on
this subject, by the late Prof.
Aug. Schleicher, has been translated by Dr. Bikkers into
English, under the title of
'Darwinism tested by the
Science of Language,' 1869.

selection we shall see that primeval man, or rather some early progenitor of man, probably first used his voice in producing true musical cadences, that is in singing, as do some of the gibbon-apes at the present day; and we may conclude from a widely-spread analogy, that this power would have been especially exerted during the courtship of the sexes,—would have expressed various emotions, such as love, jealousy, triumph,—and would have served as a challenge to rivals. It is, therefore, probable that the imitation of musical cries by articulate sounds may have given rise to words expressive of various complex emotions. The strong tendency in our nearest allies, the monkeys, in microcephalous idiots,[56] and in the barbarous races of mankind, to imitate whatever they hear deserves notice, as bearing on the subject of imitation. Since monkeys certainly understand much that is said to them by man, and when wild, utter signal-cries of danger to their fellows;[57] and since fowls give distinct warnings for danger on the ground, or in the sky from hawks (both, as well as a third cry, intelligible to dogs),[58] may not some unusually wise ape-like animal have imitated the growl of a beast of prey, and thus told his fellow-monkeys the nature of the expected danger? This would have been a first step in the formation of a language.

As the voice was used more and more, the vocal organs would have been strengthened and perfected through the principle of the inherited effects of use;

[56] Vogt, 'Mémoire sur les Microcéphales,' 1867, p. 169. With respect to savages, I have given some facts in my 'Journal of Researches,' &c., 1845, p. 206.

[57] See clear evidence on this head in the two works so often quoted, by Brehm and Rengger.

[58] Houzeau gives a very curious account of his observations on this subject in his 'Facultés Mentales des Animaux,' tom. ii. p. 348.

and this would have reacted on the power of speech. But the relation between the continued use of language and the development of the brain, has no doubt been far more important. The mental powers in some early progenitor of man must have been more highly developed than in any existing ape, before even the most imperfect form of speech could have come into use ; but we may confidently believe that the continued use and advancement of this power would have reacted on the mind itself, by enabling and encouraging it to carry on long trains of thought. A complex train of thought can no more be carried on without the aid of words, whether spoken or silent, than a long calculation without the use of figures or algebra. It appears, also, that even an ordinary train of thought almost requires, or is greatly facilitated by some form of language, for the dumb, deaf, and blind girl, Laura Bridgman, was observed to use her fingers whilst dreaming.[59] Nevertheless, a long succession of vivid and connected ideas may pass through the mind without the aid of any form of language, as we may infer from the movements of dogs during their dreams. We have, also, seen that animals are able to reason to a certain extent, manifestly without the aid of language. The intimate connection between the brain, as it is now developed in us, and the faculty of speech, is well shewn by those curious cases of brain-disease in which speech is specially affected, as when the power to remember substantives is lost, whilst other words can be correctly used, or where substantives of a certain class, or all except the initial letters of substantives

[59] See remarks on this head by Dr. Maudsley, 'The Physio-logy and Pathology of Mind,' 2nd edit. 1868, p. 199.

and proper names are forgotten.[60] There is no more improbability in the continued use of the mental and vocal organs leading to inherited changes in their structure and functions, than in the case of hand-writing, which depends partly on the form of the hand and partly on the disposition of the mind; and hand-writing is certainly inherited.[61]

Several writers, more especially Prof. Max Müller,[62] have lately insisted that the use of language implies the power of forming general concepts; and that as no animals are supposed to possess this power, an impassable barrier is formed between them and man.[63] With respect to animals, I have already endeavoured

[60] Many curious cases have been recorded. See, for instance, Dr. Bateman 'On Aphasia,' 1870, p. 27, 31, 53, 100, &c. Also, 'Inquiries Concerning the Intellectual Powers,' by Dr. Abercrombie, 1838, p. 150.

[61] 'The Variation of Animals and Plants under Domestication,' vol. ii. p. 6.

[62] Lectures on 'Mr. Darwin's Philosophy of Language,' 1873.

[63] The judgment of a distinguished philologist, such as Prof. Whitney, will have far more weight on this point than anything that I can say. He remarks ('Oriental and Linguistic Studies,' 1873, p. 297), in speaking of Bleek's views: " Because on the grand scale "language is the necessary "auxiliary of thought, indis-"pensable to the development "of the power of thinking, to "the distinctness and variety "and complexity of cogni-"tions to the full mastery "of consciousness; therefore he "would fain make thought "absolutely impossible without "speech, identifying the faculty "with its instrument. He "might just as reasonably assert "that the human hand cannot "act without a tool. With such "a doctrine to start from, he "cannot stop short of Müller's "worst paradoxes, that an "infant (*in fans*, not speaking) "is not a human being, and that "deaf-mutes do not become "possessed of reason until they "learn to twist their fingers "into imitation of spoken "words." Max Müller gives in italics ('Lectures on Mr. Darwin's Philosophy of Language,' 1873, third lecture) the following aphorism : " There is no "thought without words, as "little as there are words with-"out thought." What a strange definition must here be given to the word thought !

to shew that they have this power, at least in a rude
and incipient degree. As far as concerns infants of
from ten to eleven months old, and deaf-mutes, it
seems to me incredible, that they should be able to
connect certain sounds with certain general ideas as
quickly as they do, unless such ideas were already
formed in their minds. The same remark may be
extended to the more intelligent animals; as Mr.
Leslie Stephen observes,[64] " A dog frames a general
" concept of cats or sheep, and knows the correspond-
" ing words as well as a philosopher. And the capacity
" to understand is as good a proof of vocal intelligence,
" though in an inferior degree, as the capacity to speak."

Why the organs now used for speech should have
been originally perfected for this purpose, rather than
any other organs, it is not difficult to see. Ants have
considerable powers of intercommunication by means
of their antennæ, as shewn by Huber, who devotes
a whole chapter to their language. We might have
used our fingers as efficient instruments, for a person
with practice can report to a deaf man every word of a
speech rapidly delivered at a public meeting; but the
loss of our hands, whilst thus employed, would have been
a serious inconvenience. As all the higher mammals
possess vocal organs, constructed on the same general
plan as ours, and used as a means of communication, it
was obviously probable that these same organs would
be still further developed if the power of communication had to be improved; and this has been effected by
the aid of adjoining and well adapted parts, namely the
tongue and lips.[65] The fact of the higher apes not

[64] 'Essays on Free-thinking,'
&c., 1873, p. 82.
[65] See some good remarks to
this effect by Dr. Maudsley,
'The Physiology and Pathology
of Mind,' 1868, p. 199.

using their vocal organs for speech, no doubt depends on their intelligence not having been sufficiently advanced. The possession by them of organs, which with long-continued practice might have been used for speech, although not thus used, is paralleled by the case of many birds which possess organs fitted for singing, though they never sing. Thus, the nightingale and crow have vocal organs similarly constructed, these being used by the former for diversified song, and by the latter only for croaking.[66] If it be asked why apes have not had their intellects developed to the same degree as that of man, general causes only can be assigned in answer, and it is unreasonable to expect anything more definite, considering our ignorance with respect to the successive stages of development through which each creature has passed.

The formation of different languages and of distinct species, and the proofs that both have been developed through a gradual process, are curiously parallel.[67] But we can trace the formation of many words further back than that of species, for we can perceive how they actually arose from the imitation of various sounds. We find in distinct languages striking homologies due to community of descent, and analogies due to a similar process of formation. The manner in which

[66] Macgillivray, 'Hist. of British Birds,' vol. ii. 1839, p. 29. An excellent observer, Mr. Blackwall, remarks that the magpie learns to pronounce single words, and even short sentences, more readily than almost any other British bird; yet, as he adds, after long and closely investigating its habits, he has never known it, in a state of nature, display any unusual capacity for imitation. 'Researches in Zoology,' 1834, p. 158.

[67] See the very interesting parallelism between the development of species and languages, given by Sir C. Lyell in 'The Geolog. Evidences of the Antiquity of Man,' 1863, chap. xxiii.

certain letters or sounds change when others change is
very like correlated growth. We have in both cases
the reduplication of parts, the effects of long-continued
use, and so forth. The frequent presence of rudiments, both in languages and in species, is still more
remarkable. The letter *m* in the word *am*, means *I*;
so that in the expression *I am*, a superfluous and useless rudiment has been retained. In the spelling also
of words, letters often remain as the rudiments of
ancient forms of pronunciation. Languages, like
organic beings, can be classed in groups under groups;
and they can be classed either naturally according to
descent, or artificially by other characters. Dominant
languages and dialects spread widely, and lead to the
gradual extinction of other tongues. A language, like
a species, when once extinct, never, as Sir C. Lyell
remarks, reappears. The same language never has
two birth-places. Distinct languages may be crossed
or blended together.[68] We see variability in every
tongue, and new words are continually cropping up;
but as there is a limit to the powers of the memory,
single words, like whole languages, gradually become
extinct. As Max Müller [69] has well remarked:—" A
" struggle for life is constantly going on amongst the
" words and grammatical forms in each language. The
" better, the shorter, the easier forms are constantly
" gaining the upper hand, and they owe their success to
" their own inherent virtue." To these more important
causes of the survival of certain words, mere novelty
and fashion may be added; for there is in the mind of

[68] See remarks to this effect
by the Rev. F. W. Farrar, in an
interesting   article,   entitled
' Philology and Darwinism,' in
' Nature,' March 24th, 1870, p.
528.

[69] ' Nature,' Jan. 6th, 1870,
p. 257.

man a strong love for slight changes in all things. The survival or preservation of certain favoured words in the struggle for existence is natural selection.

The perfectly regular and wonderfully complex construction of the languages of many barbarous nations has often been advanced as a proof, either of the divine origin of these languages, or of the high art and former civilisation of their founders. Thus F. von Schlegel writes: "In those languages which appear "to be at the lowest grade of intellectual culture, "we frequently observe a very high and elaborate "degree of art in their grammatical structure. This "is especially the case with the Basque and the "Lapponian, and many of the American languages." [70] But it is assuredly an error to speak of any language as an art, in the sense of its having been elaborately and methodically formed. Philologists now admit that conjugations, declensions, &c., originally existed as distinct words, since joined together; and as such words express the most obvious relations between objects and persons, it is not surprising that they should have been used by the men of most races during the earliest ages. With respect to perfection, the following illustration will best shew how easily we may err: a Crinoid sometimes consists of no less than 150,000 pieces of shell,[71] all arranged with perfect symmetry in radiating lines; but a naturalist does not consider an animal of this kind as more perfect than a bilateral one with comparatively few parts, and with none of these parts alike, excepting on the opposite

[70] Quoted by C. S. Wake, 'Chapters on Man,' 1868, p. 101.

[71] Buckland, 'Bridgewater Treatise,' p. 411.

sides of the body. He justly considers the differentiation and specialisation of organs as the test of perfection. So with languages: the most symmetrical and complex ought not to be ranked above irregular, abbreviated, and bastardised languages, which have borrowed expressive words and useful forms of construction from various conquering, conquered, or immigrant races.

From these few and imperfect remarks I conclude that the extremely complex and regular construction of many barbarous languages, is no proof that they owe their origin to a special act of creation.[72] Nor, as we have seen, does the faculty of articulate speech in itself offer any insuperable objection to the belief that man has been developed from some lower form.

Sense of Beauty.—This sense has been declared to be peculiar to man. I refer here only to the pleasure given by certain colours, forms, and sounds, and which may fairly be called a sense of the beautiful; with cultivated men such sensations are, however, intimately associated with complex ideas and trains of thought. When we behold a male bird elaborately displaying his graceful plumes or splendid colours before the female, whilst other birds, not thus decorated, make no such display, it is impossible to doubt that she admires the beauty of her male partner. As women everywhere deck themselves with these plumes, the beauty of such ornaments cannot be disputed. As we shall see later, the nests of humming-birds, and the playing passages of bower-birds are tastefully ornamented with gaily-coloured objects; and this shews that they must receive some kind of pleasure from the sight of such things.

[72] See some good remarks on the simplification of languages, by Sir J. Lubbock, 'Origin of Civilisation, 1870, p. 278.

With the great majority of animals, however, the taste for the beautiful is confined, as far as we can judge, to the attractions of the opposite sex. The sweet strains poured forth by many male birds during the season of love, are certainly admired by the females, of which fact evidence will hereafter be given. If female birds had been incapable of appreciating the beautiful colours, the ornaments, and voices of their male partners, all the labour and anxiety exhibited by the latter in displaying their charms before the females would have been thrown away; and this it is impossible to admit. Why certain bright colours should excite pleasure cannot, I presume, be explained, any more than why certain flavours and scents are agreeable; but habit has something to do with the result, for that which is at first unpleasant to our senses, ultimately becomes pleasant, and habits are inherited. With respect to sounds, Helmholtz has explained to a certain extent on physiological principles, why harmonies and certain cadences are agreeable. But besides this, sounds frequently recurring at irregular intervals are highly disagreeable, as every one will admit who has listened at night to the irregular flapping of a rope on board ship. The same principle seems to come into play with vision, as the eye prefers symmetry or figures with some regular recurrence. Patterns of this kind are employed by even the lowest savages as ornaments; and they have been developed through sexual selection for the adornment of some male animals. Whether we can or not give any reason for the pleasure thus derived from vision and hearing, yet man and many of the lower animals are alike pleased by the same colours, graceful shading and forms, and the same sounds.

The taste for the beautiful, at least as far as female beauty is concerned, is not of a special nature in the human mind; for it differs widely in the different races of man, and is not quite the same even in the different nations of the same race. Judging from the hideous ornaments, and the equally hideous music admired by most savages, it might be urged that their æsthetic faculty was not so highly developed as in certain animals, for instance, as in birds. Obviously no animal would be capable of admiring such scenes as the heavens at night, a beautiful landscape, or refined music; but such high tastes are acquired through culture, and depend on complex associations; they are not enjoyed by barbarians or by uneducated persons.

Many of the faculties, which have been of inestimable service to man for his progressive advancement, such as the powers of the imagination, wonder, curiosity, an undefined sense of beauty, a tendency to imitation, and the love of excitement or novelty, could hardly fail to lead to capricious changes of customs and fashions. I have alluded to this point, because a recent writer [73] has oddly fixed on Caprice "as one of the most remarkable and typical differences "between savages and brutes." But not only can we partially understand how it is that man is from various conflicting influences rendered capricious, but that the lower animals are, as we shall hereafter see, likewise capricious in their affections, aversions, and sense of beauty. There is also reason to suspect that they love novelty, for its own sake.

Belief in God—Religion.—There is no evidence that

[73] 'The Spectator,' Dec. 4th, 1869, p. 1430.

man was aboriginally endowed with the ennobling belief in the existence of an Omnipotent God. On the contrary there is ample evidence, derived not from hasty travellers, but from men who have long resided with savages, that numerous races have existed, and still exist, who have no idea of one or more gods, and who have no words in their languages to express such an idea.[74] The question is of course wholly distinct from that higher one, whether there exists a Creator and Ruler of the universe; and this has been answered in the affirmative by some of the highest intellects that have ever existed.

If, however, we include under the term "religion" the belief in unseen or spiritual agencies, the case is wholly different; for this belief seems to be universal with the less civilised races. Nor is it difficult to comprehend how it arose. As soon as the important faculties of the imagination, wonder, and curiosity, together with some power of reasoning, had become partially developed, man would naturally crave to understand what was passing around him, and would have vaguely speculated on his own existence. As Mr. M'Lennan[75] has remarked, "Some explanation of "the phenomena of life, a man must feign for himself, "and to judge from the universality of it, the simplest "hypothesis, and the first to occur to men, seems to "have been that natural phenomena are ascribable to

[74] See an excellent article on this subject by the Rev. F. W. Farrar, in the 'Anthropological Review,' Aug. 1864, p. ccxvii. For further facts see Sir J. Lubbock, 'Prehistoric Times,' 2nd edit. 1869, p. 564; and especially the chapters on Religion in his 'Origin of Civilisation,' 1870.

[75] 'The Worship of Animals and Plants,' in the 'Fortnightly Review,' Oct. 1, 1869, p. 422.

" the presence in animals, plants, and things, and in
" the forces of nature, of such spirits prompting to
" action as men are conscious they themselves possess.'
It is also probable, as Mr. Tylor has shewn, that
dreams may have first given rise to the notion of
spirits; for savages do not readily distinguish between
subjective and objective impressions. When a savage
dreams, the figures which appear before him are
believed to have come from a distance, and to stand
over him; or " the soul of the dreamer goes out on its
" travels, and comes home with a remembrance of
" what it has seen." [76] But until the faculties of
imagination, curiosity, reason, &c., had been fairly
well developed in the mind of man, his dreams would
not have led him to believe in spirits, any more than
in the case of a dog.

The tendency in savages to imagine that natural
objects and agencies are animated by spiritual or
living essences, is perhaps illustrated by a little fact

[76] Tylor, 'Early History of
Mankind,' 1865, p. 6. See also
the three striking chapters on
the Development of Religion, in
Lubbock's 'Origin of Civilisation,' 1870. In a like manner
Mr. Herbert Spencer, in his ingenious essay in the 'Fortnightly Review' (May 1st, 1870,
p. 535), accounts for the earliest
forms of religious belief throughout the world, by man being
led through dreams, shadows,
and other causes, to look at
himself as a double essence,
corporeal and spiritual. As the
spiritual being is supposed to
exist after death and to be
powerful, it is propitiated by
various gifts and ceremonies,
and its aid invoked. He then
further shews that names or
nicknames given from some
animal or other object, to the
early progenitors or founders of
a tribe, are supposed after a
long interval to represent the
real progenitor of the tribe; and
such animal or object is then
naturally believed still to exist
as a spirit, is held sacred, and
worshipped as a god. Nevertheless I cannot but suspect
that there is a still earlier and
ruder stage, when anything
which manifests power or movement is thought to be endowed
with some form of life, and with
mental faculties analogous to our
own.

which I once noticed: my dog, a full-grown and very sensible animal, was lying on the lawn during a hot and still day; but at a little distance a slight breeze occasionally moved an open parasol, which would have been wholly disregarded by the dog, had any one stood near it. As it was, every time that the parasol slightly moved, the dog growled fiercely and barked. He must, I think, have reasoned to himself in a rapid and unconscious manner, that movement without any apparent cause indicated the presence of some strange living agent, and that no stranger had a right to be on his territory.

The belief in spiritual agencies would easily pass into the belief in the existence of one or more gods. For savages would naturally attribute to spirits the same passions, the same love of vengeance or simplest form of justice, and the same affections which they themselves feel. The Fuegians appear to be in this respect in an intermediate condition, for when the surgeon on board the "Beagle" shot some young ducklings as specimens, York Minster declared in the most solemn manner, "Oh, Mr. Bynoe, much rain, "much snow, blow much;" and this was evidently a retributive punishment for wasting human food. So again he related how, when his brother killed a "wild "man," storms long raged, much rain and snow fell. Yet we could never discover that the Fuegians believed in what we should call a God, or practised any religious rites; and Jemmy Button, with justifiable pride, stoutly maintained that there was no devil in his land. This latter assertion is the more remarkable, as with savages the belief in bad spirits is far more common than that in good ones.

The feeling of religious devotion is a highly complex one, consisting of love, complete submission to an exalted and mysterious superior, a strong sense of dependence,[77] fear, reverence, gratitude, hope for the future, and perhaps other elements. No being could experience so complex an emotion until advanced in his intellectual and moral faculties to at least a moderately high level. Nevertheless, we see some distant approach to this state of mind in the deep love of a dog for his master, associated with complete submission, some fear, and perhaps other feelings. The behaviour of a dog when returning to his master after an absence, and, as I may add, of a monkey to his beloved keeper, is widely different from that towards their fellows. In the latter case the transports of joy appear to be somewhat less, and the sense of equality is shewn in every action. Professor Braubach goes so far as to maintain that a dog looks on his master as on a god.[78]

The same high mental faculties which first led man to believe in unseen spiritual agencies, then in fetishism, polytheism, and ultimately in monotheism, would infallibly lead him, as long as his reasoning powers remained poorly developed, to various strange superstitions and customs. Many of these are terrible to think of—such as the sacrifice of human beings to a blood-loving god; the trial of innocent persons by the ordeal of poison or fire; witchcraft, &c.—yet it is well

[77] See an able article on the 'Physical Elements of Religion,' by Mr. L. Owen Pike, in 'Anthropolog. Review,' April, 1870, p. lxiii.

[78] 'Religion, Moral, &c., der Darwin'schen Art-Lehre,' 1869, s. 53. It is said (Dr. W. Lauder Lindsay, 'Journal of Mental Science,' 1871, p. 43), that Bacon long ago, and the poet Burns, held the same notion.

occasionally to reflect on these superstitions, for they shew us what an infinite debt of gratitude we owe to the improvement of our reason, to science, and to our accumulated knowledge.   As Sir J. Lubbock [79] has well observed, " it is not too much to say that the horrible "dread of unknown evil hangs like a thick cloud over "savage life, and embitters every pleasure."   These miserable and indirect consequences of our highest faculties may be compared with the incidental and occasional mistakes of the instincts of the lower animals.

[79] ' Prehistoric Times,' 2nd edit. p. 571. In this work (p. 571) there will be found an excellent account of the many strange and capricious customs of savages.

CHAPTER IV.

Comparison of the Mental Powers of Man and the Lower Animals—*continued.*

The moral sense—Fundamental proposition—The qualities of social animals — Origin of sociability — Struggle between opposed instincts—Man a social animal—The more enduring social instincts conquer other less persistent instincts—The social virtues alone regarded by savages—The self-regarding virtues acquired at a later stage of development—The importance of the judgment of the members of the same community on conduct—Transmission of moral tendencies—Summary.

I FULLY subscribe to the judgment of those writers[1] who maintain that of all the differences between man and the lower animals, the moral sense or conscience is by far the most important. This sense, as Mackintosh[2] remarks, "has a rightful supremacy over every other "principle of human action;" it is summed up in that short but imperious word *ought*, so full of high significance. It is the most noble of all the attributes of man, leading him without a moment's hesitation to risk his life for that of a fellow-creature; or after due deliberation, impelled simply by the deep feeling of right or duty, to sacrifice it in some great cause. Immanuel Kant exclaims, "Duty! Wondrous thought, "that workest neither by fond insinuation, flattery, "nor by any threat, but merely by holding up thy

[1] See, for instance, on this subject, Quatrefages, 'Unité de l'Espèce Humaine,' 1861, p. 21, &c.

[2] 'Dissertation on Ethical Philosophy,' 1837, p. 231, &c.

"naked law in the soul, and so extorting for thyself
"always reverence, if not always obedience; before
"whom all appetites are dumb, however secretly they
"rebel; whence thy original?"[3]

This great question has been discussed by many
writers[4] of consummate ability; and my sole excuse
for touching on it, is the impossibility of here passing
it over; and because, as far as I know, no one has
approached it exclusively from the side of natural
history. The investigation possesses, also, some independent interest, as an attempt to see how far the
study of the lower animals throws light on one of the
highest psychical faculties of man.

The following proposition seems to me in a high
degree probable—namely, that any animal whatever,
endowed with well-marked social instincts,[5] the pa-

[3] 'Metaphysics of Ethics,' translated by J. W. Semple, Edinburgh,' 1836, p. 136.

[4] Mr. Bain gives a list ('Men-tal and Moral Science,' 1868, p. 543-725) of twenty-six British authors who have written on this subject, and whose names are familiar to every reader; to these, Mr. Bain's own name, and those of Mr. Lecky, Mr. Shadworth Hodgson, Sir J. Lubbock, and others, might be added.

[5] Sir B. Brodie, after observing that man is a social animal ('Psychological Enquiries,' 1854, p. 192), asks the pregnant ques-tion, "ought not this to settle "the disputed question as to "the existence of a moral "sense?" Similar ideas have probably occurred to many per-sons, as they did long ago to

Marcus Aurelius. Mr. J. S. Mill speaks, in his celebrated work, 'Utilitarianism,' (1864, pp. 45, 46), of the social feelings as a "powerful natural sentiment," and as "the natural basis of "sentiment for utilitarian mo-"rality." Again he says, "Like "the other acquired capacities "above referred to, the moral "faculty, if not a part of our "nature, is a natural out-growth "from it; capable, like them, "in a certain small degree of "springing up spontaneously." But in opposition to all this, he also remarks, "if, as is my own "belief, the moral feelings are "not innate, but acquired, they "are not for that reason less "natural." It is with hesitation that I venture to differ at all from so profound a thinker, but it can hardly be disputed that

rental and filial affections being here included, would inevitably acquire a moral sense or conscience, as soon as its intellectual powers had become as well, or nearly as well developed, as in man. For, *firstly*, the social instincts lead an animal to take pleasure in the society of its fellows, to feel a certain amount of sympathy with them, and to perform various services for them. The services may be of a definite and evidently instinctive nature; or there may be only a wish and readiness, as with most of the higher social animals, to aid their fellows in certain general ways. But these feelings and services are by no means extended to all the individuals of the same species, only to those of the same association. *Secondly*, as soon as the mental faculties had become highly developed, images of all past actions and motives would be incessantly passing through the brain of each individual; and that feeling of dissatisfaction, or even misery, which invariably results, as we shall hereafter see, from any unsatisfied instinct, would arise, as often as it was perceived that the enduring and always present social instinct had yielded to some other instinct, at the time stronger, but neither enduring in its nature, nor leaving behind it a very vivid impression. It is clear that many instinctive desires, such as that of hunger,

---

the social feelings are instinctive or innate in the lower animals; and why should they not be so in man? Mr. Bain (see, for instance, 'The Emotions and the Will,' 1865, p. 481) and others believe that the moral sense is acquired by each individual during his lifetime. On the general theory of evolution this is at least extremely improbable. The ignoring of all transmitted mental qualities will, as it seems to me, be hereafter judged as a most serious blemish in the works of Mr. Mill.

are in their nature of short duration; and after being satisfied, are not readily or vividly recalled. *Thirdly*, after the power of language had been acquired, and the wishes of the community could be expressed, the common opinion how each member ought to act for the public good, would naturally become in a paramount degree the guide to action. But it should be borne in mind that however great weight we may attribute to public opinion, our regard for the approbation and disapprobation of our fellows depends on sympathy, which, as we shall see, forms an essential part of the social instinct, and is indeed its foundation-stone. *Lastly*, habit in the individual would ultimately play a very important part in guiding the conduct of each member; for the social instinct, together with sympathy, is, like any other instinct, greatly strengthened by habit, and so consequently would be obedience to the wishes and judgment of the community. These several subordinate propositions must now be discussed, and some of them at considerable length.

It may be well first to premise that I do not wish to maintain that any strictly social animal, if its intellectual faculties were to become as active and as highly developed as in man, would acquire exactly the same moral sense as ours. In the same manner as various animals have some sense of beauty, though they admire widely different objects, so they might have a sense of right and wrong, though led by it to follow widely different lines of conduct. If, for instance, to take an extreme case, men were reared under precisely the same conditions as hive-bees, there can hardly be a doubt that our unmarried females would, like the worker-bees, think it a sacred duty to kill their brothers, and mothers would strive to kill their fertile daughters; and no one would think of interfering.[6] Nevertheless, the bee, or any other social animal, would gain in our supposed case, as it appears to me, some feeling of right or wrong, or a conscience. For each individual would have an inward sense of possessing certain stronger or more enduring instincts, and others less strong or enduring; so that there would often be a struggle as to which impulse should be followed; and satisfaction, dissatisfaction, or even misery would be felt, as past impressions were compared during their incessant passage through the mind. In this case an inward monitor would tell the animal that it would have been better to have followed the one impulse rather than the other. The one course ought to have been followed, and the other ought not; the one would have been right and the other wrong; but to these terms I shall recur.

[6] Mr. H. Sidgwick remarks, in an able discussion on this subject (the 'Academy,' June 15th, 1872, p. 231), "a superior "bee, we may feel sure, would "aspire to a milder solution "of the population question." Judging, however, from the habits of many or most savages, man solves the problem by female infanticide, polyandry and promiscuous intercourse; therefore it may well be doubted whether it would be by a milder method. Miss Cobbe, in commenting ('Darwinism in Morals,' 'Theological Review,' April, 1872, p. 188–191) on the same illustration, says, the *principles* of social duty would be thus reversed; and by this, I pre-sume, she means that the fulfilment of a social duty would tend to the injury of individuals; but she overlooks the fact, which she would doubtless admit, that the instincts of the bee have been acquired for the good of the community. She goes so far as to say that if the theory of ethics advocated in this chapter were ever generally accepted, "I cannot but believe "that in the hour of their "triumph would be sounded "the knell of the virtue of mankind!" It is to be hoped that the belief in the permanence of virtue on this earth is not held by many persons on so weak a tenure.

Sociability.—Animals of many kinds are social; we find even distinct species living together; for example, some American monkeys; and united flocks of rooks, jackdaws, and starlings. Man shews the same feeling in his strong love for the dog, which the dog returns with interest. Every one must have noticed how miserable horses, dogs, sheep, &c., are when separated from their companions, and what strong mutual affection the two former kinds, at least, shew on their reunion. It is curious to speculate on the feelings of a dog, who will rest peacefully for hours in a room with his master or any of the family, without the least notice being taken of him; but if left for a short time by himself, barks or howls dismally. We will confine our attention to the higher social animals; and pass over insects, although some of these are social, and aid one another in many important ways. The most common mutual service in the higher animals is to warn one another of danger by means of the united senses of all. Every sportsman knows, as Dr. Jaeger remarks,[7] how difficult it is to approach animals in a herd or troop. Wild horses and cattle do not, I believe, make any danger-signal; but the attitude of any one of them who first discovers an enemy, warns the others. Rabbits stamp loudly on the ground with their hind-feet as a signal: sheep and chamois do the same with their forefeet, uttering likewise a whistle. Many birds, and some mammals, post sentinels, which in the case of seals are said[8] generally to be the females. The leader of a troop of monkeys acts as the sentinel, and utters cries expressive both of danger and

[7] 'Die Darwin'sche Theorie,' s. 101.

[8] Mr. R. Brown in 'Proc. Zoolog. Soc.' 1868, p. 409.

of safety.[9]   Social animals perform many little services
for each other : horses nibble, and cows lick each other,
on any spot which itches: monkeys search each other
for external parasites; and Brehm states that after
a troop of the *Cercopithecus griseo-viridis* has rushed
through a thorny brake, each monkey stretches itself
on a branch, and another monkey sitting by, " con-
" scientiously" examines its fur, and extracts every
thorn or burr.

Animals also render more important services to one
another: thus wolves and some other beasts of prey
hunt in packs, and aid one another in attacking their
victims.   Pelicans fish in concert.   The Hamadryas
baboons turn over stones to find insects, &c.; and
when they come to a large one, as many as can stand
round, turn it over together and share the booty.
Social animals mutually defend each other.   Bull
bisons in N. America, when there is danger, drive the
cows and calves into the middle of the herd, whilst
they defend the outside.   I shall also in a future
chapter give an account of two young wild bulls at
Chillingham attacking an old one in concert, and of
two stallions together trying to drive away a third
stallion from a troop of mares.   In Abyssinia, Brehm
encountered a great troop of baboons who were crossing
a valley : some had already ascended the opposite
mountain, and some were still in the valley : the latter

[9] Brehm, ' Thierleben,' B. i.
1864, s. 52, 79. For the case
of the monkeys extracting thorns
from each other, see s. 54. With
respect to the Hamadryas turning over stones, the fact is given
(s. 76) on the evidence of
Alvarez, whose observations
Brehm thinks quite trustworthy.
For the cases of the old male
baboons attacking the dogs, see
s. 79; and with respect to the
eagle, s. 56.

were attacked by the dogs, but the old males immediately hurried down from the rocks, and with mouths widely opened, roared so fearfully, that the dogs quickly drew back. They were again encouraged to the attack; but by this time all the baboons had reascended the heights, excepting a young one, about six months old, who, loudly calling for aid, climbed on a block of rock, and was surrounded. Now one of the largest males, a true hero, came down again from the mountain, slowly went to the young one, coaxed him, and triumphantly led him away—the dogs being too much astonished to make an attack. I cannot resist giving another scene which was witnessed by this same naturalist; an eagle seized a young Cercopithecus, which, by clinging to a branch, was not at once carried off; it cried loudly for assistance, upon which the other members of the troop, with much uproar, rushed to the rescue, surrounded the eagle, and pulled out so many feathers, that he no longer thought of his prey, but only how to escape. This eagle, as Brehm remarks, assuredly would never again attack a single monkey of a troop.[10]

It is certain that associated animals have a feeling of love for each other, which is not felt by non-social adult animals. How far in most cases they actually sympathise in the pains and pleasures of others, is more doubtful, especially with respect to pleasures.

[10] Mr. Belt gives the case of a spider-monkey (Ateles) in Nicaragua, which was heard screaming for nearly two hours in the forest, and was found with an eagle perched close by it. The bird apparently feared to attack as long as it remained face to face; and Mr. Belt believes, from what he has seen of the habits of these monkeys, that they protect themselves from eagles by keeping two or three together. 'The Naturalist in Nicaragua,' 1874, p. 118.

Mr Buxton, however, who had excellent means of observation,[11] states that his macaws, which lived free in Norfolk, took " an extravagant interest " in a pair with a nest; and whenever the female left it, she was surrounded by a troop "screaming horrible acclama-"tions in her honour." It is often difficult to judge whether animals have any feeling for the sufferings of others of their kind. Who can say what cows feel, when they surround and stare intently on a dying or dead companion; apparently, however, as Houzeau remarks, they feel no pity. That animals sometimes are far from feeling any sympathy is too certain; for they will expel a wounded animal from the herd, or gore or worry it to death. This is almost the blackest fact in natural history, unless, indeed, the explanation which has been suggested is true, that their instinct or reason leads them to expel an injured companion, lest beasts of prey, including man, should be tempted to follow the troop. In this case their conduct is not much worse than that of the North American Indians, who leave their feeble comrades to perish on the plains; or the Fijians, who, when their parents get old, or fall ill, bury them alive.[12]

Many animals, however, certainly sympathise with each other's distress or danger. This is the case even with birds. Captain Stansbury[13] found on a salt lake in Utah an old and completely blind pelican, which

[11] 'Annals of Mag. of Nat. Hist.,' November, 1868, p. 382.

[12] Sir J. Lubbock, 'Prehistoric Times,' 2nd edit. p. 446.

[13] As quoted by Mr. L. H. Morgan, 'The American Beaver,' 1868, p. 272. Capt. Stansbury also gives an interesting account of the manner in which a very young pelican, carried away by a strong stream, was guided and encouraged in its attempts to reach the shore by half a dozen old birds.

was very fat, and must have been well fed for a long time by his companions. Mr. Blyth, as he informs me, saw Indian crows feeding two or three of their companions which were blind ; and I have heard of an analogous case with the domestic cock. We may, if we choose, call these actions instinctive ; but such cases are much too rare for the development of any special instinct.[14]   I have myself seen a dog, who never passed a cat who lay sick in a basket, and was a great friend of his, without giving her a few licks with his tongue, the surest sign of kind feeling in a dog.

It must be called sympathy that leads a courageous dog to fly at any one who strikes his master, as he certainly will. I saw a person pretending to beat a lady, who had a very timid little dog on her lap, and the trial had never been made before; the little creature instantly jumped away, but after the pretended beating was over, it was really pathetic to see how perseveringly he tried to lick his mistress's face, and comfort her.   Brehm [15] states that when a baboon in confinement was pursued to be punished, the others tried to protect him.   It must have been sympathy in the cases above given which led the baboons and Cercopitheci to defend their young comrades from the dogs and the eagle.   I will give only one other instance of sympathetic and heroic conduct, in the case of a little American monkey.   Several years ago a keeper at the Zoological Gardens showed me some deep and scarcely healed wounds on the nape of his own neck, inflicted on him, whilst kneeling on the floor, by a

[14] As Mr. Bain states, " effec-"tive aid to a sufferer springs "from sympathy proper : "

'Mental and Moral Science, 1868, p. 245.

[15] ' Thierleben,' B. i. s. 85.

fierce baboon. The little American monkey, who was
a warm friend of this keeper, lived in the same large
compartment, and was dreadfully afraid of the great
baboon. Nevertheless, as soon as he saw his friend in
peril, he rushed to the rescue, and by screams and
bites so distracted the baboon that the man was able to
escape, after, as the surgeon thought, running great
risk of his life.

Besides love and sympathy, animals exhibit other
qualities connected with the social instincts, which
in us would be called moral; and I agree with
Agassiz[16] that dogs possess something very like a
conscience.

Dogs possess some power of self-command, and this
does not appear to be wholly the result of fear. As
Braubach[17] remarks, they will refrain from stealing
food in the absence of their master. They have long
been accepted as the very type of fidelity and obedience.
But the elephant is likewise very faithful to his driver
or keeper, and probably considers him as the leader of
the herd. Dr. Hooker informs me that an elephant,
which he was riding in India, became so deeply bogged
that he remained stuck fast until the next day, when
he was extricated by men with ropes. Under such
circumstances elephants will seize with their trunks
any object, dead or alive, to place under their knees, to
prevent their sinking deeper in the mud; and the
driver was dreadfully afraid lest the animal should have
seized Dr. Hooker and crushed him to death. But the
driver himself, as Dr. Hooker was assured, ran no
risk. This forbearance under an emergency so dread-

[16] 'De l'Espèce et de la
Classe,' 1869, p. 97.   [17] 'Die Darwin'sche Art-
Lehre,' 1869, s. 54.

ful for a heavy animal, is a wonderful proof of noble fidelity.[18]

All animals living in a body, which defend themselves or attack their enemies in concert, must indeed be in some degree faithful to one another; and those that follow a leader must be in some degree obedient. When the baboons in Abyssinia[19] plunder a garden, they silently follow their leader; and if an imprudent young animal makes a noise, he receives a slap from the others to teach him silence and obedience. Mr. Galton, who has had excellent opportunities for observing the half-wild cattle in S. Africa, says,[20] that they cannot endure even a momentary separation from the herd. They are essentially slavish, and accept the common determination, seeking no better lot than to be led by any one ox who has enough self-reliance to accept the position. The men who break in these animals for harness, watch assiduously for those who, by grazing apart, shew a self-reliant disposition, and these they train as fore-oxen. Mr. Galton adds that such animals are rare and valuable; and if many were born they would soon be eliminated, as lions are always on the look-out for the individuals which wander from the herd.

With respect to the impulse which leads certain animals to associate together, and to aid one another in many ways, we may infer that in most cases they are impelled by the same sense of satisfaction or pleasure which they experience in performing other

[18] See also Hooker's 'Himalayan Journals,' vol. ii., 1854, p. 333.

[19] Brehm, 'Thierleben,' B. i. s. 76.

[20] See his extremely interesting paper on 'Gregariousness in Cattle, and in Man,' 'Macmillan's Mag.' Feb. 1871, p. 353.

instinctive actions; or by the same sense of dissatisfaction as when other instinctive actions are checked.
We see this in innumerable instances, and it is illustrated in a striking manner by the acquired instincts
of our domesticated animals; thus a young shepherd-
dog delights in driving and running round a flock of
sheep, but not in worrying them; a young fox-hound
delights in hunting a fox, whilst some other kinds of
dogs, as I have witnessed, utterly disregard foxes.
What a strong feeling of inward satisfaction must
impel a bird, so full of activity, to brood day after day
over her eggs. Migratory birds are quite miserable if
stopped from migrating; perhaps they enjoy starting
on their long flight; but it is hard to believe that the
poor pinioned goose, described by Audubon, which
started on foot at the proper time for its journey of
probably more than a thousand miles, could have felt
any joy in doing so. Some instincts are determined
solely by painful feelings, as by fear, which leads to
self-preservation, and is in some cases directed towards
special enemies. No one, I presume, can analyse the
sensations of pleasure or pain. In many instances,
however, it is probable that instincts are persistently
followed from the mere force of inheritance, without
the stimulus of either pleasure or pain. A young
pointer, when it first scents game, apparently cannot
help pointing. A squirrel in a cage who pats the nuts
which it cannot eat, as if to bury them in the ground,
can hardly be thought to act thus, either from pleasure
or pain. Hence the common assumption that men
must be impelled to every action by experiencing some
pleasure or pain may be erroneous. Although a habit
may be blindly and implicitly followed, independently

of any pleasure or pain felt at the moment, yet if it be
forcibly and abruptly checked, a vague sense of dissatisfaction is generally experienced.

It has often been assumed that animals were in the
first place rendered social, and that they feel as a consequence uncomfortable when separated from each
other, and comfortable whilst together; but it is a
more probable view that these sensations were first
developed, in order that those animals which would
profit by living in society, should be induced to live
together, in the same manner as the sense of hunger
and the pleasure of eating were, no doubt, first acquired
in order to induce animals to eat. The feeling of
pleasure from society is probably an extension of the
parental or filial affections, since the social instinct
seems to be developed by the young remaining for a
long time with their parents; and this extension may
be attributed in part to habit, but chiefly to natural
selection. With those animals which were benefited
by living in close association, the individuals which
took the greatest pleasure in society would best escape
various dangers, whilst those that cared least for their
comrades, and lived solitary, would perish in greater
numbers. With respect to the origin of the parental
and filial affections, which apparently lie at the base of
the social instincts, we know not the steps by which
they have been gained; but we may infer that it has
been to a large extent through natural selection. So
it has almost certainly been with the unusual and
opposite feeling of hatred between the nearest relations,
as with the worker-bees which kill their brother-drones,
and with the queen-bees which kill their daughter-
queens; the desire to destroy their nearest relations

having been in this case of service to the community. Parental affection, or some feeling which replaces it, has been developed in certain animals extremely low in the scale, for example, in star-fishes and spiders. It is also occasionally present in a few members alone in a whole group of animals, as in the genus Forficula, or earwigs.

The all-important emotion of sympathy is distinct from that of love. A mother may passionately love her sleeping and passive infant, but she can hardly at such times be said to feel sympathy for it. The love of a man for his dog is distinct from sympathy, and so is that of a dog for his master. Adam Smith formerly argued, as has Mr. Bain recently, that the basis of sympathy lies in our strong retentiveness of former states of pain or pleasure. Hence, "the sight of "another person enduring hunger, cold, fatigue, "revives in us some recollection of these states, which "are painful even in idea." We are thus impelled to relieve the sufferings of another, in order that our own painful feelings may be at the same time relieved. In like manner we are led to participate in the pleasures of others.[21] But I cannot see how this view explains the fact that sympathy is excited, in an immeasurably stronger degree, by a beloved, than by an indifferent

[21] See the first and striking chapter in Adam Smith's 'Theory of Moral Sentiments.' Also Mr. Bain's 'Mental and Moral Science,' 1868, p. 244, and 275–282. Mr. Bain states, that, "sympathy is, indirectly, "a source of pleasure to the "sympathiser;" and he accounts for this through reciprocity. He remarks t at "the "person benefited, or others in "his stead, may make up, by "sympathy and good offices re- "turned, for all the sacrifice." But if, as appears to be the case, sympathy is strictly an instinct, its exercise would give direct pleasure, in the same manner as the exercise, as before remarked, of almost every other instinct.

person. The mere sight of suffering, independently of love, would suffice to call up in us vivid recollections and associations. The explanation may lie in the fact that, with all animals, sympathy is directed solely towards the members of the same community, and therefore towards known, and more or less beloved members, but not to all the individuals of the same species. This fact is not more surprising than that the fears of many animals should be directed against special enemies. Species which are not social, such as lions and tigers, no doubt feel sympathy for the suffering of their own young, but not for that of any other animal. With mankind, selfishness, experience, and imitation, probably add, as Mr. Bain has shown, to the power of sympathy; for we are led by the hope of receiving good in return to perform acts of sympathetic kindness to others; and sympathy is much strengthened by habit. In however complex a manner this feeling may have originated, as it is one of high importance to all those animals which aid and defend one another, it will have been increased through natural selection; for those communities, which included the greatest number of the most sympathetic members, would flourish best, and rear the greatest number of offspring.

It is, however, impossible to decide in many cases whether certain social instincts have been acquired through natural selection, or are the indirect result of other instincts and faculties, such as sympathy, reason, experience, and a tendency to imitation; or again, whether they are simply the result of long-continued habit. So remarkable an instinct as the placing sentinels to warn the community of danger, can hardly have been the indirect result of any of these faculties; it must, therefore, have been directly acquired. On the other hand, the habit followed by the males of some social animals of defending the community, and of attacking their enemies or their prey in concert, may perhaps have originated from mutual sympathy; but courage, and in most cases strength, must have been previously acquired, probably through natural selection.

Of the various instincts and habits, some are much stronger than others; that is, some either give more pleasure in their performance, and more distress in their prevention, than others; or, which is probably quite as important, they are, through inheritance, more persistently followed, without exciting any special feeling of pleasure or pain. We are ourselves conscious that some habits are much more difficult to cure or change than others. Hence a struggle may often be observed in animals between different instincts, or between an instinct and some habitual disposition; as when a dog rushes after a hare, is rebuked, pauses, hesitates, pursues again, or returns ashamed to his master; or as between the love of a female dog for her young puppies and for her master,—for she may be seen to slink away to them, as if half ashamed of not accompanying her master. But the most curious instance known to me of one instinct getting the better of another, is the migratory instinct conquering the maternal instinct. The former is wonderfully strong; a confined bird will at the proper season beat her breast against the wires of her cage, until it is bare and bloody. It causes young salmon to leap out of the fresh water, in which they could continue to exist, and thus unintentionally to commit suicide. Every one knows how strong the maternal instinct is, leading even timid birds to face great danger, though with hesitation, and in opposition to the instinct of self-preservation. Nevertheless, the migratory instinct is so powerful, that late in the autumn swallows, house-martins, and swifts frequently desert their tender young, leaving them to perish miserably in their nests.[22]

We can perceive that an instinctive impulse, if it be in any way more beneficial to a species than some other or opposed instinct, would be rendered the more potent of the two through natural selection; for the individuals which had it most strongly developed would survive in larger numbers. Whether this is the case with the migratory in comparison with the maternal instinct, may be doubted. The great persistence, or steady action of the former at certain seasons of the year during the whole day, may give it for a time paramount force.

Man a social animal.—Every one will admit that

[22] This fact, the Rev. L. Jenyns states (see his edition of ' White's Nat. Hist. of Selborne,' 1853, p. 204) was first recorded by the illustrious Jenner, in 'Phil. Transact.' 1824, and has since been confirmed by several observers, especially by Mr. Blackwall. This latter careful observer examined, late in the autumn, during two years, thirty-six nests; he found that twelve contained young dead birds, five contained eggs on the point of being hatched, and three, eggs not nearly hatched. Many birds, not yet old enough for a prolonged flight, are likewise deserted and left behind. See Blackwall, 'Researches in Zoology,' 1834, pp. 108, 118. For some additional evidence, although this is not wanted, see Leroy, 'Lettres Phil.' 1802, p. 217. For Swifts, Gould's ' Introduction to the Birds of Great Britain,' 1823, p. 5. Similar cases have been observed in Canada by Mr. Adams; ' Pop. Science Review,' July, 1873, p. 283.

man is a social being. We see this in his dislike of
solitude, and in his wish for society beyond that of his
own family. Solitary confinement is one of the severest
punishments which can be inflicted. Some authors
suppose that man primevally lived in single families;
but at the present day, though single families, or only
two or three together, roam the solitudes of some savage
lands, they always, as far as I can discover, hold
friendly relations with other families inhabiting the
same district. Such families occasionally meet in
council, and unite for their common defence. It is no
argument against savage man being a social animal,
that the tribes inhabiting adjacent districts are almost
always at war with each other; for the social instincts
never extend to all the individuals of the same species.
Judging from the analogy of the majority of the Quadrumana, it is probable that the early ape-like progenitors of man were likewise social; but this is not of
much importance for us. Although man, as he now
exists, has few special instincts, having lost any which
his early progenitors may have possessed, this is no
reason why he should not have retained from an
extremely remote period some degree of instinctive
love and sympathy for his fellows. We are indeed
all conscious that we do possess such sympathetic
feelings;[23] but our consciousness does not tell us
whether they are instinctive, having originated long
ago in the same manner as with the lower animals, or

[23] Hume remarks ('An Enquiry Concerning the Principles
of Morals,' edit. of 1751, p. 132),
"There seems a necessity for
"confessing that the happiness
"and misery of others are not
"spectacles altogether indiffer-
"ent to us, but that the view of
"the former . . . communicates
"a secret joy; the appearance
"of the latter . . . throws a
"melancholy damp over the
"imagination."

whether they have been acquired by each of us during
our early years.   As man is a social animal, it is almost
certain that he would inherit a tendency to be faithful
to his comrades, and obedient to the leader of his tribe;
for these qualities are common to most social animals.
He would consequently possess some capacity for self-
command.   He would from an inherited tendency be
willing to defend, in concert with others, his fellow-
men; and would be ready to aid them in any way,
which did not too greatly interfere with his own
welfare or his own strong desires.

The social animals which stand at the bottom of the
scale are guided almost exclusively, and those which
stand higher in the scale are largely guided, by special
instincts in the aid which they give to the members
of the same community; but they are likewise in part
impelled by mutual love and sympathy, assisted apparently by some amount of reason.   Although man,
as just remarked, has no special instincts to tell him
how to aid his fellow-men, he still has the impulse, and
with his improved intellectual faculties would naturally
be much guided in this respect by reason and experience.   Instinctive sympathy would also cause him
to value highly the approbation of his fellows; for, as
Mr. Bain has clearly shewn,[24] the love of praise and the
strong feeling of glory, and the still stronger horror of
scorn and infamy, " are due to the workings of sympathy."   Consequently man would be influenced in the
highest degree by the wishes, approbation, and blame
of his fellow-men, as expressed by their gestures and
language.   Thus the social instincts, which must have
been acquired by man in a very rude state, and probably

[24] ' Mental and Moral Science,' 1868, p. 254.

even by his early ape-like progenitors, still give the impulse to some of his best actions; but his actions are in a higher degree determined by the expressed wishes and judgment of his fellow-men, and unfortunately very often by his own strong selfish desires. But as love, sympathy and self-command become strengthened by habit, and as the power of reasoning becomes clearer, so that man can value justly the judgments of his fellows, he will feel himself impelled, apart from any transitory pleasure or pain, to certain lines of conduct. He might then declare—not that any barbarian or uncultivated man could thus think—I am the supreme judge of my own conduct, and in the words of Kant, I will not in my own person violate the dignity of humanity.

The more enduring Social Instincts conquer the less persistent Instincts.—We have not, however, as yet considered the main point, on which, from our present point of view, the whole question of the moral sense turns. Why should a man feel that he ought to obey one instinctive desire rather than another? Why is he bitterly regretful, if he has yielded to a strong sense of self-preservation, and has not risked his life to save that of a fellow-creature? or why does he regret having stolen food from hunger?

It is evident in the first place, that with mankind the instinctive impulses have different degrees of strength; a savage will risk his own life to save that of a member of the same community, but will be wholly indifferent about a stranger: a young and timid mother urged by the maternal instinct will, without a moment's hesitation, run the greatest danger for her own infant, but not for a mere fellow-creature.

Nevertheless many a civilized man, or even boy, who never before risked his life for another, but full of courage and sympathy, has disregarded the instinct of self-preservation, and plunged at once into a torrent to save a drowning man, though a stranger. In this case man is impelled by the same instinctive motive, which made the heroic little American monkey, formerly described, save his keeper, by attacking the great and dreaded baboon. Such actions as the above appear to be the simple result of the greater strength of the social or maternal instincts than that of any other instinct or motive; for they are performed too instantaneously for reflection, or for pleasure or pain to be felt at the time; though, if prevented by any cause, distress or even misery might be felt. In a timid man, on the other hand, the instinct of self-preservation might be so strong, that he would be unable to force himself to run any such risk, perhaps not even for his own child.

I am aware that some persons maintain that actions performed impulsively, as in the above cases, do not come under the dominion of the moral sense, and cannot be called moral. They confine this term to actions done deliberately, after a victory over opposing desires, or when prompted by some exalted motive. But it appears scarcely possible to draw any clear line of distinction of this kind.[25] As far as exalted motives are concerned, many instances have been recorded of

[25] I refer here to the distinction between what has been called *material* and *formal* morality. I am glad to find that Professor Huxley ('Critiques and Addresses,' 1873, p. 287) takes the same view on this subject as I do. Mr. Leslie Stephen remarks ('Essays on Freethinking and Plain Speaking,' 1873, p. 83), "the metaphysical distinction, "between material and formal "morality is as irrelevant as other "such distinctions."

savages, destitute of any feeling of general benevolence towards mankind, and not guided by any religious motive, who have deliberately sacrificed their lives as prisoners,[26] rather than betray their comrades; and surely their conduct ought to be considered as moral. As far as deliberation, and the victory over opposing motives are concerned, animals may be seen doubting between opposed instincts, in rescuing their offspring or comrades from danger; yet their actions, though done for the good of others, are not called moral. Moreover, anything performed very often by us, will at last be done without deliberation or hesitation, and can then hardly be distinguished from an instinct; yet surely no one will pretend that such an action ceases to be moral. On the contrary, we all feel that an act cannot be considered as perfect, or as performed in the most noble manner, unless it be done impulsively, without deliberation or effort, in the same manner as by a man in whom the requisite qualities are innate. He who is forced to overcome his fear or want of sympathy before he acts, deserves, however, in one way higher credit than the man whose innate disposition leads him to a good act without effort. As we cannot distinguish between motives, we rank all actions of a certain class as moral, if performed by a moral being. A moral being is one who is capable of comparing his past and future actions or motives, and of approving or disapproving of them. We have no reason to suppose that any of the lower animals have this capacity; therefore, when a Newfoundland dog drags a child out

[26] I have given one such case, namely of three Patagonian Indians who preferred being shot, one after the other, to betraying the plans of their companions in war ('Journal of Researches,' 1845, p. 103).

of the water, or a monkey faces danger to rescue its comrade, or takes charge of an orphan monkey, we do not call its conduct moral. But in the case of man, who alone can with certainty be ranked as a moral being, actions of a certain class are called moral, whether performed deliberately, after a struggle with opposing motives, or impulsively through instinct, or from the effects of slowly-gained habit.

But to return to our more immediate subject. Although some instincts are more powerful than others, and thus lead to corresponding actions, yet it is untenable, that in man the social instincts (including the love of praise and fear of blame) possess greater strength, or have, through long habit, acquired greater strength than the instincts of self-preservation, hunger, lust, vengeance, &c. Why then does man regret, even though trying to banish such regret, that he has followed the one natural impulse rather than the other ; and why does he further feel that he ought to regret his conduct ? Man in this respect differs profoundly from the lower animals. Nevertheless we can, I think, see with some degree of clearness the reason of this difference.

Man, from the activity of his mental faculties, cannot avoid reflection: past impressions and images are incessantly and clearly passing through his mind. Now with those animals which live permanently in a body, the social instincts are ever present and persistent. Such animals are always ready to utter the danger-signal, to defend the community, and to give aid to their fellows in accordance with their habits ; they feel at all times, without the stimulus of any special passion or desire, some degree of love and sympathy for them ; they are unhappy if long separated from them, and

always happy to be again in their company. So it is
with ourselves. Even when we are quite alone, how
often do we think with pleasure or pain of what others
think of us,—of their imagined approbation or disapprobation; and this all follows from sympathy, a
fundamental element of the social instincts. A man
who possessed no trace of such instincts would be an
unnatural monster. On the other hand, the desire to
satisfy hunger, or any passion such as vengeance, is in
its nature temporary, and can for a time be fully
satisfied. Nor is it easy, perhaps hardly possible, to
call up with complete vividness the feeling, for instance,
of hunger; nor indeed, as has often been remarked, of
any suffering. The instinct of self-preservation is not
felt except in the presence of danger; and many a
coward has thought himself brave until he has met his
enemy face to face. The wish for another man's
property is perhaps as persistent a desire as any that
can be named; but even in this case the satisfaction of
actual possession is generally a weaker feeling than
the desire: many a thief, if not a habitual one, after
success has wondered why he stole some article.[27]

[27] Enmity or hatred seems
also to be a highly persistent
feeling, perhaps more so than
any other that can be named.
Envy is defined as hatred of
another for some excellence or
success; and Bacon insists
(Essay ix.), "Of all other
"affections envy is the most
"importune and continual."
Dogs are very apt to hate both
strange men and strange dogs,
especially if they live near at
hand, but do not belong to the
same family, tribe, or clan; this
feeling would thus seem to be
innate, and is certainly a most
persistent one. It seems to be
the complement and converse of
the true social instinct. From
what we hear of savages, it
would appear that something of
the same kind holds good with
them. If this be so, it would
be a small step in any one to
transfer such feelings to any
member of the same tribe if he
had done him an injury and had
become his enemy. Nor is it
probable that the primitive

A man cannot prevent past impressions often re-passing through his mind; he will thus be driven to make a comparison between the impressions of past hunger, vengeance satisfied, or danger shunned at other men's cost, with the almost ever-present instinct of sympathy, and with his early knowledge of what others consider as praiseworthy or blameable. This knowledge cannot be banished from his mind, and from instinctive sympathy is esteemed of great moment. He will then feel as if he had been baulked in following a present instinct or habit, and this with all animals causes dissatisfaction, or even misery.

The above case of the swallow affords an illustration, though of a reversed nature, of a temporary though for the time strongly persistent instinct conquering another instinct, which is usually dominant over all others. At the proper season these birds seem all day long to be impressed with the desire to migrate; their habits change; they become restless, are noisy and congregate in flocks. Whilst the mother-bird is feeding, or brooding over her nestlings, the maternal instinct is probably stronger than the migratory; but the instinct which is the more persistent gains the victory, and at last, at a moment when her young ones are not in sight, she takes flight and deserts them. When arrived at the end of her long journey, and the

---

conscience would reproach a man for injuring his enemy: rather it would reproach him, if he had not revenged himself. To do good in return for evil, to love your enemy, is a height of morality to which it may be doubted whether the social instincts would, by themselves, have ever led us. It is necessary that these instincts, together with sympathy, should have been highly cultivated and ex-tended by the aid of reason, in-struction, and the love or fear of God, before any such golden rule would ever be thought of and obeyed.

migratory instinct has ceased to act, what an agony of remorse the bird would feel, if, from being endowed with great mental activity, she could not prevent the image constantly passing through her mind, of her young ones perishing in the bleak north from cold and hunger.

At the moment of action, man will no doubt be apt to follow the stronger impulse; and though this may occasionally prompt him to the noblest deeds, it will more commonly lead him to gratify his own desires at the expense of other men. But after their gratification when past and weaker impressions are judged by the ever-enduring social instinct, and by his deep regard for the good opinion of his fellows, retribution will surely come. He will then feel remorse, repentance, regret, or shame; this latter feeling, however, relates almost exclusively to the judgment of others. He will consequently resolve more or less firmly to act differently for the future; and this is conscience; for conscience looks backwards, and serves as a guide for the future.

The nature and strength of the feelings which we call regret, shame, repentance or remorse, depend apparently not only on the strength of the violated instinct, but partly on the strength of the temptation, and often still more on the judgment of our fellows. How far each man values the appreciation of others, depends on the strength of his innate or acquired feeling of sympathy; and on his own capacity for reasoning out the remote consequences of his acts. Another element is most important, although not necessary, the reverence or fear of the Gods, or Spirits believed in by each man: and this applies especially in cases of remorse. Several critics have objected that though some slight regret or repentance may be explained by the view advocated in this chapter, it is impossible thus to account for the soul-shaking feeling of remorse. But I can see little force in this objection. My critics do not define what they mean by remorse, and I can find no definition implying more than an overwhelming sense of repentance. Remorse seems to bear the same relation to repentance, as rage does to anger, or agony to pain. It is far from strange that an instinct so strong and so generally admired, as maternal love, should, if disobeyed, lead to the deepest misery, as soon as the impression of the past cause of disobedience is weakened. Even when an action is opposed to no special instinct, merely to know that our friends and equals despise us for it is enough to cause great misery. Who can doubt that the refusal to fight a duel through fear has caused many men an agony of shame? Many a Hindoo, it is said, has been stirred to the bottom of his soul by having partaken of unclean food. Here is another case of what must, I think, be called remorse. Dr. Landor acted as a magistrate in West Australia, and relates,[28] that a native on his farm, after losing one of his wives from disease, came and said that " he was going to a distant tribe to spear a " woman, to satisfy his sense of duty to his wife. I " told him that if he did so, I would send him to " prison for life. He remained about the farm for some " months, but got exceedingly thin, and complained " that he could not rest or eat, that his wife's spirit " was haunting him, because he had not taken a life

[28] 'Insanity in Relation to Law;' Ontario, United States, 1871, p. 1.

"for hers. I was inexorable, and assured him that "nothing should save him if he did." Nevertheless the man disappeared for more than a year, and then returned in high condition; and his other wife told Dr. Landor that her husband had taken the life of a woman belonging to a distant tribe; but it was impossible to obtain legal evidence of the act. The breach of a rule held sacred by the tribe, will thus, as it seems, give rise to the deepest feelings,—and this quite apart from the social instincts, excepting in so far as the rule is grounded on the judgment of the community. How so many strange superstitions have arisen throughout the world we know not; nor can we tell how some real and great crimes, such as incest, have come to be held in an abhorrence (which is not however quite universal) by the lowest savages. It is even doubtful whether in some tribes incest would be looked on with greater horror, than would the marriage of a man with a woman bearing the same name, though not a relation. " To violate this law is a crime which the Australians "hold in the greatest abhorrence, in this agreeing " exactly with certain tribes of North America. When "the question is put in either district, is it worse to " kill a girl of a foreign tribe, or to marry a girl of one's " own, an answer just opposite to ours would be given " without hesitation." [29] We may, therefore, reject the belief, lately insisted on by some writers, that the abhorrence of incest is due to our possessing a special God-implanted conscience. On the whole it is intelligible, that a man urged by so powerful a sentiment as remorse, though arising as above explained, should be led to act in a manner, which he has been taught to

[29] E. B. Tylor in 'Contemporary Review,' April, 1873, p. 707.

believe serves as an expiation, such as delivering himself up to justice.

Man prompted by his conscience, will through long habit acquire such perfect self-command, that his desires and passions will at last yield instantly and without a struggle to his social sympathies and instincts, including his feeling for the judgment of his fellows. The still hungry, or the still revengeful man will not think of stealing food, or of wreaking his vengeance. It is possible, or as we shall hereafter see, even probable, that the habit of self-command may, like other habits, be inherited. Thus at last man comes to feel, through acquired and perhaps inherited habit, that it is best for him to obey his more persistent impulses. The imperious word *ought* seems merely to imply the consciousness of the existence of a rule of conduct, however it may have originated. Formerly it must have been often vehemently urged that an insulted gentleman *ought* to fight a duel. We even say that a pointer *ought* to point, and a retriever to retrieve game. If they fail to do so, they fail in their duty and act wrongly.

If any desire or instinct leading to an action opposed to the good of others still appears, when recalled to mind, as strong as, or stronger than, the social instinct, a man will feel no keen regret at having followed it; but he will be conscious that if his conduct were known to his fellows, it would meet with their disapprobation; and few are so destitute of sympathy as not to feel discomfort when this is realised. If he has no such sympathy, and if his desires leading to bad actions are at the time strong, and when recalled are not over-mastered by the persistent social instincts, and the judgment of others, then he is essentially a bad man; [30] and the sole restraining motive left is the fear of punishment, and the conviction that in the long run it would be best for his own selfish interests to regard the good of others rather than his own.

It is obvious that every one may with an easy conscience gratify his own desires, if they do not interfere with his social instincts, that is with the good of others; but in order to be quite free from self-reproach, or at least of anxiety, it is almost necessary for him to avoid the disapprobation, whether reasonable or not, of his fellow-men. Nor must he break through the fixed habits of his life, especially if these are supported by reason; for if he does, he will assuredly feel dissatisfaction. He must likewise avoid the reprobation of the one God or gods in whom, according to his knowledge or superstition, he may believe; but in this case the additional fear of divine punishment often supervenes.

The strictly Social Virtues at first alone regarded.— The above view of the origin and nature of the moral sense, which tells us what we ought to do, and of the conscience which reproves us if we disobey it, accords well with what we see of the early and undeveloped condition of this faculty in mankind. The virtues which must be practised, at least generally, by rude men, so that they may associate in a body, are those which are

[30] Dr. Prosper Despine in his 'Psychologie Naturelle,' 1868 (tom. i. p. 243; tom. ii. p. 169) gives many curious cases of the worst criminals, who apparently have been entirely destitute of conscience.

still recognised as the most important. But they are practised almost exclusively in relation to the men of the same tribe; and their opposites are not regarded as crimes in relation to the men of other tribes. No tribe could hold together if murder, robbery, treachery, &c., were common; consequently such crimes within the limits of the same tribe "are branded with ever-"lasting infamy;" [31] but excite no such sentiment beyond these limits. A North-American Indian is well pleased with himself, and is honoured by others, when he scalps a man of another tribe; and a Dyak cuts off the head of an unoffending person, and dries it as a trophy. The murder of infants has prevailed on the largest scale throughout the world,[32] and has met with no reproach; but infanticide, especially of females, has been thought to be good for the tribe, or at least not injurious. Suicide during former times was not generally considered as a crime,[33] but rather, from the courage displayed, as an honourable act; and it is still practised by some semi-civilised and savage nations without reproach, for it does not obviously

[31] See an able article in the 'North British Review,' 1867, p. 395. See also Mr. W. Bagehot's articles on the Importance of Obedience and Coherence to Primitive Man, in the 'Fortnightly Review,' 1867, p. 529, and 1868, p. 457, &c.

[32] The fullest account which I have met with is by Dr. Gerland, in his 'Ueber dan Aussterben der Naturvölker,' 1868; but I shall have to recur to the subject of infanticide in a future chapter.

[33] See the very interesting discussion on Suicide in Lecky's 'History of European Morals, vol. i, 1869, p. 223. With respect to savages, Mr. Winwood Reade informs me that the negroes of West Africa often commit suicide. It is well known how common it was amongst the miserable aborigines of South America after the Spanish conquest. For New Zealand, see the voyage of the "Novara," and for the Aleutian Islands, Müller, as quoted by Houzeau, 'Les Facultés Mentales,' &c., tom. ii. p. 136.

concern others of the tribe. It has been recorded that
an Indian Thug conscientiously regretted that he had
not robbed and strangled as many travellers as did
his father before him. In a rude state of civilisation
the robbery of strangers is, indeed, generally considered
as honourable.

Slavery, although in some ways beneficial during
ancient times,[34] is a great crime; yet it was not so
regarded until quite recently, even by the most
civilised nations. And this was especially the case,
because the slaves belonged in general to a race
different from that of their masters. As barbarians
do not regard the opinion of their women, wives
are commonly treated like slaves. Most savages are
utterly indifferent to the sufferings of strangers, or
even delight in witnessing them. It is well known
that the women and children of the North-American
Indians aided in torturing their enemies. Some
savages take a horrid pleasure in cruelty to animals,[35]
and humanity is an unknown virtue. Nevertheless,
besides the family affections, kindness is common,
especially during sickness, between the members of the
same tribe, and is sometimes extended beyond these
limits. Mungo Park's touching account of the kindness
of the negro women of the interior to him is well known.
Many instances could be given of the noble fidelity of
savages towards each other, but not to strangers;
common experience justifies the maxim of the
Spaniard, "Never, never trust an Indian." There
cannot be fidelity without truth; and this fundamental

[34] See Mr. Bagehot, 'Physics
and Politics,' 1872, p. 72.
[35] See, for instance, Mr.
Hamilton's account of the
Kaffirs, 'Anthropological Review,' 1870, p. xv.

virtue is not rare between the members of the same tribe: thus Mungo Park heard the negro women teaching their young children to love the truth. This, again, is one of the virtues which becomes so deeply rooted in the mind, that it is sometimes practised by savages, even at a high cost, towards strangers; but to lie to your enemy has rarely been thought a sin, as the history of modern diplomacy too plainly shews. As soon as a tribe has a recognised leader, disobedience becomes a crime, and even abject submission is looked at as a sacred virtue.

As during rude times no man can be useful or faithful to his tribe without courage, this quality has universally been placed in the highest rank; and although in civilised countries a good yet timid man may be far more useful to the community than a brave one, we cannot help instinctively honouring the latter above a coward, however benevolent. Prudence, on the other hand, which does not concern the welfare of others, though a very useful virtue, has never been highly esteemed. As no man can practise the virtues necessary for the welfare of his tribe without self-sacrifice, self-command, and the power of endurance, these qualities have been at all times highly and most justly valued. The American savage voluntarily submits to the most horrid tortures without a groan, to prove and strengthen his fortitude and courage; and we cannot help admiring him, or even an Indian Fakir, who, from a foolish religious motive, swings suspended by a hook buried in his flesh.

The other so-called self-regarding virtues, which do not obviously, though they may really, affect the welfare of the tribe, have never been esteemed by savages, though now highly appreciated by civilised nations. The greatest intemperance is no reproach with savages. Utter licentiousness, and unnatural crimes, prevail to an astounding extent.[36] As soon, however, as marriage, whether polygamous, or monogamous, becomes common, jealousy will lead to the inculcation of female virtue; and this, being honoured, will tend to spread to the unmarried females. How slowly it spreads to the male sex, we see at the present day. Chastity eminently requires self-command; therefore it has been honoured from a very early period in the moral history of civilised man. As a consequence of this, the senseless practice of celibacy has been ranked from a remote period as a virtue.[37] The hatred of indecency, which appears to us so natural as to be thought innate, and which is so valuable an aid to chastity, is a modern virtue, appertaining exclusively, as Sir G. Staunton remarks,[38] to civilised life. This is shewn by the ancient religious rites of various nations, by the drawings on the walls of Pompeii, and by the practices of many savages.

We have now seen that actions are regarded by savages, and were probably so regarded by primeval man, as good or bad, solely as they obviously affect the welfare of the tribe,—not that of the species, nor that of an individual member of the tribe. This conclusion agrees well with the belief that the so-called moral sense is aboriginally derived from the social instincts, for both relate at first exclusively to the community.

[36] Mr. M'Lennan has given ('Primitive Marriage,' 1865, p. 176) a good collection of facts on this head.

[37] Lecky, 'History of Euro-pean Morals,' vol. i. 1869, p. 109.

[38] 'Embassy to China,' vol. ii. p. 348.

The chief causes of the low morality of savages, as judged by our standard, are, firstly, the confinement of sympathy to the same tribe. Secondly, powers of reasoning insufficient to recognise the bearing of many virtues, especially of the self-regarding virtues, on the general welfare of the tribe. Savages, for instance, fail to trace the multiplied evils consequent on a want of temperance, chastity, &c. And, thirdly, weak power of self-command; for this power has not been strengthened through long-continued, perhaps inherited, habit, instruction and religion.

I have entered into the above details on the immorality of savages,[39] because some authors have recently taken a high view of their moral nature, or have attributed most of their crimes to mistaken benevolence.[40] These authors appears to rest their conclusion on savages possessing those virtues which are serviceable, or even necessary, for the existence of the family and of the tribe,—qualities which they undoubtedly do possess, and often in a high degree.

Concluding Remarks.—It was assumed formerly by philosophers of the derivative [41] school of morals that the foundation of morality lay in a form of Selfishness; but more recently the " Greatest happiness principle " has been brought prominently forward. It is, however, more correct to speak of the latter principle as the standard, and not as the motive of conduct.

---

[39] See on this subject copious evidence in Chap. vii. of Sir J. Lubbock, 'Origin of Civilisation,' 1870.

[40] For instance Lecky, 'Hist. European Morals,' vol. i. p. 124.

[41] This term is used in an able article in the ' Westminster Review,' Oct. 1869, p. 498. For the " Greatest happiness " principle," see J. S. Mill, ' Utilitarianism,' p. 17.

Nevertheless, all the authors whose works I have consulted, with a few exceptions,[42] write as if there must be a distinct motive for every action, and that this must be associated with some pleasure or displeasure. But man seems often to act impulsively, that is from instinct or long habit, without any consciousness of pleasure, in the same manner as does probably a bee or ant, when it blindly follows its instincts. Under circumstances of extreme peril, as during a fire, when a man endeavours to save a fellow-creature without a moment's hesitation, he can hardly feel pleasure; and still less has he time to reflect on the dissatisfaction which he might subsequently experience if he did not make the attempt. Should he afterwards reflect over his own conduct, he would feel that there lies within him an impulsive power widely different from a search after pleasure or happiness; and this seems to be the deeply planted social instinct.

In the case of the lower animals it seems much

[42] Mill recognises ('System of Logic,' vol. ii. p. 422) in the clearest manner, that actions may be performed through habit without the anticipation of pleasure. Mr. H. Sidgwick also, in his Essay on Pleasure and Desire ('The Contemporary Review,' April 1872, p. 671), remarks: "To sum up, in contravention of the doctrine that "our conscious active impulses "are always directed towards "the production of agreeable "sensations in ourselves, I "would maintain that we find "everywhere in consciousness "extra-regarding impulse, di-"rect d towards something that "is not pleasure; that in many "cases the impulse is so far in-"compatible with the self-re-"garding that the two do not "easily co-exist in the same "moment of consciousness." A dim feeling that our impulses do not by any means always arise from any contemporaneous or anticipated pleasure, has, I cannot but think, been one chief cause of the acceptance of the intuitive theory of morality, and of the rejection of the utilitarian or "Greatest happiness" theory. With respect to the latter theory the standard and the motive of conduct have no doubt often been confused, but they are really in some degree blended.

more appropriate to speak of their social instincts, as having been developed for the general good rather than for the general happiness of the species. The term, general good, may be defined as the rearing of the greatest number of individuals in full vigour and health, with all their faculties perfect, under the conditions to which they are subjected. As the social instincts both of man and the lower animals have no doubt been developed by nearly the same steps, it would be advisable, if found practicable, to use the same definition in both cases, and to take as the standard of morality, the general good or welfare of the community, rather than the general happiness; but this definition would perhaps require some limitation on account of political ethics.

When a man risks his life to save that of a fellow-creature, it seems also more correct to say that he acts for the general good, rather than for the general happiness of mankind. No doubt the welfare and the happiness of the individual usually coincide; and a contented, happy tribe will flourish better than one that is discontented and unhappy. We have seen that even at an early period in the history of man, the expressed wishes of the community will have naturally influenced to a large extent the conduct of each member; and as all wish for happiness, the "greatest "happiness principle" will have become a most important secondary guide and object; the social instinct, however, together with sympathy (which leads to our regarding the approbation and disapprobation of others), having served as the primary impulse and guide. Thus the reproach is removed of laying the foundation of the noblest part of our nature in the base principle of selfishness; unless, indeed, the satisfaction which every animal feels, when it follows its proper instincts, and the dissatisfaction felt when prevented, be called selfish.

The wishes and opinions of the members of the same community, expressed at first orally, but later by writing also, either form the sole guides of our conduct, or greatly reinforce the social instincts; such opinions, however, have sometimes a tendency directly opposed to these instincts. This latter fact is well exemplified by the *Law of Honour*, that is, the law of the opinion of our equals, and not of all our countrymen. The breach of this law, even when the breach is known to be strictly accordant with true morality, has caused many a man more agony than a real crime. We recognise the same influence in the burning sense of shame which most of us have felt, even after the interval of years, when calling to mind some accidental breach of a trifling, though fixed, rule of etiquette. The judgment of the community will generally be guided by some rude experience of what is best in the long run for all the members; but this judgment will not rarely err from ignorance and weak powers of reasoning. Hence the strangest customs and superstitions, in complete opposition to the true welfare and happiness of mankind, have become all-powerful throughout the world. We see this in the horror felt by a Hindoo who breaks his caste, and in many other such cases. It would be difficult to distinguish between the remorse felt by a Hindoo who has yielded to the temptation of eating unclean food, from that felt after committing a theft; but the former would probably be the more severe.

How so many absurd rules of conduct, as well as so many absurd religious beliefs, have originated, we do not know; nor how it is that they have become, in all quarters of the world, so deeply impressed on the mind of men; but it is worthy of remark that a belief constantly inculcated during the early years of life, whilst the brain is impressible, appears to acquire almost the nature of an instinct; and the very essence of an instinct is that it is followed independently of reason. Neither can we say why certain admirable virtues, such as the love of truth, are much more highly appreciated by some savage tribes than by others;[43] nor, again, why similar differences prevail even amongst highly civilised nations. Knowing how firmly fixed many strange customs and superstitions have become, we need feel no surprise that the self-regarding virtues, supported as they are by reason, should now appear to us so natural as to be thought innate, although they were not valued by man in his early condition.

Notwithstanding many sources of doubt, man can generally and readily distinguish between the higher and lower moral rules. The higher are founded on the social instincts, and relate to the welfare of others. They are supported by the approbation of our fellow-men and by reason. The lower rules, though some of them when implying self-sacrifice hardly deserve to be called lower, relate chiefly to self, and arise from public opinion, matured by experience and cultivation; for they are not practised by rude tribes.

As man advances in civilisation, and small tribes are

[43] Good instances are given by Mr. Wallace in 'Scientific Opinion,' Sept. 15, 1869; and more fully in his 'Contributions to the Theory of Natural Selection,' 1870, p. 353.

united into larger communities, the simplest reason
would tell each individual that he ought to extend his
social instincts and sympathies to all the members of
the same nation, though personally unknown to him.
This point being once reached, there is only an
artificial barrier to prevent his sympathies extending
to the men of all nations and races. If, indeed, such
men are separated from him by great differences in
appearance or habits, experience unfortunately shews
us how long it is, before we look at them as our
fellow-creatures. Sympathy beyond the confines of
man, that is, humanity to the lower animals, seems to
be one of the latest moral acquisitions. It is apparently unfelt by savages, except towards their pets.
How little the old Romans knew of it is shewn by
their abhorrent gladiatorial exhibitions. The very
idea of humanity, as far as I could observe, was new to
most of the Gauchos of the Pampas. This virtue, one
of the noblest with which man is endowed, seems to
arise incidentally from our sympathies becoming more
tender and more widely diffused, until they are extended to all sentient beings. As soon as this virtue is
honoured and practised by some few men, it spreads
through instruction and example to the young, and
eventually becomes incorporated in public opinion.

The highest possible stage in moral culture is when
we recognise that we ought to control our thoughts,
and " not even in inmost thought to think again the
" sins that made the past so pleasant to us." [44] Whatever makes any bad action familiar to the mind,
renders its performance by so much the easier. As
Marcus Aurelius long ago said, " Such as are thy

[44] Tennyson, ' Idylls of the King,' p. 244.

" habitual thoughts, such also will be the character of
" thy mind; for the soul is dyed by the thoughts." [45]

Our great philosopher, Herbert Spencer, has recently
explained his views on the moral sense. He says,[46]
" I believe that the experiences of utility organised
" and consolidated through all past generations of the
" human race, have been producing corresponding
" modifications, which, by continued transmission and
" accumulation, have become in us certain faculties of
" moral intuition—certain emotions responding to right
" and wrong conduct, which have no apparent basis in
" the individual experiences of utility." There is not
the least inherent improbability, as it seems to me, in
virtuous tendencies being more or less strongly inherited; for, not to mention the various dispositions
and habits transmitted by many of our domestic animals
to their offspring, I have heard of authentic cases in
which a desire to steal and a tendency to lie appeared
to run in families of the upper ranks; and as stealing
is a rare crime in the wealthy classes, we can hardly
account by accidental coincidence for the tendency
occurring in two or three members of the same family.
If bad tendencies are transmitted, it is probable that
good ones are likewise transmitted. That the state of
the body by affecting the brain, has great influence on
the moral tendencies is known to most of those who have
suffered from chronic derangements of the digestion or
liver. The same fact is likewise shewn by the "per-
" version or destruction of the moral sense being often
" one of the earliest symptoms of mental derange-

[45] 'The Thoughts of the Emperor M. Aurelius Antoni-nus,' Eng. translat., 2nd edit., 1869, p. 112. Marcus Aurelius was born A.D. 121.

[46] Letter to Mr. Mill in Bain's 'Mental and Moral Science,' 1868, p. 722.

" ment ; " [47] and insanity is notoriously often inherited. Except through the principle of the transmission of moral tendencies, we cannot understand the differences believed to exist in this respect between the various races of mankind.

Even the partial transmission of virtuous tendencies would be an immense assistance to the primary impulse derived directly and indirectly from the social instincts. Admitting for a moment that virtuous tendencies are inherited, it appears probable, at least in such cases as chastity, temperance, humanity to animals, &c., that they become first impressed on the mental organization through habit, instruction and example, continued during several generations in the same family, and in a quite subordinate degree, or not at all, by the individuals possessing such virtues having succeeded best in the struggle for life. My chief source of doubt with respect to any such inheritance, is that senseless customs, superstitions, and tastes, such as the horror of a Hindoo for unclean food, ought on the same principle to be transmitted. I have not met with any evidence in support of the transmission of superstitious customs or senseless habits, although in itself it is perhaps not less probable than that animals should acquire inherited tastes for certain kinds of food or fear of certain foes.

Finally the social instincts, which no doubt were acquired by man as by the lower animals for the good of the community, will from the first have given to him some wish to aid his fellows, some feeling of sympathy, and have compelled him to regard their

[47] Maudsley Body and Mind,' 1870, p. 60.

approbation and disapprobation. Such impulses will
have served him at a very early period as a rude rule
of right and wrong. But as man gradually advanced
in intellectual power, and was enabled to trace the
more remote consequences of his actions; as he acquired sufficient knowledge to reject baneful customs
and superstitions; as he regarded more and more, not
only the welfare, but the happiness of his fellow-men;
as from habit, following on beneficial experience, instruction and example, his sympathies became more
tender and widely diffused, extending to men of all
races, to the imbecile, maimed, and other useless
members of society, and finally to the lower animals,—
so would the standard of his morality rise higher
and higher. And it is admitted by moralists of the
derivative school and by some intuitionists, that the
standard of morality has risen since an early period in
the history of man.[48]

As a struggle may sometimes be seen going on
between the various instincts of the lower animals, it
is not surprising that there should be a struggle in
man between his social instincts, with their derived
virtues, and his lower, though momentarily stronger
impulses or desires. This, as Mr. Galton [49] has remarked, is all the less surprising, as man has emerged
from a state of barbarism within a comparatively
recent period. After having yielded to some tempta-

---

[48] A writer in the 'North
British Review' (July 1869, p.
531), well capable of forming a
sound judgment, expresses himself strongly in favour of this
conclusion. Mr. Lecky ('Hist.
of Morals,' vol. i. p. 143) seems
to a certain extent to coincide
therein.

[49] See his remarkable work
on 'Hereditary Genius,' 1869,
p. 349. The Duke of Argyll
('Primeval Man,' 1869, p. 188)
has some good remarks on the
contest in man's nature between
right and wrong.

tion we feel a sense of dissatisfaction, shame, repentance, or remorse, analogous to the feelings caused
by other powerful instincts or desires, when left
unsatisfied or baulked. We compare the weakened
impression of a past temptation with the ever present
social instincts, or with habits, gained in early youth
and strengthened during our whole lives, until they
have become almost as strong as instincts. If with
the temptation still before us we do not yield, it is
because either the social instinct or some custom is at
the moment predominant, or because we have learnt
that it will appear to us hereafter the stronger, when
compared with the weakened impression of the temptation, and we realise that its violation would cause us
suffering. Looking to future generations, there is
no cause to fear that the social instincts will grow
weaker, and we may expect that virtuous habits will
grow stronger, becoming perhaps fixed by inheritance.
In this case the struggle between our higher and
lower impulses will be less severe, and virtue will be
triumphant.

Summary of the last two Chapters.—There can be no
doubt that the difference between the mind of the
lowest man and that of the highest animal is immense.
An anthropomorphous ape, if he could take a dis-
passionate view of his own case, would admit that
though he could form an artful plan to plunder a
garden—though he could use stones for fighting or
for breaking open nuts, yet that the thought of
fashioning a stone into a tool was quite beyond his
scope. Still less, as he would admit, could he follow
out a train of metaphysical reasoning, or solve a

mathematical problem, or reflect on God, or admire a grand natural scene. Some apes, however, would probably declare that they could and did admire the beauty of the coloured skin and fur of their partners in marriage. They would admit, that though they could make other apes understand by cries some of their perceptions and simpler wants, the notion of expressing definite ideas by definite sounds had never crossed their minds. They might insist that they were ready to aid their fellow-apes of the same troop in many ways, to risk their lives for them, and to take charge of their orphans; but they would be forced to acknowledge that disinterested love for all living creatures, the most noble attribute of man, was quite beyond their comprehension.

Nevertheless the difference in mind between man and the higher animals, great as it is, certainly is one of degree and not of kind. We have seen that the senses and intuitions, the various emotions and faculties, such as love, memory, attention, curiosity, imitation, reason, &c., of which man boasts, may be found in an incipient, or even sometimes in a well-developed condition, in the lower animals. They are also capable of some inherited improvement, as we see in the domestic dog compared with the wolf or jackal. If it could be proved that certain high mental powers, such as the formation of general concepts, self-consciousness, &c., were absolutely peculiar to man, which seems extremely doubtful, it is not improbable that these qualities are merely the incidental results of other highly-advanced intellectual faculties; and these again mainly the result of the continued use of a perfect language. At what age does the new-born

infant possess the power of abstraction, or become
self-conscious, and reflect on its own existence? We
cannot answer; nor can we answer in regard to the
ascending organic scale. The half-art, half-instinct of
language still bears the stamp of its gradual evolution.
The ennobling belief in God is not universal with
man; and the belief in spiritual agencies naturally
follows from other mental powers. The moral sense
perhaps affords the best and highest distinction between man and the lower animals; but I need say
nothing on this head, as I have so lately endeavoured
to shew that the social instincts,—the prime principle
of man's moral constitution [50]—with the aid of active
intellectual powers and the effects of habit, naturally
lead to the golden rule, "As ye would that men should
do to you, do ye to them likewise;" and this lies at
the foundation of morality.

In the next chapter I shall make some few remarks
on the probable steps and means by which the several
mental and moral faculties of man have been gradually
evolved. That such evolution is at least possible,
ought not to be denied, for we daily see these faculties
developing in every infant; and we may trace a perfect
gradation from the mind of an utter idiot, lower than
that of an animal low in the scale, to the mind of a
Newton.

[50] 'The Thoughts of Marcus Aurelius,' &c., p. 139.

CHAPTER V.

On the Development of the Intellectual and Moral Faculties during Primeval and Civilised Times.

Advancement of the intellectual powers through natural selection—Importance of imitation—Social and moral faculties—Their development within the limits of the same tribe—Natural selection as affecting civilised nations—Evidence that civilised nations were once barbarous.

The subjects to be discussed in this chapter are of the highest interest, but are treated by me in an imperfect and fragmentary manner. Mr. Wallace, in an admirable paper before referred to,[1] argues that man, after he had partially acquired those intellectual and moral faculties which distinguish him from the lower animals, would have been but little liable to bodily modifications through natural selection or any other means. For man is enabled through his mental faculties "to keep with an unchanged body in harmony "with the changing universe." He has great power of adapting his habits to new conditions of life. He invents weapons, tools, and various stratagems to procure food and to defend himself. When he migrates into a colder climate he uses clothes, builds sheds, and makes fires ; and by the aid of fire cooks food otherwise indigestible. He aids his fellow-men in many ways,

[1] 'Anthropological Review,' May 1864, p. clviii.

o 2

and anticipates future events. Even at a remote period he practised some division of labour.

The lower animals, on the other hand, must have their bodily structure modified in order to survive under greatly changed conditions. They must be rendered stronger, or acquire more effective teeth or claws, for defence against new enemies; or they must be reduced in size, so as to escape detection and danger. When they migrate into a colder climate, they must become clothed with thicker fur, or have their constitutions altered. If they fail to be thus modified, they will cease to exist.

The case, however, is widely different, as Mr. Wallace has with justice insisted, in relation to the intellectual and moral faculties of man. These faculties are variable; and we have every reason to believe that the variations tend to be inherited. Therefore, if they were formerly of high importance to primeval man and to his ape-like progenitors, they would have been perfected or advanced through natural selection. Of the high importance of the intellectual faculties there can be no doubt, for man mainly owes to them his predominant position in the world. We can see, that in the rudest state of society, the individuals who were the most sagacious, who invented and used the best weapons or traps, and who were best able to defend themselves, would rear the greatest number of offspring. The tribes, which included the largest number of men thus endowed, would increase in number and supplant other tribes. Numbers depend primarily on the means of subsistence, and this depends partly on the physical nature of the country, but in a much higher degree on the arts which are there practised. As a tribe increases and is victorious, it is often still further increased by the absorption of other tribes.[2] The stature and strength of the men of a tribe are likewise of some importance for its success, and these depend in part on the nature and amount of the food which can be obtained. In Europe the men of the Bronze period were supplanted by a race more powerful, and, judging from their sword-handles, with larger hands;[3] but their success was probably still more due to their superiority in the arts.

All that we know about savages, or may infer from their traditions and from old monuments, the history of which is quite forgotten by the present inhabitants, shew that from the remotest times successful tribes have supplanted other tribes. Relics of extinct or forgotten tribes have been discovered throughout the civilised regions of the earth, on the wild plains of America, and on the isolated islands in the Pacific Ocean. At the present day civilised nations are everywhere supplanting barbarous nations, excepting where the climate opposes a deadly barrier; and they succeed mainly, though not exclusively, through their arts, which are the products of the intellect. It is, therefore, highly probable that with mankind the intellectual faculties have been mainly and gradually perfected through natural selection; and this conclusion is sufficient for our purpose. Undoubtedly it would be interesting to trace the development of each

[2] After a time the members or tribes which are absorbed into another tribe assume, as Sir Henry Maine remarks ('Ancient Law,' 1861, p. 131), that they are the co-descendants of the same ancestors.

[3] Morlot, 'Soc. Vaud. Sc. Nat.' 1860, p. 294.

separate faculty from the state in which it exists in
the lower animals to that in which it exists in man;
but neither my ability nor knowledge permits the
attempt.

It deserves notice that, as soon as the progenitors
of man became social (and this probably occurred at
a very early period), the principle of imitation, and
reason, and experience would have increased, and
much modified the intellectual powers in a way, of
which we see only traces in the lower animals. Apes
are much given to imitation, as are the lowest savages;
and the simple fact previously referred to, that after a
time no animal can be caught in the same place by
the same sort of trap, shews that animals learn by
experience, and imitate the caution of others. Now, if
some one man in a tribe, more sagacious than the
others, invented a new snare or weapon, or other
means of attack or defence, the plainest self-interest,
without the assistance of much reasoning power, would
prompt the other members to imitate him; and all
would thus profit. The habitual practice of each new
art must likewise in some slight degree strengthen the
intellect. If the new invention were an important
one, the tribe would increase in number, spread, and
supplant other tribes. In a tribe thus rendered more
numerous there would always be a rather greater
chance of the birth of other superior and inventive
members. If such men left children to inherit their
mental superiority, the chance of the birth of still
more ingenious members would be somewhat better,
and in a very small tribe decidedly better. Even if
they left no children, the tribe would still include
their blood-relations; and it has been ascertained by

agriculturists[4] that by preserving and breeding from the family of an animal, which when slaughtered was found to be valuable, the desired character has been obtained.

Turning now to the social and moral faculties. In order that primeval men, or the ape-like progenitors of man, should become social, they must have acquired the same instinctive feelings, which impel other animals to live in a body; and they no doubt exhibited the same general disposition. They would have felt uneasy when separated from their comrades, for whom they would have felt some degree of love; they would have warned each other of danger, and have given mutual aid in attack or defence. All this implies some degree of sympathy, fidelity, and courage. Such social qualities, the paramount importance of which to the lower animals is disputed by no one, were no doubt acquired by the progenitors of man in a similar manner, namely, through natural selection, aided by inherited habit. When two tribes of primeval man, living in the same country, came into competition, if (other circumstances being equal) the one tribe included a great number of courageous, sympathetic and faithful members, who were always ready to warn each other of danger, to aid and defend each other, this tribe would succeed better and conquer the other. Let it be borne in mind how all-important in the never-ceasing wars of savages, fidelity and courage must be. The advantage which disciplined soldiers have over undisciplined hordes follows chiefly from the

[4] I have given instances in my 'Variation of Animals under Domestication,' vol. ii. p. 196.

confidence which each man feels in his comrades. Obedience, as Mr. Bagehot has well shewn,[5] is of the highest value, for any form of government is better than none. Selfish and contentious people will not cohere, and without coherence nothing can be effected. A tribe rich in the above qualities would spread and be victorious over other tribes: but in the course of time it would, judging from all past history, be in its turn overcome by some other tribe still more highly endowed. Thus the social and moral qualities would tend slowly to advance and be diffused throughout the world.

But it may be asked, how within the limits of the same tribe did a large number of members first become endowed with these social and moral qualities, and how was the standard of excellence raised? It is extremely doubtful whether the offspring of the more sympathetic and benevolent parents, or of those who were the most faithful to their comrades, would be reared in greater numbers than the children of selfish and treacherous parents belonging to the same tribe. He who was ready to sacrifice his life, as many a savage has been, rather than betray his comrades, would often leave no offspring to inherit his noble nature. The bravest men, who were always willing to come to the front in war, and who freely risked their lives for others, would on an average perish in larger numbers than other men. Therefore it hardly seems probable, that the number of men gifted with such virtues, or that the standard of their excellence, could

[5] See a remarkable series of articles on 'Physics and Politics,' in the 'Fortnightly Review,' Nov. 1867; April 1, 1868; July 1, 1869, since separately published.

be increased through natural selection, that is, by the survival of the fittest; for we are not here speaking of one tribe being victorious over another.

Although the circumstances, leading to an increase in the number of those thus endowed within the same tribe, are too complex to be clearly followed out, we can trace some of the probable steps. In the first place, as the reasoning powers and foresight of the members became improved, each man would soon learn that if he aided his fellow-men, he would commonly receive aid in return. From this low motive he might acquire the habit of aiding his fellows; and the habit of performing benevolent actions certainly strengthens the feeling of sympathy which gives the first impulse to benevolent actions. Habits, moreover, followed during many generations probably tend to be inherited.

But another and much more powerful stimulus to the development of the social virtues, is afforded by the praise and the blame of our fellow-men. To the instinct of sympathy, as we have already seen, it is primarily due, that we habitually bestow both praise and blame on others, whilst we love the former and dread the latter when applied to ourselves; and this instinct no doubt was originally acquired, like all the other social instincts, through natural selection. At how early a period the progenitors of man in the course of their development, became capable of feeling and being impelled by, the praise or blame of their fellow-creatures, we cannot of course say. But it appears that even dogs appreciate encouragement, praise, and blame. The rudest savages feel the sentiment of glory, as they clearly show by preserving the trophies of their prowess, by their habit of excessive boasting, and even by the extreme care which they take of their personal appearance and decorations; for unless they regarded the opinion of their comrades, such habits would be senseless.

They certainly feel shame at the breach of some of their lesser rules, and apparently remorse, as shewn by the case of the Australian who grew thin and could not rest from having delayed to murder some other woman, so as to propitiate his dead wife's spirit. Though I have not met with any other recorded case, it is scarcely credible that a savage, who will sacrifice his life rather than betray his tribe, or one who will deliver himself up as a prisoner rather than break his parole,[6] would not feel remorse in his inmost soul, if he had failed in a duty, which he held sacred.

We may therefore conclude that primeval man, at a very remote period, was influenced by the praise and blame of his fellows. It is obvious, that the members of the same tribe would approve of conduct which appeared to them to be for the general good, and would reprobate that which appeared evil. To do good unto others—to do unto others as ye would they should do unto you—is the foundation-stone of morality. It is, therefore, hardly possible to exaggerate the importance during rude times of the love of praise and the dread of blame. A man who was not impelled by any deep, instinctive feeling, to sacrifice his life for the good of others, yet was roused to such actions by a sense of glory, would by his example excite the same wish for glory in other men,

[6] Mr. Wallace gives cases in his 'Contributions to the Theory of Natural Selection,' 1870, p. 354.

and would strengthen by exercise the noble feeling of admiration. He might thus do far more good to his tribe than by begetting offspring with a tendency to inherit his own high character.

With increased experience and reason, man perceives the more remote consequences of his actions, and the self-regarding virtues, such as temperance, chastity, &c., which during early times are, as we have before seen, utterly disregarded, come to be highly esteemed or even held sacred. I need not, however, repeat what I have said on this head in the fourth chapter. Ultimately our moral sense or conscience becomes a highly complex sentiment—originating in the social instincts, largely guided by the approbation of our fellow-men, ruled by reason, self-interest, and in later times by deep religious feelings, and confirmed by instruction and habit.

It must not be forgotten that although a high standard of morality gives but a slight or no advantage to each individual man and his children over the other men of the same tribe, yet that an increase in the number of well-endowed men and an advancement in the standard of morality will certainly give an immense advantage to one tribe over another. A tribe including many members who, from possessing in a high degree the spirit of patriotism, fidelity, obedience, courage, and sympathy, were always ready to aid one another, and to sacrifice themselves for the common good, would be victorious over most other tribes; and this would be natural selection. At all times throughout the world tribes have supplanted other tribes; and as morality is one important element in their success, the standard of morality and the number of well-endowed men will thus everywhere tend to rise and increase.

It is, however, very difficult to form any judgment why one particular tribe and not another has been successful and has risen in the scale of civilisation. Many savages are in the same condition as when first discovered several centuries ago. As Mr. Bagehot has remarked, we are apt to look at progress as normal in human society; but history refutes this. The ancients did not even entertain the idea, nor do the Oriental nations at the present day. According to another high authority, Sir Henry Maine,[7] "the greatest part "of mankind has never shewn a particle of desire that "its civil institutions should be improved." Progress seems to depend on many concurrent favourable conditions, far too complex to be followed out. But it has often been remarked, that a cool climate, from leading to industry and to the various arts, has been highly favourable thereto. The Esquimaux, pressed by hard necessity, have succeeded in many ingenious inventions, but their climate has been too severe for continued progress. Nomadic habits, whether over wide plains, or through the dense forests of the tropics, or along the shores of the sea, have in every case been highly detrimental. Whilst observing the barbarous inhabitants of Tierra del Fuego, it struck me that the possession of some property, a fixed abode, and the union of many families under a chief, were the indispensable requisites for civilisation. Such habits almost necessitate the cultivation of the ground; and the first steps in cultivation would probably result, as

[7] 'Ancient Law,' 1861, p. 22. For Mr. Bagehot's remarks,   'Fortnightly Review,' April 1, 1868, p. 452.

I have elsewhere shewn,[8] from some such accident as
the seeds of a fruit-tree falling on a heap of refuse,
and producing an unusually fine variety. The problem,
however, of the first advance of savages towards
civilisation is at present much too difficult to be
solved.

Natural Selection as affecting Civilised Nations.—I have
hitherto only considered the advancement of man from
a semi-human condition to that of the modern savage.
But some remarks on the action of natural selection on
civilised nations may be worth adding. This subject
has been ably discussed by Mr. W. R. Greg,[9] and
previously by Mr. Wallace and Mr. Galton.[10] Most
of my remarks are taken from these three authors.
With savages, the weak in body or mind are soon
eliminated; and those that survive commonly exhibit a
vigorous state of health. We civilised men, on the
other hand, do our utmost to check the process of
elimination; we build asylums for the imbecile, the
maimed, and the sick; we institute poor-laws; and
our medical men exert their utmost skill to save the
life of every one to the last moment. There is reason

[8] 'The Variation of Animals
and Plants under Domestication,'
vol. i. p. 309.

[9] 'Fraser's Magazine,' Sept.
1868, p. 353. This article seems
to have struck many persons,
and has given rise to two remarkable essays and a rejoinder
in the 'Spectator,' Oct. 3rd and
17th, 1868. It has also been
discussed in the 'Q. Journal of
Science,' 1869, p. 152, and by
Mr. Lawson Tait in the 'Dublin
Q. Journal of Medical Science,'

Feb. 1869, and by Mr. E. Ray
Lankester in his 'Comparative
Longevity,' 1870, p. 128. Similar views appeared previously in
the 'Australasian,' July 13,
1867. I have borrowed ideas
from several of these writers.

[10] For Mr. Wallace, see 'Anthropolog. Review,' as before
cited. Mr. Galton in 'Macmillan's Magazine,' Aug. 1865,
p. 318; also his great work,
'Hereditary Genius,' 1870.

to believe that vaccination has preserved thousands, who from a weak constitution would formerly have succumbed to small-pox. Thus the weak members of civilised societies propagate their kind. No one who has attended to the breeding of domestic animals will doubt that this must be highly injurious to the race of man. It is surprising how soon a want of care, or care wrongly directed, leads to the degeneration of a domestic race; but excepting in the case of man himself, hardly any one is so ignorant as to allow his worst animals to breed.

The aid which we feel impelled to give to the helpless is mainly an incidental result of the instinct of sympathy, which was originally acquired as part of the social instincts, but subsequently rendered, in the manner previously indicated, more tender and more widely diffused. Nor could we check our sympathy, even at the urging of hard reason, without deterioration in the noblest part of our nature. The surgeon may harden himself whilst performing an operation, for he knows that he is acting for the good of his patient; but if we were intentionally to neglect the weak and helpless, it could only be for a contingent benefit, with an overwhelming present evil. We must therefore bear the undoubtedly bad effects of the weak surviving and propagating their kind; but there appears to be at least one check in steady action, namely that the weaker and inferior members of society do not marry so freely as the sound; and this check might be indefinitely increased by the weak in body or mind refraining from marriage, though this is more to be hoped for than expected.

In every country in which a large standing army is

kept up, the finest young men are taken by the con-
scription or are enlisted. They are thus exposed to
early death during war, are often tempted into vice,
and are prevented from marrying during the prime of
life. On the other hand the shorter and feebler men,
with poor constitutions, are left at home, and consequently have a much better chance of marrying and
propagating their kind.[11]

Man accumulates property and bequeaths it to his
children, so that the children of the rich have an
advantage over the poor in the race for success,
independently of bodily or mental superiority. On
the other hand, the children of parents who are short-
lived, and are therefore on an average deficient in
health and vigour, come into their property sooner
than other children, and will be likely to marry earlier,
and leave a larger number of offspring to inherit their
inferior constitutions. But the inheritance of property
by itself is very far from an evil; for without the
accumulation of capital the arts could not progress;
and it is chiefly through their power that the civilised
races have extended, and are now everywhere extending
their range, so as to take the place of the lower races.
Nor does the moderate accumulation of wealth interfere
with the process of selection. When a poor man
becomes moderately rich, his children enter trades or
professions in which there is struggle enough, so that
the able in body and mind succeed best. The presence
of a body of well-instructed men, who have not to
labour for their daily bread, is important to a degree

[11] Prof. H. Fick ('Einfluss
der Naturwissenschaft auf das
Recht,' June, 1872) has some
good remarks on this head, and
on other such points.

which cannot be over-estimated ; as all high intellectual work is carried on by them, and on such work, material progress of all kinds mainly depends, not to mention other and higher advantages. No doubt wealth when very great tends to convert men into useless drones, but their number is never large ; and some degree of elimination here occurs, for we daily see rich men, who happen to be fools or profligate, squandering away their wealth.

Primogeniture with entailed estates is a more direct evil, though it may formerly have been a great advantage by the creation of a dominant class, and any government is better than none. Most eldest sons, though they may be weak in body or mind, marry, whilst the younger sons, however superior in these respects, do not so generally marry. Nor can worthless eldest sons with entailed estates squander their wealth. But here, as elsewhere, the relations of civilised life are so complex that some compensatory checks intervene. The men who are rich through primogeniture are able to select generation after generation the more beautiful and charming women ; and these must generally be healthy in body and active in mind. The evil consequences, such as they may be, of the continued preservation of the same line of descent, without any selection, are checked by men of rank always wishing to increase their wealth and power ; and this they effect by marrying heiresses. But the daughters of parents who have produced single children, are themselves, as Mr. Galton [12] has shewn, apt to be sterile ; and thus noble families are continually cut off in the direct line, and their wealth

[12] 'Hereditary Genius,' 1870, pp. 132–140.

flows into some side channel; but unfortunately this channel is not determined by superiority of any kind.

Although civilisation thus checks in many ways the action of natural selection, it apparently favours the better development of the body, by means of good food and the freedom from occasional hardships. This may be inferred from civilised men having been found, wherever compared, to be physically stronger than savages.[13] They appear also to have equal powers of endurance, as has been proved in many adventurous expeditions. Even the great luxury of the rich can be but little detrimental; for the expectation of life of our aristocracy, at all ages and of both sexes, is very little inferior to that of healthy English lives in the lower classes.[14]

We will now look to the intellectual faculties. If in each grade of society the members were divided into two equal bodies, the one including the intellectually superior and the other the inferior, there can be little doubt that the former would succeed best in all occupations, and rear a greater number of children. Even in the lowest walks of life, skill and ability must be of some advantage; though in many occupations, owing to the great division of labour, a very small one. Hence in civilised nations there will be some tendency to an increase both in the number and in the standard of the intellectually able. But I do not wish to assert that this tendency may not be more than counterbalanced in other ways, as by the multiplication

[13] Quatrefages, 'Revue des Cours Scientifiques,' 1867–68, p. 659.

[14] See the fifth and sixth columns, compiled from good authorities, in the table given in Mr. E. R. Lankester's 'Comparative Longevity,' 1870, p. 115.

of the reckless and improvident; but even to such as these, ability must be some advantage.

It has often been objected to views like the foregoing, that the most eminent men who have ever lived have left no offspring to inherit their great intellect. Mr. Galton says,[15] "I regret I am unable to solve the "simple question whether, and how far, men and "women who are prodigies of genius are infertile. I "have, however, shewn that men of eminence are by "no means so." Great lawgivers, the founders of beneficent religions, great philosophers and discoverers in science, aid the progress of mankind in a far higher degree by their works than by leaving a numerous progeny. In the case of corporeal structures, it is the selection of the slightly better-endowed and the elimination of the slightly less well-endowed individuals, and not the preservation of strongly-marked and rare anomalies, that leads to the advancement of a species.[16] So it will be with the intellectual faculties, since the somewhat abler men in each grade of society succeed rather better than the less able, and consequently increase in number, if not otherwise prevented. When in any nation the standard of intellect and the number of intellectual men have increased, we may expect from the law of the deviation from an average, that prodigies of genius will, as shewn by Mr. Galton, appear somewhat more frequently than before.

In regard to the moral qualities, some elimination of the worst dispositions is always in progress even in the most civilised nations. Malefactors are executed,

---

[15] 'Hereditary Genius,' 1870, p. 330.

[16] 'Origin of Species' (fifth edition, 1869), p. 104.

or imprisoned for long periods, so that they cannot freely transmit their bad qualities. Melancholic and insane persons are confined, or commit suicide. Violent and quarrelsome men often come to a bloody end. The restless who will not follow any steady occupation —and this relic of barbarism is a great check to civilisation [17]—emigrate to newly-settled countries, where they prove useful pioneers. Intemperance is so highly destructive, that the expectation of life of the intemperate, at the age of thirty for instance, is only 13·8 years; whilst for the rural labourers of England at the same age it is 40·59 years.[18] Profligate women bear few children, and profligate men rarely marry; both suffer from disease. In the breeding of domestic animals, the elimination of those individuals, though few in number, which are in any marked manner inferior, is by no means an unimportant element towards success. This especially holds good with injurious characters which tend to reappear through reversion, such as blackness in sheep; and with mankind some of the worst dispositions, which occasionally without any assignable cause make their appearance in families, may perhaps be reversions to a savage state, from which we are not removed by very many generations. This view seems indeed recognised in the common expression that such men are the black sheep of the family.

With civilised nations, as far as an advanced standard

---

[17] 'Hereditary Genius,' 1870, p. 347.

[18] E. Ray Lankester, 'Comparative Longevity,' 1870, p. 115. The table of the intemperate is from Neison's 'Vital Statistics.' In regard to profligacy, see Dr. Farr, 'Influence of Marriage on Mortality,' 'Nat. Assoc. for the Premotion of Social Science,' 1858.

of morality, and an increased number of fairly good
men are concerned, natural selection apparently effects
but little; though the fundamental social instincts
were originally thus gained. But I have already said
enough, whilst treating of the lower races, on the
causes which lead to the advance of morality, namely,
the approbation of our fellow-men—the strengthening
of our sympathies by habit—example and imitation—
reason—experience, and even self-interest—instruction
during youth, and religious feelings.

A most important obstacle in civilised countries to
an increase in the number of men of a superior class
has been strongly insisted on by Mr. Greg and Mr.
Galton,[19] namely, the fact that the very poor and
reckless, who are often degraded by vice, almost invariably marry early, whilst the careful and frugal,
who are generally otherwise virtuous, marry late in
life, so that they may be able to support themselves
and their children in comfort. Those who marry
early produce within a given period not only a greater
number of generations, but, as shewn by Dr. Duncan,[20]
they produce many more children. The children,
moreover, that are born by mothers during the prime
of life are heavier and larger, and therefore probably
more vigorous, than those born at other periods.
Thus the reckless, degraded, and often vicious members of society, tend to increase at a quicker rate than

[19] 'Fraser's Magazine,' Sept.
1868, p. 353. 'Macmillan's
Magazine,' Aug. 1865, p. 318.
The Rev. F. W. Farrar (' Fraser's
Mag.,' Aug. 1870, p. 264) takes
a different view.
[20] 'On the Laws of the Fertility of Women,' in 'Transact.
Royal Soc.,' Edinburgh, vol.
xxiv. p. 287; now published
separately under the title of
'Fecundity, Fertility, and Sterility,' 1871. See, also, Mr.
Galton, 'Hereditary Genius,' pp.
352–357, for observations to the
above effect.

the provident and generally virtuous members. Or as Mr. Greg puts the case: "The careless, squalid, un-" aspiring Irishman multiplies like rabbits: the frugal, "foreseeing, self-respecting, ambitious Scot, stern in "his morality, spiritual in his faith, sagacious and "disciplined in his intelligence, passes his best years "in struggle and in celibacy, marries late, and leaves "few behind him. Given a land originally peopled by "a thousand Saxons and a thousand Celts—and in a "dozen generations five-sixths of the population would "be Celts, but five-sixths of the property, of the "power, of the intellect, would belong to the one-"sixth of Saxons that remained. In the eternal "'struggle for existence,' it would be the inferior and "*less* favoured race that had prevailed—and prevailed "by virtue not of its good qualities but of its faults."

There are, however, some checks to this downward tendency. We have seen that the intemperate suffer from a high rate of mortality, and the extremely profligate leave few offspring. The poorest classes crowd into towns, and it has been proved by Dr Stark from the statistics of ten years in Scotland,[21] that at all ages the death-rate is higher in towns than in rural districts, "and during the first five years of life "the town death-rate is almost exactly double that of "the rural districts." As these returns include both the rich and the poor, no doubt more than twice the number of births would be requisite to keep up the number of the very poor inhabitants in the towns, relatively to those in the country. With women, marriage at too early an age is highly injurious; for

[21] 'Tenth Annual Report of Births, Deaths, &c., in Scotland,' 1867, p. xxix.

it has been found in France that, "twice as many "wives under twenty die in the year, as died out of "the same number of the unmarried." The mortality, also, of husbands under twenty is "excessively high,"[22] but what the cause of this may be, seems doubtful. Lastly, if the men who prudently delay marrying until they can bring up their families in comfort, were to select, as they often do, women in the prime of life, the rate of increase in the better class would be only slightly lessened.

It was established from an enormous body of statistics, taken during 1853, that the unmarried men throughout France, between the ages of twenty and eighty, die in a much larger proportion than the married: for instance, out of every 1000 unmarried men, between the ages of twenty and thirty, $11 \cdot 3$ annually died, whilst of the married only $6 \cdot 5$ died.[23] A similar law was proved to hold good, during the years 1863 and 1864, with the entire population above the age of twenty in Scotland: for instance, out of every 1000 unmarried men, between the ages of twenty and thirty, $14 \cdot 97$ annually died, whilst of the married only $7 \cdot 24$ died, that is less than half.[24] Dr. Stark remarks on this, "Bachelorhood is more de- "structive to life than the most unwholesome trades,

[22] These quotations are taken from our highest authority on such questions, namely, Dr. Farr, in his paper 'On the Influence of Marriage on the Mortality of the French People,' read before the Nat. Assoc. for the Promotion of Social Science, 1858.

[23] Dr. Farr, ibid. The quotations given below are extracted from the same striking paper.

[24] I have taken the mean of the quinquennial means, given in 'The Tenth Annual Report of Births, Deaths, &c., in Scotland,' 1867. The quotation from Dr. Stark is copied from an article in the 'Daily News,' Oct. 17th, 1868, which Dr. Farr considers very carefully written.

" or than residence in an unwholesome house or district
" where there has never been the most distant attempt
" at sanitary improvement." He considers that the
lessened mortality is the direct result of " marriage,
" and the more regular domestic habits which attend
" that state." He admits, however, that the intemperate, profligate, and criminal classes, whose duration
of life is low, do not commonly marry; and it must
likewise be admitted that men with a weak constitution,
ill health, or any great infirmity in body or mind, will
often not wish to marry, or will be rejected. Dr.
Stark seems to have come to the conclusion that
marriage in itself is a main cause of prolonged life,
from finding that aged married men still have a
considerable advantage in this respect over the unmarried of the same advanced age; but every one
must have known instances of men, who with weak
health during youth did not marry, and yet have
survived to old age, though remaining weak, and
therefore always with a lessened chance of life or of
marrying. There is another remarkable circumstance
which seems to support Dr. Stark's conclusion, namely,
that widows and widowers in France suffer in comparison with the married a very heavy rate of
mortality; but Dr. Farr attributes this to the poverty
and evil habits consequent on the disruption of the
family, and to grief. On the whole we may conclude
with Dr. Farr that the lesser mortality of married
than of unmarried men, which seems to be a general
law, " is mainly due to the constant elimination of
" imperfect types, and to the skilful selection of the
" finest individuals out of each successive generation;"
the selection relating only to the marriage state,

and acting on all corporeal, intellectual, and moral qualities.[25] We may, therefore, infer that sound and good men who out of prudence remain for a time unmarried, do not suffer a high rate of mortality.

If the various checks specified in the two last paragraphs, and perhaps others as yet unknown, do not prevent the reckless, the vicious and otherwise inferior members of society from increasing at a quicker rate than the better class of men, the nation will retrograde, as has too often occurred in the history of the world. We must remember that progress is no invariable rule. It is very difficult to say why one civilised nation rises, becomes more powerful, and spreads more widely, than another; or why the same nation progresses more quickly at one time than at another. We can only say that it depends on an increase in the actual number of the population, on the number of the men endowed with high intellectual and moral faculties, as well as on their standard of excellence. Corporeal structure appears to have little influence, except so far as vigour of body leads to vigour of mind.

It has been urged by several writers that as high intellectual powers are advantageous to a nation, the old Greeks, who stood some grades higher in intellect than any race that has ever existed,[26] ought, if the power of natural selection were real, to have risen still higher in the scale, increased in number, and stocked

[25] Dr. Duncan remarks ('Fecundity, Fertility,' &c., 1871, p. 334) on this subject; "At every "age the healthy and beautiful "go over from the unmarried "side to the married, leaving "the unmarried columns crowded "with the sickly and unfortu- "nate."

[26] See the ingenious and original argument on this subject by Mr. Galton, 'Hereditary Genius,' pp. 340–342.

the whole of Europe. Here we have the tacit assumption, so often made with respect to corporeal structures, that there is some innate tendency towards continued development in mind and body. But development of all kinds depends on many concurrent favourable circumstances. Natural selection acts only tentatively. Individuals and races may have acquired certain indisputable advantages, and yet have perished from failing in other characters. The Greeks may have retrograded from a want of coherence between the many small states, from the small size of their whole country, from the practice of slavery, or from extreme sensuality; for they did not succumb until "they "were enervated and corrupt to the very core." [27] The western nations of Europe, who now so immeasurably surpass their former savage progenitors, and stand at the summit of civilisation, owe little or none of their superiority to direct inheritance from the old Greeks, though they owe much to the written works of that wonderful people.

Who can positively say why the Spanish nation, so dominant at one time, has been distanced in the race. The awakening of the nations of Europe from the dark ages is a still more perplexing problem. At that early period, as Mr. Galton has remarked, almost all the men of a gentle nature, those given to meditation or culture of the mind, had no refuge except in the bosom of a Church which demanded celibacy; [28] and this could hardly fail to have had a deteriorating

[27] Mr. Greg, ' Fraser's Magazine,' Sept. 1868, p. 357.
[28] 'Hereditary Genius,' 1870, pp. 357–359. The Rev. F. W. Farrar ('Fraser's Mag.,' Aug.

1870, p. 257) advances arguments on the other side. Sir C. Lyell had already ('Principles of Geology,' vol. ii. 1868, p. 489) in a striking passage called

influence on each successive generation. During this same period the Holy Inquisition selected with extreme care the freest and boldest men in order to burn or imprison them. In Spain alone some of the best men—those who doubted and questioned, and without doubting there can be no progress—were eliminated during three centuries at the rate of a thousand a year. The evil which the Catholic Church has thus effected is incalculable, though no doubt counterbalanced to a certain, perhaps to a large, extent in other ways; nevertheless, Europe has progressed at an unparalleled rate.

The remarkable success of the English as colonists, compared to other European nations, has been ascribed to their "daring and persistent energy;" a result which is well illustrated by comparing the progress of the Canadians of English and French extraction; but who can say how the English gained their energy? There is apparently much truth in the belief that the wonderful progress of the United States, as well as the character of the people, are the results of natural selection; for the more energetic, restless, and courageous men from all parts of Europe have emigrated during the last ten or twelve generations to that great country, and have there succeeded best.[29] Looking to the distant future, I do not think that the Rev. Mr. Zincke takes an exaggerated view when he says:[30] "All other series of events—as that which

---

attention to the evil influence of the Holy Inquisition in having, through selection, lowered the general standard of intelligence in Europe.

[29] Mr. Galton, 'Macmillan's Magazine,' August, 1865, p. 325. See also, 'Nature,' 'On Darwinism and National Life,' Dec. 1869, p. 184.

[30] 'Last Winter in the United States,' 1868, p. 29.

"resulted in the culture of mind in Greece, and that "which resulted in the empire of Rome—only appear "to have purpose and value when viewed in connection "with, or rather as subsidiary to . . . . the great "stream of Anglo-Saxon emigration to the west." Obscure as is the problem of the advance of civilisation, we can at least see that a nation which produced during a lengthened period the greatest number of highly intellectual, energetic, brave, patriotic, and benevolent men, would generally prevail over less favoured nations.

Natural selection follows from the struggle for existence; and this from a rapid rate of increase. It is impossible not to regret bitterly, but whether wisely is another question, the rate at which man tends to increase; for this leads in barbarous tribes to infanticide and many other evils, and in civilised nations to abject poverty, celibacy, and to the late marriages of the prudent. But as man suffers from the same physical evils as the lower animals, he has no right to expect an immunity from the evils consequent on the struggle for existence. Had he not been subjected during primeval times to natural selection, assuredly he would never have attained to his present rank. Since we see in many parts of the world enormous areas of the most fertile land capable of supporting numerous happy homes, but peopled only by a few wandering savages, it might be argued that the struggle for existence had not been sufficiently severe to force man upwards to his highest standard. Judging from all that we know of man and the lower animals, there has always been sufficient variability in their intellectual and moral faculties, for a steady advance through natural selection. No doubt such advance demands many favourable concurrent circumstances; but it may well be doubted whether the most favourable would have sufficed, had not the rate of increase been rapid, and the consequent struggle for existence extremely severe. It even appears from what we see, for instance, in parts of S. America, that a people which may be called civilised, such as the Spanish settlers, is liable to become indolent and to retrograde, when the conditions of life are very easy. With highly civilised nations continued progress depends in a subordinate degree on natural selection; for such nations do not supplant and exterminate one another as do savage tribes. Nevertheless the more intelligent members within the same community will succeed better in the long run than the inferior, and leave a more numerous progeny, and this is a form of natural selection. The more efficient causes of progress seem to consist of a good education during youth whilst the brain is impressible, and of a high standard of excellence, inculcated by the ablest and best men, embodied in the laws, customs and traditions of the nation, and enforced by public opinion. It should, however, be borne in mind, that the enforcement of public opinion depends on our appreciation of the approbation and disapprobation of others; and this appreciation is founded on our sympathy, which it can hardly be doubted was originally developed through natural selection as one of the most important elements of the social instincts.[31]

[31] I am much indebted to Mr. John Morley for some good criticisms on this subject: see, also, Broca, 'Les Sélections,' 'Revue d'Anthropologie,' 1872.

On the evidence that all civilised nations were once barbarous.—The present subject has been treated in so full and admirable a manner by Sir J. Lubbock,[32] Mr. Tylor, Mr. M'Lennan, and others, that I need here give only the briefest summary of their results. The arguments recently advanced by the Duke of Argyll[33] and formerly by Archbishop Whately, in favour of the belief that man came into the world as a civilised being, and that all savages have since undergone degradation, seem to me weak in comparison with those advanced on the other side. Many nations, no doubt, have fallen away in civilisation, and some may have lapsed into utter barbarism, though on this latter head I have met with no evidence. The Fuegians were probably compelled by other conquering hordes to settle in their inhospitable country, and they may have become in consequence somewhat more degraded; but it would be difficult to prove that they have fallen much below the Botocudos, who inhabit the finest parts of Brazil.

The evidence that all civilised nations are the descendants of barbarians, consists, on the one side, of clear traces of their former low condition in still-existing customs, beliefs, language, &c.; and on the other side, of proofs that savages are independently able to raise themselves a few steps in the scale of civilisation, and have actually thus risen. The evidence on the first head is extremely curious, but cannot be here given: I refer to such cases as that of the art of enumeration, which, as Mr. Tylor clearly shews by reference to the words still used in some

---

[32] 'On the Origin of Civilisation,' 'Proc. Ethnological Soc.,' Nov. 26, 1867.

[33] 'Primeval Man,' 1869.

places, originated in counting the fingers, first of one
hand and then of the other, and lastly of the toes.
We have traces of this in our own decimal system, and
in the Roman numerals, where, after the V., which
is supposed to be an abbrevated picture of a human
hand, we pass on to VI., &c , when the other hand no
doubt was used. So again, " when we speak of three-
" score and ten, we are counting by the vigesimal
" system, each score thus ideally made, standing for
" 20—for ' one man ' as a Mexican or Carib would put
" it." [34]   According to a large and increasing school of
philologists, every language bears the marks of its
slow and gradual evolution. So it is with the art
of writing, for letters are rudiments of pictorial
representations. It is hardly possible to read Mr.
M'Lennan's work [35] and not admit that almost all
civilised nations still retain traces of such rude habits
as the forcible capture of wives. What ancient
nation, as the same author asks, can be named that
was originally monogamous? The primitive idea of
justice, as shewn by the law of battle and other
customs of which vestiges still remain, was likewise
most rude. Many existing superstitions are the
remnants of former false religious beliefs. The
highest form of religion—the grand idea of God

[34] ' Royal Institution of Great
Britain,' March 15, 1867. Also,
' Researches into the Early His-
tory of Mankind,' 1865.

[35] ' Primitive Marriage,' 1865.
See, likewise, an excellent article,
evidently by the same author,
in the ' North British Review,'
July, 1869. Also, Mr. L. H.
Morgan, 'A Conjectural Solution of the Origin of the Class,
System of Relationship,' in
' Proc. American Acad. of Sciences,' vol. vii. Feb. 1868.
Prof. Schaaffhausen ('Anthropolog. Review,' Oct. 1869, p.
373) remarks on "the vestiges
"of human sacrifices found both
"in Homer and the Old Testa-
"ment."

hating sin and loving righteousness—was unknown during primeval times.

Turning to the other kind of evidence: Sir J. Lubbock has shewn that some savages have recently improved a little in some of their simpler arts. From the extremely curious account which he gives of the weapons, tools, and arts, in use amongst savages in various parts of the world, it cannot be doubted that these have nearly all been independent discoveries, excepting perhaps the art of making fire.[36] The Australian boomerang is a good instance of one such independent discovery. The Tahitians when first visited had advanced in many respects beyond the inhabitants of most of the other Polynesian islands. There are no just grounds for the belief that the high culture of the native Peruvians and Mexicans was derived from abroad;[37] many native plants were there cultivated, and a few native animals domesticated. We should bear in mind that, judging from the small influence of most missionaries, a wandering crew from some semi-civilised land, if washed to the shores of America, would not have produced any marked effect on the natives, unless they had already become somewhat advanced. Looking to a very remote period in the history of the world, we find, to use Sir J. Lubbock's well-known terms, a paleolithic and neolithic period; and no one will pretend that the art of grinding rough flint tools was a borrowed one. In all

[36] Sir J. Lubbock, 'Prehistoric Times,' 2nd edit. 1869, chap. xv. and xvi. *et passim*. See also the excellent 9th Chapter in Tylor's 'Early History of Mankind,' 2nd edit., 1870.

[37] Dr. F. Müller has made some good remarks to this effect in the 'Reise der Novara: Anthropolog. Theil,' Abtheil. iii. 1868, s. 127.

parts of Europe, as far east as Greece, in Palestine, India, Japan, New Zealand, and Africa, including Egypt. flint tools have been discovered in abundance; and of their use the existing inhabitants retain no tradition. There is also indirect evidence of their former use by the Chinese and ancient Jews. Hence there can hardly be a doubt that the inhabitants of these countries, which include nearly the whole civilised world, were once in a barbarous condition. To believe that man was aboriginally civilised and then suffered utter degradation in so many regions, is to take a pitiably low view of human nature. It is apparently a truer and more cheerful view that progress has been much more general than retrogression; that man has risen, though by slow and interrupted steps, from a lowly condition to the highest standard as yet attained by him in knowledge, morals and religion.

CHAPTER VI.

On the Affinities and Genealogy of Man.

Position of man in the animal series—The natural system genealogical—Adaptive characters of slight value—Various small
points of resemblance between man and the Quadrumana—Rank
of man in the natural system—Birthplace and antiquity of man—
Absence of fossil connecting links—Lower stages in the genealogy
of man, as inferred, firstly from his affinities and secondly from
his structure—Early androgynous condition of the Vertebrata—
Conclusion.

Even if it be granted that the difference between man
and his nearest allies is as great in corporeal structure
as some naturalists maintain, and although we must
grant that the difference between them is immense in
mental power, yet the facts given in the earlier
chapters appear to declare, in the plainest manner,
that man is descended from some lower form, notwithstanding that connecting-links have not hitherto been
discovered.

Man is liable to numerous, slight, and diversified
variations, which are induced by the same general
causes, are governed and transmitted in accordance with
the same general laws, as in the lower animals.   Man
has multiplied so rapidly, that he has necessarily been
exposed to struggle for existence, and consequently
to natural selection.   He has given rise to many races,
some of which differ so much from each other, that
they have often been ranked by naturalists as distinct

species. His body is constructed on the same homological plan as that of other mammals. He passes
through the same phases of embryological development.
He retains many rudimentary and useless structures,
which no doubt were once serviceable. Characters
occasionally make their re-appearance in him, which
we have reason to believe were possessed by his
early progenitors. If the origin of man had been
wholly different from that of all other animals, these
various appearances would be mere empty deceptions;
but such an admission is incredible. These appearances, on the other hand, are intelligible, at least to a
large extent, if man is the co-descendant with other
mammals of some unknown and lower form.

Some naturalists, from being deeply impressed with
the mental and spiritual powers of man, have divided the
whole organic world into three kingdoms, the Human,
the Animal, and the Vegetable, thus giving to man a separate kingdom.[1] Spiritual powers cannot be compared
or classed by the naturalist: but he may endeavour to
shew, as I have done, that the mental faculties of man
and the lower animals do not differ in kind, although
immensely in degree. A difference in degree, however
great, does not justify us in placing man in a distinct
kingdom, as will perhaps be best illustrated by comparing the mental powers of two insects, namely, a coccus
or scale-insect and an ant, which undoubtedly belong
to the same class. The difference is here greater than,
though of a somewhat different kind from, that between
man and the highest mammal. The female coccus,

[1] Isidore Geoffroy St.-Hilaire
gives a detailed account of the
position assigned to man by
various naturalists in their classifications: 'Hist. Nat. Gén.' tom.
ii. 1859, pp. 170–189.

whilst young, attaches itself by its proboscis to a plant; sucks the sap, but never moves again; is fertilised and lays eggs; and this is its whole history. On the other hand, to describe the habits and mental powers of worker-ants, would require, as Pierre Huber has shewn, a large volume; I may, however, briefly specify a few points. Ants certainly communicate information to each other, and several unite for the same work, or for games of play. They recognise their fellow-ants after months of absence, and feel sympathy for each other. They build great edifices, keep them clean, close the doors in the evening, and post sentries. They make roads as well as tunnels under rivers, and temporary bridges over them, by clinging together. They collect food for the community, and when an object, too large for entrance, is brought to the nest, they enlarge the door, and afterwards build it up again. They store up seeds, of which they prevent the germination, and which, if damp, are brought up to the surface to dry. They keep aphides and other insects as milch-cows. They go out to battle in regular bands, and freely sacrifice their lives for the common weal. They emigrate according to a preconcerted plan. They capture slaves. They move the eggs of their aphides, as well as their own eggs and cocoons, into warm parts of the nest, in order that they may be quickly hatched; and endless similar facts could be given.[2] On the whole, the difference in mental power between an ant and a coccus is immense; yet no one has ever dreamed

[2] Some of the most interesting facts ever published on the habits of ants are given by Mr. Belt, in his 'Naturalist in Nicaragua,' 1874. See also Mr. Moggridge's admirable work, 'Harvesting Ants,' &c., 1873, also 'L'Instinct chez les Insectes,' by M. George Pouchet, 'Revue des Deux Mondes,' Feb. 1870, p. 682.

of placing these insects in distinct classes, much less in distinct kingdoms. No doubt the difference is bridged over by other insects; and this is not the case with man and the higher apes. But we have every reason to believe that the breaks in the series are simply the results of many forms having become extinct.

Professor Owen, relying chiefly on the structure of the brain, has divided the mammalian series into four sub-classes. One of these he devotes to man; in another he places both the Marsupials and the Mono-tremata; so that he makes man as distinct from all other mammals as are these two latter groups conjoined. This view has not been accepted, as far as I am aware, by any naturalist capable of forming an independent judgment, and therefore need not here be further considered.

We can understand why a classification founded on any single character or organ—even an organ so wonderfully complex and important as the brain—or on the high development of the mental faculties, is almost sure to prove unsatisfactory. This principle has indeed been tried with hymenopterous insects; but when thus classed by their habits or instincts, the arrangement proved thoroughly artificial.[3] Classifications may, of course, be based on any character whatever, as on size, colour, or the element inhabited; but naturalists have long felt a profound conviction that there is a natural system. This system, it is now generally admitted, must be, as far as possible, genealogical in arrangement, —that is the co-descendants of the same form must be kept together in one group, apart from the co-descend-

[3] Westwood, 'Modern Class of Insects,' vol. ii. 1840, p. 87.

ants of any other form; but if the parent-forms are related, so will be their descendants, and the two groups together will form a larger group. The amount of difference between the several groups—that is the amount of modification which each has undergone—is expressed by such terms as genera, families, orders, and classes. As we have no record of the lines of descent, the pedigree can be discovered only by observing the degrees of resemblance between the beings which are to be classed. For this object numerous points of resemblance are of much more importance than the amount of similarity or dissimilarity in a few points. If two languages were found to resemble each other in a multitude of words and points of construction, they would be universally recognised as having sprung from a common source, notwithstanding that they differed greatly in some few words or points of construction. But with organic beings the points of resemblance must not consist of adaptations to similar habits of life: two animals may, for instance, have had their whole frames modified for living in the water, and yet they will not be brought any nearer to each other in the natural system. Hence we can see how it is that resemblances in several unimportant structures, in useless and rudimentary organs, or not now functionally active, or in an embryological condition, are by far the most serviceable for classification; for they can hardly be due to adaptations within a late period; and thus they reveal the old lines of descent or of true affinity.

We can further see why a great amount of modification in some one character ought not to lead us to separate widely any two organisms. A part which

already differs much from the same part in other allied
forms has already, according to the theory of evolution,
varied much; consequently it would (as long as the
organism remained exposed to the same exciting conditions) be liable to further variations of the same
kind; and these, if beneficial, would be preserved, and
thus be continually augmented. In many cases the
continued development of a part, for instance, of the
beak of a bird, or of the teeth of a mammal, would not
aid the species in gaining its food, or for any other
object; but with man we can see no definite limit to
the continued development of the brain and mental
faculties, as far as advantage is concerned. Therefore
in determining the position of man in the natural
or genealogical system, the extreme development of
his brain ought not to outweigh a multitude of
resemblances in other less important or quite unimportant points.

The greater number of naturalists who have taken
into consideration the whole structure of man, including his mental faculties, have followed Blumenbach and Cuvier, and have placed man in a separate
Order, under the title of the Bimana, and therefore on
an equality with the orders of the Quadrumana,
Carnivora, &c. Recently many of our best naturalists
have recurred to the view first propounded by
Linnæus, so remarkable for his sagacity, and have
placed man in the same Order with the Quadrumana,
under the title of the Primates. The justice of this
conclusion will be admitted: for in the first place, we
must bear in mind the comparative insignificance for
classification of the great development of the brain
in man, and that the strongly-marked differences

between the skulls of man and the Quadrumana (lately insisted upon by Bischoff, Aeby, and others) apparently follow from their differently developed brains. In the second place, we must remember that nearly all the other and more important differences between man and the Quadrumana are manifestly adaptive in their nature, and relate chiefly to the erect position of man; such as the structure of his hand, foot, and pelvis, the curvature of his spine, and the position of his head. The family of Seals offers a good illustration of the small importance of adaptive characters for classification. These animals differ from all other Carnivora in the form of their bodies and in the structure of their limbs, far more than does man from the higher apes; yet in most systems, from that of Cuvier to the most recent one by Mr. Flower,[4] seals are ranked as a mere family in the Order of the Carnivora. If man had not been his own classifier, he would never have thought of founding a separate order for his own reception.

It would be beyond my limits, and quite beyond my knowledge, even to name the innumerable points of structure in which man agrees with the other Primates. Our great anatomist and philosopher, Prof. Huxley, has fully discussed this subject,[5] and concludes that man in all parts of his organization differs less from the higher apes, than these do from the lower members of the same group. Consequently there "is no "justification for placing man in a distinct order."

In an early part of this work I brought forward various facts, shewing how closely man agrees in

[4] 'Proc. Zoolog. Soc.' 1863, p. 4.
[5] 'Evidence as to Man's Place in Nature,' 1863, p. 70, *et passim.*

constitution with the higher mammals; and this agreement must depend on our close similarity in minute structure and chemical composition. I gave, as instances, our liability to the same diseases, and to the attacks of allied parasites; our tastes in common for the same stimulants, and the similar effects produced by them, as well as by various drugs, and other such facts.

As small unimportant points of resemblance between man and the Quadrumana are not commonly noticed in systematic works, and as, when numerous, they clearly reveal our relationship, I will specify a few such points. The relative position of our features is manifestly the same; and the various emotions are displayed by nearly similar movements of the muscles and skin, chiefly above the eyebrows and round the mouth. Some few expressions are, indeed, almost the same, as in the weeping of certain kinds of monkeys and in the laughing noise made by others, during which the corners of the mouth are drawn backwards, and the lower eyelids wrinkled. The external ears are curiously alike. In man the nose is much more prominent than in most monkeys; but we may trace the commencement of an aquiline curvature in the nose of the Hoolock Gibbon; and this in the *Semnopithecus nasica* is carried to a ridiculous extreme.

The faces of many monkeys are ornamented with beards, whiskers, or moustaches. The hair on the head grows to a great length in some species of Semnopithecus;[6] and in the Bonnet monkey (*Macacus radiatus*) it radiates from a point on the crown, with a parting down the middle. It is commonly said that

[6] Isid. Geoffroy, ' Hist. Nat. Gén.' tom. ii. 1859, p. 217.

the forehead gives to man his noble and intellectual appearance; but the thick hair on the head of the Bonnet monkey terminates downwards abruptly, and is succeeded by hair so short and fine that at a little distance the forehead, with the exception of the eyebrows, appears quite naked. It has been erroneously asserted that eyebrows are not present in any monkey. In the species just named the degree of nakedness of the forehead differs in different individuals; and Eschricht states [7] that in our children the limit between the hairy scalp and the naked forehead is sometimes not well defined; so that here we seem to have a trifling case of reversion to a progenitor, in whom the forehead had not as yet become quite naked.

It is well known that the hair on our arms tends to converge from above and below to a point at the elbow. This curious arrangement, so unlike that in most of the lower mammals, is common to the gorilla, chimpanzee, orang, some species of Hylobates, and even to some few American monkeys. But in *Hylobates agilis* the hair on the fore-arm is directed downwards or towards the wrist in the ordinary manner; and in *H. lar* it is nearly erect, with only a very slight forward inclination; so that in this latter species it is in a transitional state. It can hardly be doubted that with most mammals the thickness of the hair on the back and its direction, is adapted to throw off the rain; even the transverse hairs on the fore-legs of a dog may serve for this end when he is coiled up asleep. Mr. Wallace, who has carefully studied the habits of the orang, remarks that the convergence of the hair

[7] 'Ueber die Richtung der Haare,' &c., Müller's 'Archiv für Anat. und Phys.' 1837, s. 51.

towards the elbow on the arms of the orang may be explained as serving to throw off the rain, for this animal during rainy weather sits with its arms bent, and with the hands clasped round a branch or over its head. According to Livingstone, the gorilla also " sits in pelting rain with his hands over his head." [8] If the above explanation is correct, as seems probable, the direction of the hair on our own arms offers a curious record of our former state; for no one supposes that it is now of any use in throwing off the rain; nor, in our present erect condition, is it properly directed for this purpose.

It would, however, be rash to trust too much to the principle of adaptation in regard to the direction of the hair in man or his early progenitors; for it is impossible to study the figures given by Eschricht of the arrangement of the hair on the human fœtus (this being the same as in the adult) and not agree with this excellent observer that other and more complex causes have intervened. The points of convergence seem to stand in some relation to those points in the embryo which are last closed in during development. There appears, also, to exist some relation between the arrangement of the hair on the limbs, and the course of the medullary arteries.[9]

It must not be supposed that the resemblances between man and certain apes in the above and in

[8] Quoted by Reade, ' The African Sketch Book,' vol. i., 1873, p. 152.

[9] On the hair in Hylobates, see ' Nat. Hist. of Mammals,' by C. L. Martin, 1841, p. 415. Also, Isid. Geoffroy on the American monkeys and other kinds, ' Hist. Nat. Gén.' vol. ii. 1859, p. 216, 243, Eschricht, ibid. s. 46, 55, 61. Owen, ' Anat. of Vertebrates,' vol. iii. p. 619. Wallace, ' Contributions to the Theory of Natural Selection,' 1870, p. 344.

many other points—such as in having a naked fore-head, long tresses on the head, &c.—are all necessarily the result of unbroken inheritance from a common progenitor, or of subsequent reversion. Many of these resemblances are more probably due to analogous variation, which follows, as I have elsewhere attempted to shew,[10] from co-descended organisms having a similar constitution, and having been acted on by like causes inducing similar modifications. With respect to the similar direction of the hair on the fore-arms of man and certain monkeys, as this character is common to almost all the anthropomorphous apes, it may probably be attributed to inheritance; but this is not certain, as some very distinct American monkeys are thus characterised.

Although, as we have now seen, man has no just right to form a separate Order for his own reception, he may perhaps claim a distinct Sub-order or Family. Prof. Huxley, in his last work,[11] divides the Primates into three Sub-orders; namely, the Anthropidæ with man alone, the Simiadæ including monkeys of all kinds, and the Lemuridæ with the diversified genera of lemurs. As far as differences in certain important points of structure are concerned, man may no doubt rightly claim the rank of a Sub-order; and this rank is too low, if we look chiefly to his mental faculties. Nevertheless, from a genealogical point of view it appears that this rank is too high, and that man ought to form merely a Family, or possibly even only a Sub-family. If we imagine three lines of descent proceeding

[10] 'Origin of Species,' 5th edit. 1869, p. 194. 'The Variation of Animals and Plants under Domestication,' vol. ii. 1868, p. 348.
[11] 'An Introduction to the Classification of Animals,' 1869, p. 99.

from a common stock, it is quite conceivable that two
of them might after the lapse of ages be so slightly
changed as still to remain as species of the same
genus, whilst the third line might become so greatly
modified as to deserve to rank as a distinct Sub-family,
Family, or even Order. But in this case it is almost
certain that the third line would still retain through
inheritance numerous small points of resemblance with
the other two. Here, then, would occur the difficulty,
at present insoluble, how much weight we ought to
assign in our classifications to strongly-marked differences in some few points,—that is, to the amount
of modification undergone; and how much to close
resemblance in numerous unimportant points, as indicating the lines of descent or genealogy. To attach
much weight to the few but strong differences is the
most obvious and perhaps the safest course, though it
appears more correct to pay great attention to the
many small resemblances, as giving a truly natural
classification.

In forming a judgment on this head with reference
to man, we must glance at the classification of the
Simiadæ. This family is divided by almost all naturalists into the Catarrhine group, or Old World monkeys,
all of which are characterised (as their name expresses)
by the peculiar structure of their nostrils, and by
having four premolars in each jaw; and into the
Platyrrhine group or New World monkeys (including
two very distinct sub-groups), all of which are characterised by differently constructed nostrils, and by having
six premolars in each jaw. Some other small differences
might be mentioned. Now man unquestionably belongs
in his dentition, in the structure of his nostrils, and

some other respects, to the Catarhine or Old World division ; nor does he resemble the Platyrhines more closely than the Catarhines in any characters, excepting in a few of not much importance and apparently of an adaptive nature. It is therefore against all probability that some New World species should have formerly varied and produced a man-like creature, with all the distinctive characters proper to the Old World division ; losing at the same time all its own distinctive characters. There can, consequently, hardly be a doubt that man is an off-shoot from the Old World Simian stem ; and that under a genealogical point of view he must be classed with the Catarhine division.[12]

The anthropomorphous apes, namely the gorilla, chimpanzee, orang, and hylobates, are by most naturalists separated from the other Old World monkeys, as a distinct sub-group. I am aware that Gratiolet, relying on the structure of the brain, does not admit the existence of this sub-group, and no doubt it is a broken one. Thus the orang, as Mr. St. G. Mivart remarks, [13] "is one of the most peculiar and aberrant "forms to be found in the Order." The remaining non-anthropomorphous Old World monkeys, are again divided by some naturalists into two or three smaller sub-groups ; the genus Semnopithecus, with its peculiar sacculated stomach, being the type of one such sub-group. But it appears from M. Gaudry's wonderful

[12] This is nearly the same classification as that provisionally adopted by Mr. St. George Mivart ('Transact. Philosoph. Soc.' 1867, p. 300), who, after separating the Lemuridæ, divides the remainder of the Primates into the Hominidæ, the Simiadæ which answer to the Catarhines, the Cebidæ, and the Hapalidæ,—these two latter groups answering to the Platyrhines. Mr. Mivart still abides by the same view ; see 'Nature,' 1871, p. 481.

[13] 'Transact. Zoolog. Soc.' vol. vi. 1867, p. 214.

discoveries in Attica, that during the Miocene period a form existed there, which connected Semnopithecus and Macacus; and this probably illustrates the manner in which the other and higher groups were once blended together.

If the anthropomorphous apes be admitted to form a natural sub-group, then as man agrees with them, not only in all those characters which he possesses in common with the whole Catarhine group, but in other peculiar characters, such as the absence of a tail and of callosities, and in general appearance, we may infer that some ancient member of the anthropomorphous sub-group gave birth to man. It is not probable that, through the law of analogous variation, a member of one of the other lower sub-groups should have given rise to a man-like creature, resembling the higher anthropomorphous apes in so many respects. No doubt man, in comparison with most of his allies, has undergone an extraordinary amount of modification, chiefly in consequence of the great development of his brain and his erect position; nevertheless, we should bear in mind that he " is but one of several exceptional forms of " Primates." [14]

Every naturalist, who believes in the principle of evolution, will grant that the two main divisions of the Simiadæ, namely the Catarhine and Platyrhine monkeys, with their sub-groups, have all proceeded from some one extremely ancient progenitor. The early descendants of this progenitor, before they had diverged to any considerable extent from each other, would still have formed a single natural group; but some of the species or incipient genera would have already begun to indicate

[14] Mr. St. G. Mivart, 'Transact. Phil. Soc.' 1867, p. 410.

by their diverging characters the future distinctive
marks of the Catarhine and Platyrhine divisions. Hence
the members of this supposed ancient group would not
have been so uniform in their dentition, or in the
structure of their nostrils, as are the existing Catarhine
monkeys in one way and the Platyrhines in another way,
but would have resembled in this respect the allied
Lemuridæ, which differ greatly from each other in the
form of their muzzles,[15] and to an extraordinary degree
in their dentition.

The Catarhine and Platyrhine monkeys agree in a
multitude of characters, as is shewn by their unquestionably belonging to one and the same Order. The
many characters which they possess in common can
hardly have been independently acquired by so many
distinct species; so that these characters must have
been inherited. But a naturalist would undoubtedly
have ranked as an ape or a monkey, an ancient form
which possessed many characters common to the Catarhine and Platyrhine monkeys, other characters in an
intermediate condition, and some few, perhaps, distinct
from those now found in either group. And as man
from a genealogical point of view belongs to the
Catarhine or Old World stock, we must conclude,
however much the conclusion may revolt our pride,
that our early progenitors would have been properly
thus designated.[16] But we must not fall into the
error of supposing that the early progenitor of the

[15] Messrs. Murie and Mivart on the Lemuroidea, 'Transact. Zoolog. Soc.' vol. vii. 1869, p. 5.

[16] Häckel has come to this same conclusion. See 'Ueber die Entstehung des Men-schengeschlechts,' in Virchow's 'Sammlung. gemein. wissen. Vortrage,' 1868, s. 61. Also his 'Natürliche Schöpfungsge-schichte,' 1868, in which he gives in detail his views on the genea-logy of man.

whole Simian stock, including man, was identical with, or even closely resembled, any existing ape or monkey.

On the Birthplace and Antiquity of Man.—We are naturally led to enquire, where was the birthplace of man at that stage of descent when our progenitors diverged from the Catarhine stock? The fact that they belonged to this stock clearly shews that they inhabitated the Old World; but not Australia nor any oceanic island, as we may infer from the laws of geographical distribution. In each great region of the world the living mammals are closely related to the extinct species of the same region. It is therefore probable that Africa was formerly inhabited by extinct apes closely allied to the gorilla and chimpanzee; and as these two species are now man's nearest allies, it is somewhat more probable that our early progenitors lived on the African continent than elsewhere. But it is useless to speculate on this subject; for two or three anthropomorphous apes, one the Dryopithecus [17] of Lartet, nearly as large as a man, and closely allied to Hylobates, existed in Europe during the Miocene age; and since so remote a period the earth has certainly undergone many great revolutions, and there has been ample time for migration on the largest scale.

At the period and place, whenever and wherever it was, when man first lost his hairy covering, he probably inhabited a hot country; a circumstance favourable for the frugiferous diet on which, judging from analogy, he subsisted. We are far from knowing how long ago

[17] Dr. C. Forsyth Major, 'Sur les Singes Fossiles trouvés en Italie:' 'Soc. Ital. des Sc. Nat.' tom. xv. 1872.

it was when man first diverged from the Catarhine stock; but it may have occurred at an epoch as remote as the Eocene period; for that the higher apes had diverged from the lower apes as early as the Upper Miocene period is shewn by the existence of the Dryopithecus. We are also quite ignorant at how rapid a rate organisms, whether high or low in the scale, may be modified under favourable circumstances; we know, however, that some have retained the same form during an enormous lapse of time. From what we see going on under domestication, we learn that some of the co-descendants of the same species may be not at all, some a little, and some greatly changed, all within the same period. Thus it may have been with man, who has undergone a great amount of modification in certain characters in comparison with the higher apes.

The great break in the organic chain between man and his nearest allies, which cannot be bridged over by any extinct or living species, has often been advanced as a grave objection to the belief that man is descended from some lower form; but this objection will not appear of much weight to those who, from general reasons, believe in the general principle of evolution. Breaks often occur in all parts of the series, some being wide, sharp and defined, others less so in various degrees; as between the orang and its nearest allies—between the Tarsius and the other Lemuridæ—between the elephant, and in a more striking manner between the Ornithorhynchus or Echidna, and all other mammals. But these breaks depend merely on the number of related forms which have become extinct. At some future period, not very distant as measured by centuries, the civilised races of

man will almost certainly exterminate, and replace, the
savage races throughout the world. At the same time
the anthropomorphous apes, as Professor Schaaffhausen
has remarked,[18] will no doubt be exterminated. The
break between man and his nearest allies will then be
wider, for it will intervene between man in a more
civilised state, as we may hope, even than the Caucasian, and some ape as low as a baboon, instead of as
now between the negro or Australian and the gorilla.

With respect to the absence of fossil remains, serving
to connect man with his ape-like progenitors, no one
will lay much stress on this fact who reads Sir C.
Lyell's discussion,[19] where he shews that in all the
vertebrate classes the discovery of fossil remains has
been a very slow and fortuitous process. Nor should
it be forgotten that those regions which are the most
likely to afford remains connecting man with some
extinct ape-like creature, have not as yet been searched
by geologists.

Lower Stages in the Genealogy of Man.—We have
seen that man appears to have diverged from the
Catarhine or Old World division of the Simiadæ, after
these had diverged from the New World division. We
will now endeavour to follow the remote traces of his
genealogy, trusting principally to the mutual affinities
between the various classes and orders, with some
slight reference to the periods, as far as ascertained,
of their successive appearance on the earth. The
Lemuridæ stand below and near to the Simiadæ, and
constitute a very distinct family of the Primates, or,

[18] Anthropological Review,' April, 1867, p. 236.
1865, pp. 583–585. 'Antiquity of Man,' 1863, p. 145.
[19] 'Elements of Geology,'

according to Häckel and others, a distinct Order.
This group is diversified and broken to an extraordinary degree, and includes many aberrant forms.
It has, therefore, probably suffered much extinction.
Most of the remnants survive on islands, such as
Madagascar and the Malayan archipelago, where they
have not been exposed to so severe a competition as
they would have been on well-stocked continents.
This group likewise presents many gradations, leading,
as Huxley remarks,[20] "insensibly from the crown and
"summit of the animal creation down to creatures
"from which there is but a step, as it seems, to the
"lowest, smallest, and least intelligent of the placental
"mammalia."   From these various considerations it is
probable that the Simiadæ were originally developed
from the progenitors of the existing Lemuridæ; and
these in their turn from forms standing very low in
the mammalian series.

The Marsupials stand in many important characters
below the placental mammals.   They appeared at an
earlier geological period, and their range was formerly
much more extensive than at present.   Hence the
Placentata are generally supposed to have been derived
from the Implacentata or Marsupials; not, however,
from forms closely resembling the existing Marsupials,
but from their early progenitors.   The Monotremata
are plainly allied to the Marsupials, forming a third
and still lower division in the great mammalian series.
They are represented at the present day solely by the
Ornithorhynchus and Echidna; and these two forms
may be safely considered as relics of a much larger
group, representatives of which have been preserved in

[20] 'Man's Place in Nature,' p. 105.

Australia through some favourable concurrence of circumstances. The Monotremata are eminently interesting, as leading in several important points of structure towards the class of reptiles.

In attempting to trace the genealogy of the Mammalia, and therefore of man, lower down in the series, we become involved in greater and greater obscurity; but as a most capable judge, Mr. Parker, has remarked, we have good reason to believe, that no true bird or reptile intervenes in the direct line of descent. He who wishes to see what ingenuity and knowledge can effect, may consult Prof. Häckel's works.[21] I will content myself with a few general remarks. Every evolutionist will admit that the five great vertebrate classes, namely, mammals, birds, reptiles, amphibians, and fishes, are descended from some one prototype; for they have much in common, especially during their embryonic state. As the class of fishes is the most lowly organised, and appeared before the others, we may conclude that all the members of the vertebrate kingdom are derived from some fishlike animal. The belief that animals so distinct as a monkey, an elephant, a humming-bird, a snake, a frog, and a fish, &c., could all have sprung from the same parents, will appear monstrous to those who have not attended to the recent progress of natural history. For this belief implies

----

[21] Elaborate tables are given in his 'Generelle Morphologie' (B. ii. s. cliii. and s. 425); and with more especial reference to man in his 'Natürliche Schöpfungsgeschichte,' 1868. Prof. Huxley, in reviewing this latter work ('The Academy,' 1869, p. 42) says, that he considers the phylum or lines of descent of the Vertebrata to be admirably discussed by Häckel, although he differs on some points. He expresses, also, his high estimate of the general tenor and spirit of the whole work.

the former existence of links binding closely together all these forms, now so utterly unlike.

Nevertheless, it is certain that groups of animals have existed, or do now exist, which serve to connect several of the great vertebrate classes more or less closely. We have seen that the Ornithorhynchus graduates towards reptiles; and Prof. Huxley has discovered, and is confirmed by Mr. Cope and others, that the Dinosaurians are in many important characters intermediate between certain reptiles and certain birds —the birds referred to being the ostrich-tribe (itself evidently a widely-diffused remnant of a larger group) and the Archeopteryx, that strange Secondary bird, with a long lizard-like tail. Again, according to Prof. Owen,[22] the Ichthyosaurians—great sea-lizards furnished with paddles—present many affinities with fishes, or rather, according to Huxley, with amphibians; a class which, including in its highest division frogs and toads, is plainly allied to the Ganoid fishes. These latter fishes swarmed during the earlier geological periods, and were constructed on what is called a generalised type, that is, they presented diversified affinities with other groups of organisms. The Lepidosiren is also so closely allied to amphibians and fishes, that naturalists long disputed in which of these two classes to rank it; it, and also some few Ganoid fishes, have been preserved from utter extinction by inhabiting rivers, which are harbours of refuge, and are related to the great waters of the ocean in the same way that islands are to continents.

Lastly, one single member of the immense and diversified class of fishes, namely, the lancelet or

[22] 'Palæontology,' 1860, p. 199.

amphioxus, is so different from all other fishes, that Häckel maintains that it ought to form a distinct class in the vertebrate kingdom. This fish is remarkable for its negative characters; it can hardly be said to possess a brain, vertebral column, or heart, &c.; so that it was classed by the older naturalists amongst the worms. Many years ago Prof. Goodsir perceived that the lancelet presented some affinities with the Ascidians, which are invertebrate, hermaphrodite, marine creatures permanently attached to a support. They hardly appear like animals, and consist of a simple, tough, leathery sack, with two small projecting orifices. They belong to the Mulluscoida of Huxley— a lower division of the great kingdom of the Mollusca; but they have recently been placed by some naturalists amongst the Vermes or worms. Their larvæ somewhat resemble tadpoles in shape,[23] and have the power of swimming freely about. M. Kovalevsky[24] has lately observed that the larvæ of Ascidians are related to the Vertebrata, in their manner of development, in the relative position of the nervous system, and in possessing a structure closely like the *chorda dorsalis* of vertebrate animals; and in this he has been since confirmed by Prof. Kupffer. M. Kovalevsky writes to

[23] At the Falkland Islands I had the satisfaction of seeing, in April 1833, and therefore some years before any other naturalist, the locomotive larvæ of a compound Ascidian, closely allied to Synoicum, but apparently generically distinct from it. The tail was about five times as long as the oblong head, and terminated in a very fine filament. It was, as sketched by me under a simple microscope, plainly divided by transverse opaque partitions, which I presume represent the great cells figured by Kovalevsky. At an early stage of development the tail was closely coiled round the head of the larva.

[24] 'Mémoires de l'Acad. des Sciences de St. Pétersbourg,' tom. x. No. 15, 1866.

me from Naples, that he has now carried these observations yet further, and should his results be well established, the whole will form a discovery of the very greatest value.   Thus, if we may rely on embryology, ever the safest guide in classification, it seems that we have at last gained a clue to the source whence the Vertebrata were derived.[25]   We should then be justified in believing that at an extremely remote period a group of animals existed, resembling in many respects the larvæ of our present Ascidians, which diverged into two great branches—the one retrograding in development and producing the present class of Ascidians, the other rising to the crown and summit of the animal kingdom by giving birth to the Vertebrata.

We have thus far endeavoured rudely to trace the genealogy of the Vertebrata by the aid of their mutual affinities.   We will now look to man as he exists; and we shall, I think, be able partially to restore the structure of our early progenitors, during successive periods, but not in due order of time.   This can be effected by means of the rudiments which man still retains, by the characters which occasionally make their appearance in him through reversion, and by the aid of the principles of morphology and embryology.

---

[25] But I am bound to add that some competent judges dispute this conclusion; for instance, M. Giard, in a series of papers in the 'Archives de Zoologie Expérimentale,' for 1872.   Nevertheless, this naturalist remarks, p. 281, " L'organisation de la " larve ascidienne en dehors de " toute hypothèse et de toute " théorie, nous montre comment " la nature peut produire la dis- " position fondamentale du type " vertébré (l'existence d'une " corde dorsale) chez un inver- " tébré par la seule condition " vitale de l'adaptation, et cette " simple possibilité du passage " supprime l'abîme entre les deux " sous-règnes, encore bien qu'en " ignore par où le passage s'est " fait en réalité."

The various facts, to which I shall here allude, have been given in the previous chapters.

The early progenitors of man must have been once covered with hair, both sexes having beards; their ears were probably pointed, and capable of movement; and their bodies were provided with a tail, having the proper muscles. Their limbs and bodies were also acted on by many muscles which now only occasionally reappear, but are normally present in the Quadrumana. At this or some earlier period, the great artery and nerve of the humerus ran through a supra-condyloid foramen. The intestine gave forth a much larger diverticulum or cæcum than that now existing. The foot was then prehensile, judging from the condition of the great toe in the fœtus; and our progenitors, no doubt, were arboreal in their habits, and frequented some warm, forest-clad land. The males had great canine teeth, which served them as formidable weapons. At a much earlier period the uterus was double; the excreta were voided through a cloaca; and the eye was protected by a third eyelid or nictitating membrane. At a still earlier the progenitors of man must have been aquatic in their habits; for morphology plainly tells us that our lungs consist of a modified swim-bladder, which once served as a float. The clefts on the neck in the embryo of man show where the branchiæ once existed. In the lunar or weekly recurrent periods of some of our functions we apparently still retain traces of our primordial birthplace, a shore washed by the tides. At about this same early period the true kidneys were replaced by the corpora wolffiana. The heart existed as a simple pulsating vessel; and the chorda dorsalis took the place of a vertebral column. These early ancestors of man, thus seen in the dim recesses of time, must have been as simply, or even still more simply organised than the lancelet or amphioxus.

There is one other point deserving a fuller notice. It has long been known that in the vertebrate kingdom one sex bears rudiments of various accessory parts, appertaining to the reproductive system, which properly belong to the opposite sex; and it has now been ascertained that at a very early embryonic period both sexes possess true male and female glands. Hence some remote progenitor of the whole vertebrate kingdom appears to have been hermaphrodite or androgynous.[26] But here we encounter a singular difficulty. In the mammalian class the males possess rudiments of a uterus with the adjacent passage, in their vesiculæ prostaticæ; they bear also rudiments of mammæ, and some male Marsupials have traces of a marsupial sack.[27] Other analogous facts could be added. Are we, then, to suppose that some extremely ancient mammal continued androgynous, after it had acquired the chief distinctions of its class, and therefore after it had diverged from the lower classes of the vertebrate kingdom? This seems very improbable, for we have to look to fishes, the lowest of all the classes, to find any

[26] This is the conclusion of Prof. Gegenbaur, one of the highest authorities in comparative anatomy; see 'Grundzüge der vergleich. Anat.' 1870, s. 876. The result has been arrived at chiefly from the study of the Amphibia; but it appears from the researches of Waldeyer (as quoted in 'Journal of Anat. and Phys.' 1869, p. 161), that the sexual organs of even "the "higher vertebrata are, in their "early condition, hermaphrodite." Similar views have long been held by some authors, though until recently without a firm basis.

[27] The male Thylacinus offers the best instance. Owen, 'Anatomy of Vertebrates,' vol. iii. p. 771.

still existent androgynous forms.[28] That various accessory parts, proper to each sex, are found in a rudimentary condition in the opposite sex, may be explained by such organs having been gradually acquired by the one sex, and then transmitted in a more or less imperfect state to the other. When we treat of sexual selection, we shall meet with innumerable instances of this form of transmission,—as in the case of the spurs, plumes, and brilliant colours, acquired for battle or ornament by male birds, and inherited by the females in an imperfect or rudimentary condition.

The possession by male mammals of functionally imperfect mammary organs is, in some respects, especially curious. The Monotremata have the proper milk-secreting glands with orifices, but no nipples; and as these animals stand at the very base of the mammalian series, it is probable that the progenitors of the class also had milk-secreting glands, but no nipples. This conclusion is supported by what is known of their manner of development; for Professor Turner informs me, on the authority of Kölliker and Langer, that in the embryo the mammary glands can be distinctly traced before the nipples are in the least visible; and the development of successive parts in the individual generally represents and accords with the

[28] Hermaphroditism has been observed in several species of Serranus, as well as in some other fishes, where it is either normal and symmetrical, or abnormal and unilateral. Dr. Zouteveen has given me references on this subject, more especially to a paper by Prof. Halbertsma, in the 'Transact. of the Dutch Acad. of Sciences,' vol. xvi. Dr. Günther doubts the fact, but it has now been recorded by too many good observers to be any longer disputed. Dr. M. Lessona writes to me, that he has verified the observations made by Cavolini on Serranus. Prof. Ercolani has recently shewn ('Accad. delle Scienze,' Bologna, Dec. 28, 1871) that eels are androgynous.

development of successive beings in the same line of descent. The Marsupials differ from the Monotremata by possessing nipples; so that probably these organs were first acquired by the Marsupials, after they had diverged from, and risen above, the Monotremata, and were then transmitted to the placental mammals.[29] No one will suppose that the Marsupials still remained androgynous, after they had approximately acquired their present structure. How then are we to account for male mammals possessing mammæ? It is possible that they were first developed in the females and then transferred to the males, but from what follows this is hardly probable.

It may be suggested, as another view, that long after the progenitors of the whole mammalian class had ceased to be androgynous, both sexes yielded milk, and thus nourished their young; and in the case of the Marsupials, that both sexes carried their young marsupial sacks. This will not appear altogether improbable, if we reflect that the males of existing syngnathous fishes receive the eggs of the females in their abdominal pouches, hatch them, and afterwards, as some believe, nourish the young;[30]—that certain

[29] Prof. Gegenbaur has shewn ('Jenaische Zeitschrift,' Bd. vii. p. 212) that two distinct types of nipples prevail throughout the several mammalian orders, but that it is quite intelligible how both could have been derived from the nipples of the Marsupials, and the latter from those of the Monotremata. See, also, a memoir by Dr. Max Huss, on the mammary glands, ibid. B. viii. p. 176.

[30] Mr. Lockwood believes (as quoted in 'Quart. Journal of Science,' April, 1868, p. 269), from what he has observed of the development of Hippocampus, that the walls of the abdominal pouch of the male in some way afford nourishment. On male fishes hatching the ova in their mouths, see a very interesting paper by Prof. Wyman, in 'Proc. Boston Soc. of Nat. Hist.' Sept. 15, 1857; also Prof.

other male fishes hatch the eggs within their mouths or branchial cavities;—that certain male toads take the chaplets of eggs from the females, and wind them round their own thighs, keeping them there until the tadpoles are born; —that certain male birds undertake the whole duty of incubation, and that male pigeons, as well as the females, feed their nestlings with a secretion from their crops. But the above suggestion first occurred to me from the mammary glands of male mammals being so much more perfectly developed than the rudiments of the other accessory reproductive parts, which are found in the one sex though proper to the other. The mammary glands and nipples, as they exist in male mammals, can indeed hardly be called rudimentary; they are merely not fully developed, and not functionally active. They are sympathetically affected under the influence of certain diseases, like the same organs in the female. They often secrete a few drops of milk at birth and at puberty: this latter fact occurred in the curious case, before referred to, where a young man possessed two pairs of mammæ. In man and some other male mammals these organs have been known occasionally to become so well developed during maturity as to yield a fair supply of milk. Now if we suppose that during a former prolonged period male mammals aided the females in nursing their offspring, [31] and that afterwards from some cause (as from the production of a smaller number of young) the males ceased to give this aid, disuse of the organs during

---

Turner, in 'Journal of Anat. and Phys.' Nov. 1, 1866, p. 78. Dr. Günther has likewise described similar cases.

[31] Maddle. C. Royer has suggested a similar view in her 'Origine de l'Homme,' &c., 1870.

maturity would lead to their becoming inactive ; and from two well-known principles of inheritance, this state of inactivity would probably be transmitted to the males at the corresponding age of maturity. But at an earlier age these organs would be left unaffected, so that they would be almost equally well developed in the young of both sexes.

Conclusion.—Von Baer has defined advancement or progress in the organic scale better than any one else, as resting on the amount of differentiation and speciali-sation of the several parts of a being,—when arrived at maturity, as I should be inclined to add. Now as organisms have become slowly adapted to diversified lines of life by means of natural selection, their parts will have become more and more differentiated and specialised for various functions from the advantage gained by the division of physiological labour. The same part appears often to have been modified first for one purpose, and then long afterwards for some other and quite distinct purpose ; and thus all the parts are rendered more and more complex. But each organism still retains the general type of structure of the pro-genitor from which it was aboriginally derived. In ac-cordance with this view it seems, if we turn to geo-logical evidence, that organisation on the whole has advanced throughout the world by slow and interrupted steps. In the great kingdom of the Vertebrata it has culminated in man. It must not, however, be supposed that groups of organic beings are always supplanted, and disappear as soon as they have given birth to other and more perfect groups. The latter, though victorious over their predecessors, may not have become better adapted for all places in the economy of nature. Some old forms appear to have survived from inhabiting protected sites, where they have not been exposed to very severe competition; and these often aid us in constructing our genealogies, by giving us a fair idea of former and lost populations. But we must not fall into the error of looking at the existing members of any lowly-organised group as perfect representatives of their ancient predecessors.

The most ancient progenitors in the kingdom of the Vertebrata, at which we are able to obtain an obscure glance, apparently consisted of a group of marine animals,[32] resembling the larvæ of existing Ascidians.

---

[32] The inhabitants of the sea-shore must be greatly affected by the tides; animals living either about the *mean* high-water mark, or about the *mean* low-water mark, pass through a complete cycle of tidal changes in a fortnight. Consequently, their food supply will undergo marked changes week by week. The vital functions of such animals, living under these conditions for many generations, can hardly fail to run their course in regular weekly periods. Now it is a mysterious fact that in the higher and now terrestrial Vertebrata, as well as in other classes, many normal and abnormal processes have one or more whole weeks as their periods; this would be rendered intelligible if the Vertebrata are descended from an animal allied to the existing tidal Ascidians. Many instances of such periodic processes might be given, as the gestation of mammals, the dura-tion of fevers, &c. The hatching of eggs affords also a good example, for, according to Mr. Bartlett ('Land and Water,' Jan. 7, 1871), the eggs of the pigeon are hatched in two weeks; those of the fowl in three; those of the duck in four; those of the goose in five; and those of the ostrich in seven weeks. As far as we can judge, a recurrent period, if approximately of the right duration for any process or function, would not, when once gained, be liable to change; consequently it might be thus transmitted through almost any number of generations. But if the function changed, the period would have to change, and would be apt to change almost abruptly by a whole week. This conclusion, if sound, is highly remarkable; for the period of gestation in each mammal, and the hatching of each bird's eggs, and many other vital processes, thus betray to us the primordial birthplace of these animals.

These animals probably gave rise to a group of fishes, as lowly organised as the lancelet; and from these the Ganoids, and other fishes like the Lepidosiren, must have been developed. From such fish a very small advance would carry us on to the Amphibians. We have seen that birds and reptiles were once intimately connected together; and the Monotremata now connect mammals with reptiles in a slight degree. But no one can at present say by what line of descent the three higher and related classes, namely, mammals, birds, and reptiles, were derived from the two lower vertebrate classes, namely, amphibians and fishes. In the class of mammals the steps are not difficult to conceive which led from the ancient Monotremata to the ancient Marsupials; and from these to the early progenitors of the placental mammals. We may thus ascend to the Lemuridæ; and the interval is not very wide from these to the Simiadæ. The Simiadæ then branched off into two great stems, the New World and Old World monkeys; and from the latter, at a remote period, Man, the wonder and glory of the Universe, proceeded.

Thus we have given to man a pedigree of prodigious length, but not, it may be said, of noble quality. The world, it has often been remarked, appears as if it had long been preparing for the advent of man: and this, in one sense is strictly true, for he owes his birth to a long line of progenitors. If any single link in this chain had never existed, man would not have been exactly what he now is. Unless we wilfully close our eyes, we may, with our present knowledge, approximately recognise our parentage; nor need we feel ashamed of it. The most humble organism is something much higher than the inorganic dust under our feet; and no one with an unbiassed mind can study any living creature, however humble, without being struck with enthusiasm at its marvellous structure and properties.

CHAPTER VII.

On the Races of Man.

The nature and value of specific characters—Application to the
races of man—Arguments in favour of, and opposed to, ranking
the so-called races of man as distinct species—Sub-species—
Monogenists and polygenists—Convergence of character—
Numerous points of resemblance in body and mind between the
most distinct races of man—The state of man when he first
spread over the earth—Each race not descended from a single
pair—The extinction of races—The formation of races—The
effects of crossing—Slight influence of the direct action of the
conditions of life—Slight or no influence of natural selection—
Sexual selection.

It is not my intention here to describe the several
so-called races of men; but I am about to enquire
what is the value of the differences between them
under a classificatory point of view, and how they
have originated. In determining whether two or
more allied forms ought to be ranked as species or
varieties, naturalists are practically guided by the following considerations; namely, the amount of difference between them, and whether such differences relate
to few or many points of structure, and whether they
are of physiological importance; but more especially
whether they are constant. Constancy of character is
what is chiefly valued and sought for by naturalists.
Whenever it can be shewn, or rendered probable, that
the forms in question have remained distinct for a

long period, this becomes an argument of much weight in favour of treating them as species. Even a slight degree of sterility between any two forms when first crossed, or in their offspring, is generally considered as a decisive test of their specific distinctness; and their continued persistence without blending within the same area, is usually accepted as sufficient evidence, either of some degree of mutual sterility, or in the case of animals of some mutual repugnance to pairing.

Independently of fusion from intercrossing, the complete absence, in a well-investigated region, of varieties linking together any two closely-allied forms, is probably the most important of all the criterions of their specific distinctness; and this is a somewhat different consideration from mere constancy of character, for two forms may be highly variable and yet not yield intermediate varieties. Geographical distribution is often brought into play unconsciously and sometimes consciously; so that forms living in two widely separated areas, in which most of the other inhabitants are specifically distinct, are themselves usually looked at as distinct; but in truth this affords no aid in distinguishing geographical races from so-called good or true species.

Now let us apply these generally-admitted principles to the races of man, viewing him in the same spirit as a naturalist would any other animal. In regard to the amount of difference between the races, we must make some allowance for our nice powers of discrimination gained by the long habit of observing ourselves. In India, as Elphinstone remarks, although a newly-arrived European cannot at first distinguish the

various native races, yet they soon appear to him
extremely dissimilar;[1] and the Hindoo cannot at first
perceive any difference between the several European
nations. Even the most distinct races of man are
much more like each other in form than would at first
be supposed; certain negro tribes must be excepted,
whilst others, as Dr. Rohlfs writes to me, and as I
have myself seen, have Caucasian features. This
general similarity is well shewn by the French photo-
graphs in the Collection Anthropologique du Muséum
de Paris of the men belonging to various races, the
greater number of which might pass for Europeans,
as many persons to whom I have shewn them have
remarked. Nevertheless, these men, if seen alive,
would undoubtedly appear very distinct, so that we
are clearly much influenced in our judgment by the
mere colour of the skin and hair, by slight differences
in the features, and by expression.

There is, however, no doubt that the various races,
when carefully compared and measured, differ much
from each other,—as in the texture of the hair, the
relative proportions of all parts of the body,[2] the
capacity of the lungs, the form and capacity of the
skull, and even in the convolutions of the brain.[3] But
it would be an endless task to specify the numerous

[1] 'History of India,' 1841,
vol. i. p. 323. Father Ripa
makes exactly the same remark
with respect to the Chinese.

[2] A vast number of measurements of Whites, Blacks, and
Indians, are given in the 'Investigations in the Military
and Anthropolog. Statistics of
American Soldiers,' by B. A.
Gould, 1869, pp. 298–358; 'On

the capacity of the lungs,' p.
471. See also the numerous
and valuable tables, by Dr.
Weisbach, from the observations
of Dr. Scherzer and Dr. Schwarz,
in the 'Reise der Novara: Anthropolog. Theil,' 1867.

[3] See, for instance, Mr. Marshall's account of the brain of a
Bushwoman, in 'Phil. Transact.'
1864, p. 519.

points of difference.   The races differ also in constitution, in acclimatisation and in liability to certain
diseases.   Their mental characteristics are likewise
very distinct; chiefly as it would appear in their
emotional, but partly in their intellectual faculties.
Every one who has had the opportunity of comparison,
must have been struck with the contrast between the
taciturn, even morose, aborigines of S. America and
the light-hearted, talkative negroes.   There is a nearly
similar contrast between the Malays and the Papuans,[4]
who live under the same physical conditions, and are
separated from each other only by a narrow space of
sea.

We will first consider the arguments which may be
advanced in favour of classing the races of man as
distinct species, and then the arguments on the other
side.   If a naturalist, who had never before seen a
Negro, Hottentot, Australian, or Mongolian, were to
compare them, he would at once perceive that they
differed in a multitude of characters, some of slight
and some of considerable importance.   On enquiry he
would find that they were adapted to live under widely
different climates, and that they differed somewhat in
bodily constitution and mental disposition.   If he
were then told that hundreds of similar specimens
could be brought from the same countries, he would
assuredly declare that they were as good species as
many to which he had been in the habit of affixing
specific names.   This conclusion would be greatly
strengthened as soon as he had ascertained that these
forms had all retained the same character for many
centuries; and that negroes, apparently identical with

---

[4] Wallace, 'The Malay Archipelago,' vol. ii. 1869, p. 178.

existing negroes, had lived at least 4000 years ago.[5]
He would also hear, on the authority of an excellent
observer, Dr. Lund,[6] that the human skulls found in
the caves of Brazil, entombed with many extinct
mammals, belonged to the same type as that now
prevailing throughout the American Continent.

Our naturalist would then perhaps turn to geographical distribution, and he would probably declare
that those forms must be distinct species, which differ
not only in appearance, but are fitted for hot, as well as
damp or dry countries, and for the Arctic regions. He
might appeal to the fact that no species in the group
next to man—namely, the Quadrumana, can resist a
low temperature, or any considerable change of climate;
and that the species which come nearest to man have
never been reared to maturity, even under the temperate climate of Europe. He would be deeply im-

[5] With respect to the figures
in the famous Egyptian caves
of Abou-Simbel, M. Pouchet
says ('The Plurality of the
Human Races,' Eng. translat.,
1864, p. 50), that he was far
from finding recognisable representations of the dozen or more
nations which some authors believe that they can recognise.
Even some of the most strongly-
marked races cannot be identi-
fied with that degree of una-
nimity which might have been
expected from what has been
written on the subject. Thus
Messrs. Nott and Gliddon
('Types of Mankind,' p. 148),
state that Rameses II., or the
Great, has features superbly
European; whereas Knox, another firm believer in the specific
distinctness of the races of man

('Races of Man,' 1850, p. 201),
speaking of young Memnon (the
same as Rameses II., as I am
informed by Mr. Birch), insists
in the strongest manner that he
is identical in character with the
Jews of Antwerp. Again, when
I looked at the statue of Amu-
noph III., I agreed with two
officers of the establishment,
both competent judges, that he
had a strongly-marked negro
type of features; but Messrs.
Nott and Gliddon (ibid. p. 146,
fig. 53), describe him as a hybrid, but not of "negro inter-
mixture."

[6] As quoted by Nott and
Gliddon, 'Types of Mankind,'
1854, p. 439. They give also
corroborative evidence; but C.
Vogt thinks that the subject
requires further investigation.

pressed with the fact, first noticed by Agassiz,[7] that the different races of man are distributed over the world in the same zoological provinces, as those inhabited by undoubtedly distinct species and genera of mammals. This is manifestly the case with the Australian, Mongolian, and Negro races of man; in a less well-marked manner with the Hottentots; but plainly with the Papuans and Malays, who are separated, as Mr. Wallace has shewn, by nearly the same line which divides the great Malayan and Australian zoological provinces. The Aborigines of America range throughout the Continent; and this at first appears opposed to the above rule, for most of the productions of the Southern and Northern halves differ widely: yet some few living forms, as the opossum, range from the one into the other, as did formerly some of the gigantic Edentata. The Esquimaux, like other Arctic animals, extend round the whole polar regions. It should be observed that the amount of difference between the mammals of the several zoological provinces does not correspond with the degree of separation between the latter; so that it can hardly be considered as an anomaly that the Negro differs more, and the American much less from the other races of man, than do the mammals of the African and American continents from the mammals of the other provinces. Man, it may be added, does not appear to have aboriginally inhabited any oceanic island; and in this respect, he resembles the other members of his class.

In determining whether the supposed varieties of the same kind of domestic animal should be ranked as

[7] 'Diversity of Origin of the Human Races,' in the 'Christian Examiner,' July, 1850.

such, or as specifically distinct, that is, whether any of
them are descended from distinct wild species, every
naturalist would lay much stress on the fact of their
external parasites being specifically distinct. All the
more stress would be laid on this fact, as it would be
an exceptional one; for I am informed by Mr. Denny
that the most different kinds of dogs, fowls, and
pigeons, in England, are infested by the same species
of Pediculi or lice. Now Mr. A. Murray has carefully
examined the Pediculi collected in different countries
from the different races of man;[8] and he finds that
they differ, not only in colour, but in the structure of
their claws and limbs. In every case in which many
specimens were obtained the differences were constant.
The surgeon of a whaling ship in the Pacific assured
me that when the Pediculi, with which some Sandwich
Islanders on board swarmed, strayed on to the bodies
of the English sailors, they died in the course of three
or four days. These Pediculi were darker coloured,
and appeared different from those proper to the natives
of Chiloe in South America, of which he gave me
specimens. These, again, appeared larger and much
softer than European lice. Mr. Murray procured four
kinds from Africa, namely, from the Negroes of the
Eastern and Western coasts, from the Hottentots and
Kaffirs; two kinds from the natives of Australia; two
from North and two from South America. In these
latter cases it may be presumed that the Pediculi came
from natives inhabiting different districts. With
insects slight structural differences, if constant, are
generally esteemed of specific value: and the fact of
the races of man being infested by parasites, which

[8] 'Transact. R. Soc. of Edinburgh,' vol. xxii. 1861, p. 567.

appear to be specifically distinct, might fairly be urged as an argument that the races themselves ought to be classed as distinct species.

Our supposed naturalist having proceeded thus far in his investigation, would next enquire whether the races of men, when crossed, were in any degree sterile. He might consult the work[9] of Professor Broca, a cautious and philosophical observer, and in this he would find good evidence that some races were quite fertile together, but evidence of an opposite nature in regard to other races. Thus it has been asserted that the native women of Australia and Tasmania rarely produce children to European men; the evidence, however, on this head has now been shewn to be almost valueless. The half-castes are killed by the pure blacks: and an account has lately been published of eleven half-caste youths murdered and burnt at the same time, whose remains were found by the police.[10] Again, it has often been said that when mulattoes intermarry, they produce few children; on the other hand, Dr. Bachman, of Charleston,[11] positively asserts that he has known mulatto families which have intermarried for several generations, and have continued on an average as fertile as either pure whites or pure blacks. Enquiries formerly made by Sir C. Lyell on

[9] 'On the Phenomena of Hybridity in the Genus Homo,' Eng. translat. 1864.

[10] See the interesting letter by Mr. T. A. Murray, in the 'Anthropolog. Review,' April, 1868, p. liii. In this letter Count Strzelecki's statement that Australian women who have borne children to a white man, are afterwards sterile with their own race, is disproved. M. A. de Quatrefages has also collected ('Revue des Cours Scientifiques,' March, 1869, p. 239), much evidence that Australians and Europeans are not sterile when crossed.

[11] 'An Examination of Prof. Agassiz's Sketch of the Nat. Provinces of the Animal World,' Charleston, 1855, p. 44.

this subject led him, as he informs me, to the same conclusion.[12]   In the United States the census for the year 1854 included, according to Dr. Bachman, 405,751 mulattoes; and this number, considering all the circumstances of the case, seems small; but it may partly be accounted for by the degraded and anomalous position of the class, and by the profligacy of the women.   A certain amount of absorption of mulattoes into negroes must always be in progress; and this would lead to an apparent diminution of the former. The inferior vitality of mulattoes is spoken of in a trustworthy work[13] as a well-known phenomenon; and this, although a different consideration from their lessened fertility, may perhaps be advanced as a proof of the specific distinctness of the parent races.   No doubt both animal and vegetable hybrids, when produced from extremely distinct species, are liable to premature death; but the parents of mulattoes cannot be put under the category of extremely distinct species. The common Mule, so notorious for long life and vigour, and yet so sterile, shews how little necessary connection there is in hybrids between lessened fertility and vitality; other analogous cases could be cited.

[12] Dr. Rohlfs writes to me that he found the mixed races in the Great Sahara, derived from Arabs, Berbers, and Negroes of three tribes, extraordinarily fertile.   On the other hand, Mr. Winwood Reade informs me that the Negroes on the Gold Coast, though admiring white men and mulattoes, have a maxim that mulattoes should not intermarry, as the children are few and sickly.   This belief, as Mr. Reade remarks, deserves attention, as white men have visited and resided on the Gold Coast for four hundred years, so that the natives have had ample time to gain knowledge through experience.

[13] 'Military and Anthropolog. Statistics of American Soldiers,' by B. A. Gould, 1869, p. 319.

Even if it should hereafter be proved that all the races of men were perfectly fertile together, he who was inclined from other reasons to rank them as distinct species, might with justice argue that fertility and sterility are not safe criterions of specific distinctness. We know that these qualities are easily affected by changed conditions of life, or by close inter-breeding, and that they are governed by highly complex laws, for instance, that of the unequal fertility of converse crosses between the same two species. With forms which must be ranked as undoubted species, a perfect series exists from those which are absolutely sterile when crossed, to those which are almost or completely fertile. The degrees of sterility do not coincide strictly with the degrees of difference between the parents in external structure or habits of life. Man in many respects may be compared with those animals which have long been domesticated, and a large body of evidence can be advanced in favour of the Pallasian doctrine,[14] that domestication tends to eliminate the

[14] 'The Variation of Animals and Plants under Domestication,' vol. ii. p. 109. I may here remind the reader that the sterility of species when crossed is not a specially-acquired quality, but, like the incapacity of certain trees to be grafted together, is incidental on other acquired differences. The nature of these differences is unknown, but they relate more especially to the reproductive system, and much less so to external structure or to ordinary differences in constitution. One important element in the sterility of crossed species apparently lies in one or both having been long habituated to fixed conditions; for we know that changed conditions have a special influence on the reproductive system, and we have good reason to believe (as before remarked) that the fluctuating conditions of domestication tend to eliminate that sterility which is so general with species, in a natural state, when crossed. It has elsewhere been shewn by me (ibid. vol. ii. p. 185, and 'Origin of Species,' 5th edit. p. 317), that the sterility of crossed species has not been acquired through natural selection: we can see that when two

sterility which is so general a result of the crossing of
species in a state of nature.   From these several considerations, it may be justly urged that the perfect
fertility of the intercrossed races of man, if established,
would not absolutely preclude us from ranking them
as distinct species.

Independently of fertility, the characters presented
by the offspring from a cross have been thought to
indicate whether or not the parent-forms ought to be
ranked as species or varieties; but after carefully
studying the evidence, I have come to the conclusion
that no general rules of this kind can be trusted.   The
ordinary result of a cross is the production of a blended
or intermediate form; but in certain cases some of the
offspring take closely after one parent-form, and some
after the other.   This is especially apt to occur when
the parents differ in characters which first appeared as
sudden variations or monstrosities.[15]   I refer to this

---

forms have already been rendered very sterile, it is scarcely
possible that their sterility
should be augmented by the
preservation or survival of the
more and more sterile individuals; for, as the sterility increases, fewer and fewer offspring
will be produced from which to
breed, and at last only single
individuals will be produced at
the rarest intervals.   But there
is even a higher grade of sterility
than this.   Both Gärtner and
Kölreuter have proved that in
genera of plants, including many
species, a series can be formed
from species which, when crossed,
yield fewer and fewer seeds, to
species which never produce a

single seed, but yet are affected
by the pollen of the other species,
as shewn by the swelling of the
germen.   It is here manifestly
impossible to select the more
sterile individuals, which have
already ceased to yield seeds; so
that the acme of sterility, when
the germen alone is affected,
cannot have been gained through
selection.   This acme, and no
doubt the other grades of sterility, are the incidental results
of certain unknown differences
in the constitution of the reproductive system of the species
which are crossed.

[15] 'The Variation of Animals,'
&c., vol. ii. p. 92.

point, because Dr. Rohlfs informs me that he has frequently seen in Africa the offspring of negroes crossed with members of other races, either completely black or completely white, or rarely piebald. On the other hand, it is notorious that in America mulattoes commonly present an intermediate appearance.

We have now seen that a naturalist might feel himself fully justified in ranking the races of man as distinct species; for he has found that they are distinguished by many differences in structure and constitution, some being of importance. These differences have, also, remained nearly constant for very long periods of time. Our naturalist will have been in some degree influenced by the enormous range of man, which is a great anomaly in the class of mammals, if mankind be viewed as a single species. He will have been struck with the distribution of the several so-called races, which accords with that of other undoubtedly distinct species of mammals. Finally, he might urge that the mutual fertility of all the races has not as yet been fully proved, and even if proved would not be an absolute proof of their specific identity.

On the other side of the question, if our supposed naturalist were to enquire whether the forms of man keep distinct like ordinary species, when mingled together in large numbers in the same country, he would immediately discover that this was by no means the case. In Brazil he would behold an immense mongrel population of Negroes and Portuguese; in Chiloe, and other parts of South America, he would behold the whole population consisting of Indians and

Spaniards blended in various degrees.[16] In many parts
of the same continent he would meet with the most
complex crosses between Negroes, Indians, and Europeans; and judging from the vegetable kingdom, such
triple crosses afford the severest test of the mutual
fertility of the parent forms. In one island of the
Pacific he would find a small population of mingled
Polynesian and English blood; and in the Fiji Archipelago a population of Polynesian and Negritos crossed
in all degrees. Many analogous cases could be added;
for instance, in Africa. Hence the races of man are
not sufficiently distinct to inhabit the same country
without fusion; and the absence of fusion affords the
usual and best test of specific distinctness.

Our naturalist would likewise be much disturbed as
soon as he perceived that the distinctive characters of
all the races were highly variable. This fact strikes
every one on first beholding the negro slaves in Brazil,
who have been imported from all parts of Africa. The
same remark holds good with the Polynesians, and with
many other races. It may be doubted whether any
character can be named which is distinctive of a race
and is constant. Savages, even within the limits of
the same tribe, are not nearly so uniform in character,
as has been often asserted. Hottentot women offer
certain peculiarities, more strongly marked than those
occurring in any other race, but these are known not to
be of constant occurrence. In the several American
tribes, colour and hairiness differ considerably; as does

[16] M. de Quatrefages has given
('Anthropolog. Review,' Jan.
1869, p. 22), an interesting account of the success and energy
of the Paulistas in Brazil, who
are a much crossed race of Portuguese and Indians, with a
mixture of the blood of other
races.

colour to a certain degree, and the shape of the features greatly, in the Negroes of Africa. The shape of the skull varies much in some races;[17] and so it is with every other character. Now all naturalists have learnt by dearly bought experience, how rash it is to attempt to define species by the aid of inconstant characters.

But the most weighty of all the arguments against treating the races of man as distinct species, is that they graduate into each other, independently in many cases, as far as we can judge, of their having intercrossed. Man has been studied more carefully than any other animal, and yet there is the greatest possible diversity amongst capable judges whether he should be classed as a single species or race, or as two (Virey), as three (Jacquinot), as four (Kant), five (Blumenbach), six (Buffon), seven (Hunter), eight (Agassiz), eleven (Pickering), fifteen (Bory St. Vincent), sixteen (Desmoulins), twenty-two (Morton), sixty (Crawfurd), or as sixty-three, according to Burke.[18] This diversity of judgment does not prove that the races ought not to be ranked as species, but it shews that they graduate into each other, and that it is hardly possible to discover clear distinctive characters between them.

Every naturalist who has had the misfortune to undertake the description of a group of highly varying organisms, has encountered cases (I speak after expe-

[17] For instance, with the aborigines of America and Australia. Prof. Huxley says ('Transact. Internat. Congress of Prehist. Arch.' 1868, p. 105), that the skulls of many South Germans and Swiss are "as "short and as broad as those of "the Tartars," &c.

[18] See a good discussion on this subject in Waitz, 'Introduct. to Anthropology,' Eng. translat. 1863, pp. 198–208, 227. I have taken some of the above statements from H. Tuttle's 'Origin and Antiquity of Physical Man,' Boston, 1866, p. 35.

rience) precisely like that of man; and if of a cautious
disposition, he will end by uniting all the forms which
graduate into each other, under a single species; for
he will say to himself that he has no right to give
names to objects which he cannot define. Cases of this
kind occur in the Order which includes man, namely in
certain genera of monkeys; whilst in other genera, as
in Cercopithecus, most of the species can be determined
with certainty. In the American genus Cebus, the
various forms are ranked by some naturalists as species,
by others as mere geographical races. Now if numerous specimens of Cebus were collected from all parts
of South America, and those forms which at present
appear to be specifically distinct, were found to graduate
into each other by close steps, they would usually be
ranked as mere varieties or races; and this course has
been followed by most naturalists with respect to the
races of man. Nevertheless, it must be confessed that
there are forms, at least in the vegetable kingdom,[19]
which we cannot avoid naming as species, but which
are connected together by numberless gradations, independently of intercrossing.

Some naturalists have lately employed the term
" sub-species " to designate forms which possess many
of the characteristics of true species, but which hardly
deserve so high a rank. Now if we reflect on the
weighty arguments above given, for raising the races
of man to the dignity of species, and the insuperable
difficulties on the other side in defining them, it seems
that the term " sub-species " might here be used with

[19] Prof. Nägeli has carefully
described several striking cases
in his ' Botanische Mittheilun-
gen,' B. ii. 1866, ss. 294–369.
Prof. Asa Gray has made analogous remarks on some intermediate forms in the Compositæ of
N. America.

propriety. But from long habit the term " race " will perhaps always be employed. The choice of terms is only so far important in that it is desirable to use, as far as possible, the same terms for the same degrees of difference. Unfortunately this can rarely be done : for the larger genera generally include closely-allied forms, which can be distinguished only with much difficulty, whilst the smaller genera within the same family include forms that are perfectly distinct ; yet all must be ranked equally as species. So again, species within the same large genus by no means resemble each other to the same degree : on the contrary, some of them can generally be arranged in little groups round other species, like satellites round planets.[20]

The question whether mankind consists of one or several species has of late years been much discussed by anthropologists, who are divided into the two schools of monogenists and polygenists. Those who do not admit the principle of evolution, must look at species as separate creations, or as in some manner as distinct entities ; and they must decide what forms of man they will consider as species by the analogy of the method commonly pursued in ranking other organic beings as species. But it is a hopeless endeavour to decide this point, until some definition of the term " species " is generally accepted ; and the definition must not include an indeterminate element such as an act of creation. We might as well attempt without any definition to decide whether a certain number of houses should be called a village, town, or city. We have a practical illustration of the difficulty in the never-ending doubts

[20] 'Origin of Species,' 5th edit. p. 68.

whether many closely-allied mammals, birds, insects, and plants, which represent each other respectively in North America and Europe, should be ranked as species or geographical races; and the like holds true of the productions of many islands situated at some little distance from the nearest continent.

Those naturalists, on the other hand, who admit the principle of evolution, and this is now admitted by the majority of rising men, will feel no doubt that all the races of man are descended from a single primitive stock; whether or not they may think fit to designate the races as distinct species, for the sake of expressing their amount of difference.[21] With our domestic animals the question whether the various races have arisen from one or more species is somewhat different. Although it may be admitted that all the races, as well as all the natural species within the same genus, have sprung from the same primitive stock, yet it is a fit subject for discussion, whether all the domestic races of the dog, for instance, have acquired their present amount of difference since some one species was first domesticated by man; or whether they owe some of their characters to inheritance from distinct species, which had already been differentiated in a state of nature. With man no such question can arise, for he cannot be said to have been domesticated at any particular period.

During an early stage in the divergence of the races of man from a common stock, the differences between the races and their number must have been small; consequently as far as their distinguishing characters

[21] See Prof. Huxley to this effect in the 'Fortnightly Review,' 1865, p. 275.

are concerned, they then had less claim to rank as distinct species than the existing so-called races. Nevertheless, so arbitrary is the term of species, that such early races would perhaps have been ranked by some naturalists as distinct species, if their differences, although extremely slight, had been more constant than they are at present, and had not graduated into each other.

It is however possible, though far from probable, that the early progenitors of man might formerly have diverged much in character, until they became more unlike each other than any now existing races; but that subsequently, as suggested by Vogt,[22] they converged in character. When man selects the offspring of two distinct species for the same object, he sometimes induces a considerable amount of convergence, as far as general appearance is concerned. This is the case, as shown by Von Nathusius,[23] with the improved breeds of the pig, which are descended from two distinct species; and in a less marked manner with the improved breeds of cattle. A great anatomist, Gratiolet, maintains that the anthropomorphous apes do not form a natural sub-group; but that the orang is a highly developed gibbon or semnopithecus, the chimpanzee a highly developed macacus, and the gorilla a highly developed mandrill. If this conclusion, which rests almost exclusively on brain-characters, be admitted, we should have a case of convergence at least in external characters, for the

---

[22] 'Lectures on Man,' Eng. translat. 1864, p. 468.

[23] 'Die Racen des Schweines,' 1860, s. 46. 'Vorstudien für Geschichte, &c., Schweineschädel,' 1864, s. 104. With respect to cattle, see M. de Quatrefages, 'Unité de l'Espèce Humaine,' 1861, p. 119.

anthropomorphous apes are certainly more like each other in many points, than they are to other apes. All analogical resemblances, as of a whale to a fish, may indeed be said to be cases of convergence; but this term has never been applied to superficial and adaptive resemblances. It would, however, be extremely rash to attribute to convergence close similarity of character in many points of structure amongst the modified descendants of widely distinct beings. The form of a crystal is determined solely by the molecular forces, and it is not surprising that dissimilar substances should sometimes assume the same form; but with organic beings we should bear in mind that the form of each depends on an infinity of complex relations, namely on variations, due to causes far too intricate to be followed,—on the nature of the variations preserved, these depending on the physical conditions, and still more on the surrounding organisms which compete with each,—and lastly, on inheritance (in itself a fluctuating element) from innumerable progenitors, all of which have had their forms determined through equally complex relations. It appears incredible that the modified descendants of two organisms, if these differed from each other in a marked manner, should ever afterwards converge so closely as to lead to a near approach to identity throughout their whole organisation. In the case of the convergent races of pigs above referred to, evidence of their descent from two primitive stocks is, according to Von Nathusius, still plainly retained, in certain bones of their skulls. If the races of man had descended, as is supposed by some naturalists, from two or more species, which differed from each other as much, or nearly as much, as does the orang from the gorilla, it can hardly be doubted that marked differences in the structure of certain bones would still be discoverable in man as he now exists.

Although the existing races of man differ in many respects, as in colour, hair, shape of skull, proportions of the body, &c., yet if their whole structure be taken into consideration they are found to resemble each other closely in a multitude of points. Many of these are of so unimportant or of so singular a nature, that it is extremely improbable that they should have been independently acquired by aboriginally distinct species or races. The same remark holds good with equal or greater force with respect to the numerous points of mental similarity between the most distinct races of man. The American aborigines, Negroes and Europeans are as different from each other in mind as any three races that can be named; yet I was incessantly struck, whilst living with the Fuegians on board the " Beagle," with the many little traits of character, shewing how similar their minds were to ours; and so it was with a full-blooded negro with whom I happened once to be intimate.

He who will read Mr. Tylor's and Sir J. Lubbock's interesting works[24] can hardly fail to be deeply impressed with the close similarity between the men of all races in tastes, dispositions and habits. This is shewn by the pleasure which they all take in dancing, rude music, acting, painting, tattooing, and otherwise

[24] Tylor's 'Early History of Mankind,' 1865: with respect to gesture-language, see p. 54.   Lubbock's 'Prehistoric Times,' 2nd edit. 1869.

decorating themselves; in their mutual comprehension of gesture-language, by the same expression in their features, and by the same inarticulate cries, when excited by the same emotions. This similarity, or rather identity, is striking, when contrasted with the different expressions and cries made by distinct species of monkeys. There is good evidence that the art of shooting with bows and arrows has not been handed down from any common progenitor of mankind, yet as Westropp and Nilsson have remarked,[25] the stone arrow-heads, brought from the most distant parts of the world, and manufactured at the most remote periods, are almost identical; and this fact can only be accounted for by the various races having similar inventive or mental powers. The same observation has been made by archæologists[26] with respect to certain widely-prevalent ornaments, such as zig-zags, &c.; and with respect to various simple beliefs and customs, such as the burying of the dead under megalithic structures. I remember observing in South America,[27] that there, as in so many other parts of the world, men have generally chosen the summits of lofty hills, to throw up piles of stones, either as a record of some remarkable event, or for burying their dead.

Now when naturalists observe a close agreement in numerous small details of habits, tastes, and dispositions between two or more domestic races, or

[25] 'On Analogous Forms of Implements,' in ' Memoirs of Anthropolog. Soc.' by H. M. Westropp. 'The Primitive Inhabitants of Scandinavia,' Eng. translat. edited by Sir J. Lubbock, 1868, p. 104.

[26] Westropp, 'On Cromlechs,' &c., 'Journal of Ethnological Soc.' as given in 'Scientific Opinion,' June 2nd, 1869, p. 3.

[27] 'Journal of Researches: Voyage of the "Beagle," ' p. 46.

between nearly-allied natural forms, they use this fact as an argument that they are descended from a common progenitor who was thus endowed; and consequently that all should be classed under the same species. The same argument may be applied with much force to the races of man.

As it is improbable that the numerous and unimportant points of resemblance between the several races of man in bodily structure and mental faculties (I do not here refer to similar customs) should all have been independently acquired, they must have been inherited from progenitors who had these same characters. We thus gain some insight into the early state of man, before he had spread step by step over the face of the earth. The spreading of man to regions widely separated by the sea, no doubt, preceded any great amount of divergence of character in the several races; for otherwise we should sometimes meet with the same race in distinct continents; and this is never the case. Sir J. Lubbock, after comparing the arts now practised by savages in all parts of the world, specifies those which man could not have known, when he first wandered from his original birthplace; for if once learnt they would never have been forgotten.[28] He thus shews that " the spear, which is " but a development of the knife-point, and the club, " which is but a long hammer, are the only things left." He admits, however, that the art of making fire probably had been already discovered, for it is common to all the races now existing, and was known to the ancient cave-inhabitants of Europe. Perhaps the art of making rude canoes or rafts was likewise known;

[28] 'Prehistoric Times,' 1869, p. 574.

but as man existed at a remote epoch, when the land
in many places stood at a very different level to what
it does now, he would have been able, without the aid
of canoes, to have spread widely. Sir J. Lubbock
further remarks how improbable it is that our earliest
ancestors could have " counted as high as ten, con-
" sidering that so many races now in existence cannot
" get beyond four." Nevertheless, at this early period,
the intellectual and social faculties of man could
hardly have been inferior in any extreme degree to
those possessed at present by the lowest savages;
otherwise primeval man could not have been so
eminently successful in the struggle for life, as proved
by his early and wide diffusion.

From the fundamental differences between certain
languages, some philologists have inferred that when
man first became widely diffused, he was not a
speaking animal; but it may be suspected that languages, far less perfect than any now spoken, aided by
gestures, might have been used, and yet have left
no traces on subsequent and more highly-developed
tongues. Without the use of some language, however
imperfect, it appears doubtful whether man's intellect could have risen to the standard implied by his
dominant position at an early period.

Whether primeval man, when he possessed but few
arts, and those of the rudest kind, and when his power
of language was extremely imperfect, would have
deserved to be called man, must depend on the
definition which we employ. In a series of forms
graduating insensibly from some ape-like creature to
man as he now exists, it would be impossible to fix on
any definite point when the term " man " ought to be

used. But this is a matter of very little importance. So again, it is almost a matter of indifference whether the so-called races of man are thus designated, or are ranked as species or sub-species; but the latter term appears the more appropriate. Finally, we may conclude that when the principle of evolution is generally accepted, as it surely will be before long, the dispute between the monogenists and the polygenists will die a silent and unobserved death.

One other question ought not to be passed over without notice, namely, whether, as is sometimes assumed, each sub-species or race of man has sprung from a single pair of progenitors. With our domestic animals a new race can readily be formed by carefully matching the varying offspring from a single pair, or even from a single individual possessing some new character; but most of our races have been formed, not intentionally from a selected pair, but unconsciously by the preservation of many individuals which have varied, however slightly, in some useful or desired manner. If in one country stronger and heavier horses, and in another country lighter and fleeter ones, were habitually preferred, we may feel sure that two distinct sub-breeds would be produced in the course of time, without any one pair having been separated and bred from, in either country. Many races have been thus formed, and their manner of formation is closely analogous to that of natural species. We know, also, that the horses taken to the Falkland Islands have, during successive generations, become smaller and weaker, whilst those which have run wild on the Pampas have acquired larger and coarser heads; and such changes are manifestly due, not to any one pair, but to all the individuals having been subjected to the same conditions, aided, perhaps, by the principle of reversion. The new sub-breeds in such cases are not descended from any single pair, but from many individuals which have varied in different degrees, but in the same general manner; and we may conclude that the races of man have been similarly produced, the modifications being either the direct result of exposure to different conditions, or the indirect result of some form of selection. But to this latter subject we shall presently return.

On the Extinction of the Races of Man.—The partial or complete extinction of many races and sub-races of man is historically known. Humboldt saw in South America a parrot which was the sole living creature that could speak a word of the language of a lost tribe. Ancient monuments and stone implements found in all parts of the world, about which no tradition has been preserved by the present inhabitants, indicate much extinction. Some small and broken tribes, remnants of former races, still survive in isolated and generally mountainous districts. In Europe the ancient races were all, according to Schaaffhausen,[29] " lower in the " scale than the rudest living savages; " they must therefore have differed, to a certain extent, from any existing race. The remains described by Professor Broca from Les Eyzies, though they unfortunately appear to have belonged to a single family, indicate a race with a most singular combination of low or simious, and of high characteristics. This race

[29] Translation in 'Anthropological Review,' Oct. 1868, p. 431.

is "entirely different from any other, ancient or "modern, that we have heard of."[30] It differed, therefore, from the quaternary race of the caverns of Belgium.

Man can long resist conditions which appear extremely unfavourable for his existence.[31] He has long lived in the extreme regions of the North, with no wood for his canoes or implements, and with only blubber as fuel, and melted snow as drink. In the southern extremity of America the Fuegians survive without the protection of clothes, or of any building worthy to be called a hovel. In South Africa the aborigines wander over arid plains, where dangerous beasts abound. Man can withstand the deadly influence of the Terai at the foot of the Himalaya, and the pestilential shores of tropical Africa.

Extinction follows chiefly from the competition of tribe with tribe, and race with race. Various checks are always in action, serving to keep down the numbers of each savage tribe,—such as periodical famines, nomadic habits and the consequent deaths of infants, prolonged suckling, wars, accidents, sickness, licentiousness, the stealing of women, infanticide, and especially lessened fertility. If any one of these checks increases in power, even slightly, the tribe thus affected tends to decrease; and when of two adjoining tribes one becomes less numerous and less powerful than the other, the contest is soon settled by war, slaughter, cannibalism, slavery, and absorption. Even when a weaker tribe is not thus abruptly swept away, if it

[30] 'Transact. Internat. Congress of Prehistoric Arch.' 1868, pp. 172–175. See also Broca (translation) in 'Anthropological Review,' Oct., 1868, p. 410.

[31] Dr. Gerland, 'Ueber das Aussterben der Naturvölker,' 1868, s. 82.

once begins to decrease, it generally goes on decreasing until it becomes extinct.[32]

When civilised nations come into contact with barbarians the struggle is short, except where a deadly climate gives its aid to the native race. Of the causes which lead to the victory of civilised nations, some are plain and simple, others complex and obscure. We can see that the cultivation of the land will be fatal in many ways to savages, for they cannot, or will not, change their habits. New diseases and vices have in some cases proved highly destructive; and it appears that a new disease often causes much death, until those who are most susceptible to its destructive influence are gradually weeded out;[33] and so it may be with the evil effects from spirituous liquors, as well as with the unconquerably strong taste for them shewn by so many savages. It further appears, mysterious as is the fact, that the first meeting of distinct and separated people generates disease.[34] Mr. Sproat, who in Vancouver Island closely attended to the subject of extinction, believed that changed habits of life, consequent on the advent of Europeans, induces much ill health. He lays, also, great stress on the apparently trifling cause that the natives become " bewildered and dull " by the new life around them; they lose the motives " for exertion, and get no new ones in their place."[35]

[32] Gerland (ibid. s. 12) gives facts in support of this statement.

[33] See remarks to this effect in Sir H. Holland's 'Medical Notes and Reflections,' 1839, p. 390.

[34] I have collected ('Journal of Researches, Voyage of the "Beagle,"' p. 435) a good many cases bearing on this subject; see also Gerland, ibid. s. 8. Poeppig speaks of the "breath "of civilisation as poisonous to " savages."

[35] Sproat, 'Scenes and Studies of Savage Life,' 1868, p. 284.

The grade of their civilisation seems to be a most important element in the success of competing nations. A few centuries ago Europe feared the inroads of Eastern barbarians; now any such fear would be ridiculous. It is a more curious fact, as Mr. Bagehot has remarked, that savages did not formerly waste away before the classical nations, as they now do before modern civilised nations; had they done so, the old moralists would have mused over the event; but there is no lament in any writer of that period over the perishing barbarians.[36] The most potent of all the causes of extinction, appears in many cases to be lessened fertility and ill-health, especially amongst the children, arising from changed conditions of life, notwithstanding that the new conditions may not be injurious in themselves. I am much indebted to Mr. H. H. Howorth for having called my attention to this subject, and for having given me information respecting it. I have collected the following cases.

When Tasmania was first colonised the natives were roughly estimated by some at 7000 and by others at 20,000. Their number was soon greatly reduced, chiefly by fighting with the English and with each other. After the famous hunt by all the colonists, when the remaining natives delivered themselves up to the government, they consisted only of 120 individuals,[37] who were in 1832 transported to Flinders Island. This island, situated between Tasmania and Australia, is forty miles long, and from twelve to eighteen miles

---

[36] Bagehot, ' Physics and Politics,' ' Fortnightly Review,' April 1, 1868, p. 455.

[37] All the statements here given are taken from ' The last of the Tasmanians,' by J. Bonwick, 1870.

broad : it seems healthy, and the natives were well
treated.   Nevertheless, they suffered greatly in health.
In 1834 they consisted (Bonwick, p. 250) of forty-seven
adult males, forty-eight adult females, and sixteen
children, or in all of 111 souls.   In 1835 only one
hundred were left.   As they continued rapidly to decrease, and as they themselves thought that they
should not perish so quickly elsewhere, they were
removed in 1847 to Oyster Cove in the southern part
of Tasmania.   They then consisted (Dec. 20th, 1847)
of fourteen men, twenty-two women and ten children.[38]
But the change of site did no good.   Disease and death
still pursued them, and in 1864 one man (who died in
1869), and three elderly women alone survived.   The
infertility of the women is even a more remarkable
fact than the liability of all to ill-health and death.
At the time when only nine women were left at Oyster
Cove, they told Mr. Bonwick (p. 386), that only two
had ever borne children : and these two had together
produced only three children !

With respect to the cause of this extraordinary state
of things, Dr. Story remarks that death followed the
attempts to civilise the natives.   "If left to themselves
"to roam as they were wont and undisturbed, they
"would have reared more children, and there would
"have been less mortality."   Another careful observer
of the natives, Mr. Davis, remarks, "The births have
"been few and the deaths numerous.   This may have
"been in a great measure owing to their change of
"living and food ; but more so to their banishment
"from the mainland of Van Diemen's Land, and con-

[38] This is the statement of the Governor of Tasmania, Sir W.
Denison, 'Varieties of Vice-Regal Life,' 1870, vol. i. p. 67.

"sequent depression of spirits" (Bonwick, pp. 388, 390).

Similar facts have been observed in two widely different parts of Australia. The celebrated explorer, Mr. Gregory, told Mr. Bonwick, that in Queensland "the want of reproduction was being already felt with "the blacks, even in the most recently settled parts, "and that decay would set in." Of thirteen aborigines from Shark's Bay who visited Murchison River, twelve died of consumption within three months.[39]

The decrease of the Maories of New Zealand has been carefully investigated by Mr. Fenton, in an admirable Report, from which all the following statements, with one exception, are taken.[40] The decrease in number since 1830 is admitted by every one, including the natives themselves, and is still steadily progressing. Although it has hitherto been found impossible to take an actual census of the natives, their numbers were carefully estimated by residents in many districts. The result seems trustworthy, and shows that during the fourteen years, previous to 1858, the decrease was 19·42 per cent. Some of the tribes, thus carefully examined, lived above a hundred miles apart, some on the coast, some inland ; and their means of subsistence and habits differed to a certain extent (p. 28). The total number in 1858 was believed to be 53,700, and in 1872, after a second interval of fourteen years, another census was taken, and the number is given as only 36,359, shewing a decrease of 32·29 per cent ![41] Mr. Fenton, after shewing in detail the

[39] For these cases, see Bonwick's ' Daily Life of the Tasmanians,' 1870, p. 90 ; and the ' Last of the Tasmanians,' 1870, p. 386.
[40] ' Observations on the Ab-original Inhabitants of New Zealand,' published by the Government, 1859.
[41] ' New Zealand,' by Alex. Kennedy, 1873, p. 47.

insufficiency of the various causes, usually assigned in explanation of this extraordinary decrease, such as new diseases, the profligacy of the women, drunkenness, wars, &c., concludes on weighty grounds that it depends chiefly on the unproductiveness of the women, and on the extraordinary mortality of the young children (pp. 31, 34). In proof of this he shews (p. 33) that in 1844 there was one non-adult for every 2·57 adults; whereas in 1858 there was only one non-adult for every 3·27 adults. The mortality of the adults is also great. He adduces as a further cause of the decrease the inequality of the sexes; for fewer females are born than males. To this latter point, depending perhaps on a widely distinct cause, I shall return in a future chapter. Mr. Fenton contrasts with astonishment the decrease in New Zealand with the increase in Ireland; countries not very dissimilar in climate, and where the inhabitants now follow nearly similar habits. The Maories themselves (p. 35) " attribute their de- " cadence, in some measure, to the introduction of new " food and clothing, and the attendant change of " habits; " and it will be seen, when we consider the influence of changed conditions on fertility, that they are probably right. The diminution began between the years 1830 and 1840; and Mr. Fenton shews (p. 40) that about 1830, the art of manufacturing putrid corn (maize), by long steeping in water, was discovered and largely practised; and this proves that a change of habits was beginning amongst the natives, even when New Zealand was only thinly inhabited by Europeans. When I visited the Bay of Islands in 1835, the dress and food of the inhabitants had already been much modified: they raised potatoes, maize, and

other agricultural produce, and exchanged them for
English manufactured goods and tobacco.

It is evident from many statements in the life of
Bishop Patteson,[42] that the Melanesians of the New
Hebrides and neighbouring archipelagoes, suffered to
an extraordinary degree in health, and perished in
large numbers, when they were removed to New
Zealand, Norfolk Island, and other salubrious places,
in order to be educated as missionaries.

The decrease of the native population of the Sandwich Islands is as notorious as that of New Zealand.
It has been roughly estimated by those best capable of
judging, that when Cook discovered the Islands in
1779, the population amounted to about 300,000.
According to a loose census in 1823, the numbers then
were 142,050. In 1832, and at several subsequent
periods, an accurate census was officially taken, but I
have been able to obtain only the following returns:

YEAR.	NATIVE POPULATION. (Except during 1832 and 1836, when the few foreigners in the islands were included.)	Annual rate of decrease per cent., assuming it to have been uniform between the successive censuses; these censuses being taken at irregular intervals.
1832	130,313	
		4·46
1836	108,579	
		2·47
1853	71,019	
		0·81
1860	67,084	
		2·18
1866	58,765	
		2·17
1872	51,531	

[42] 'Life of J. C. Patteson,' by C. M. Younge, 1874; see more
especially vol. i. p. 530.

We here see that in the interval of forty years, between 1832 and 1872, the population has decreased no less than sixty-eight per cent.! This has been attributed by most writers to the profligacy of the women, to former bloody wars, and to the severe labour imposed on conquered tribes and to newly introduced diseases, which have been on several occasions extremely destructive. No doubt these and other such causes have been highly efficient, and may account for the extraordinary rate of decrease between the years 1832 and 1836; but the most potent of all the causes seems to be lessened fertility. According to Dr. Ruschenberger of the U.S. Navy, who visited these islands between 1835 and 1837, in one district of Hawaii, only twenty-five men out of 1134, and in another district only ten out of 637, had a family with as many as three children. Of eighty married women, only thirty-nine had ever borne children; and "the "official report gives an average of half a child to each "married couple in the whole island." This is almost exactly the same average as with the Tasmanians at Oyster Cove. Jarves, who published his History in 1843, says that "families who have three children are "freed from all taxes; those having more, are rewarded "by gifts of land and other encouragements." This unparalleled enactment by the government well shews how infertile the race had become. The Rev. A. Bishop stated in the Hawaiian 'Spectator' in 1839, that a large proportion of the children die at early ages, and Bishop Staley informs me that this is still the case, just as in New Zealand. This has been attributed to the neglect of the children by the women, but it is probably in large part due to innate weakness of constitution in the children, in relation to the lessened fertility of their parents. There is, moreover, a further resemblance to the case of New Zealand, in the fact that there is a large excess of male over female births: the census of 1872 gives 31,650 males to 25,247 females of all ages, that is 125·36 males for every 100 females; whereas in all civilised countries the females exceed the males. No doubt the profligacy of the women may in part account for their small fertility; but their changed habits of life is a much more probable cause, and which will at the same time account for the increased mortality, especially of the children. The islands were visited by Cook in 1779, by Vancouver in 1794, and often subsequently by whalers. In 1819 missionaries arrived, and found that idolatry had been already abolished, and other changes effected by the king. After this period there was a rapid change in almost all the habits of life of the natives, and they soon became " the most civilised of " the Pacific Islanders." One of my informants, Mr. Coan, who was born on the islands, remarks that the natives have undergone a greater change in their habits of life in the course of fifty years than Englishmen during a thousand years. From information received from Bishop Staley, it does not appear that the poorer classes have ever much changed their diet, although many new kinds of fruit have been introduced, and the sugar-cane is in universal use. Owing, however, to their passion for imitating Europeans, they altered their manner of dressing at an early period, and the use of alcoholic drinks became very general. Although these changes appear inconsiderable, I can well believe, from what is known with respect to animals, that they might suffice to lessen the fertility of the natives.[43]

Lastly, Mr. Macnamara states [44] that the low and degraded inhabitants of the Andaman Islands, on the eastern side of the Gulf of Bengal, are " eminently " susceptible to any change of climate : in fact, take " them away from their island homes, and they are " almost certain to die, and that independently of diet " or extraneous influences." He further states that the inhabitants of the Valley of Nepâl, which is extremely hot in summer, and also the various hill-tribes of India, suffer from dysentery and fever when on the plains ; and they die if they attempt to pass the whole year there.

We thus see that many of the wilder races of man are apt to suffer much in health when subjected to changed conditions or habits of life, and not exclusively from being transported to a new climate.   Mere altera-tions in habits, which do not appear injurious in themselves, seem to have this same effect ; and in several cases the children are particularly liable to suffer.   It has often been said, as Mr. Macnamara remarks, that man can resist with impunity the greatest diversities of climate and other changes ; but

[43] The foregoing statements are taken chiefly from the fol-lowing works : 'Jarves' History of the Hawaiian Islands,' 1843, p. 400–407.   Cheever, 'Life in the Sandwich Islands,' 1851, p. 277.   Ruschenberger is quoted by Bonwick, 'Last of the Tas-manians,' 1870, p. 378.   Bishop is quoted by Sir E. Belcher, 'Voyage Round the World,' 1843, vol. i. p. 272.   I owe the census of the several years to the kindness of Mr. Coan, at the request of Dr. Youmans of New York ; and in most cases I have compared the Youmans figures with those given in several of the above-named works.   I have omitted the census for 1850, as I have seen two widely different numbers given.

[44] 'The Indian Medical Ga-zette,' Nov. 1, 1871, p. 240.

this is true only of the civilised races. Man in his wild condition seems to be in this respect almost as susceptible as his nearest allies, the anthropoid apes, which have never yet survived long, when removed from their native country.

Lessened fertility from changed conditions, as in the case of the Tasmanians, Maories, Sandwich Islanders, and apparently the Australians, is still more interesting than their liability to ill-health and death; for even a slight degree of infertility, combined with those other causes which tend to check the increase of every population, would sooner or later lead to extinction. The diminution of fertility may be explained in some cases by the profligacy of the women (as until lately with the Tahitians), but Mr. Fenton has shewn that this explanation by no means suffices with the New Zealanders, nor does it with the Tasmanians.

In the paper above quoted, Mr. Macnamara gives reasons for believing that the inhabitants of districts subject to malaria are apt to be sterile; but this cannot apply in several of the above cases. Some writers have suggested that the aborigines of islands have suffered in fertility and health from long continued inter-breeding; but in the above cases infertility has coincided too closely with the arrival of Europeans for us to admit this explanation. Nor have we at present any reason to believe that man is highly sensitive to the evil effects of inter-breeding, especially in areas so large as New Zealand, and the Sandwich archipelago with its diversified stations. On the contrary, it is known that the present inhabitants of Norfolk Island are nearly all cousins or near relations, as are the Todas in India, and the inhabitants of some of the Western Islands of Scotland ; and yet they seem not to have suffered in fertility.[45]

A much more probable view is suggested by the analogy of the lower animals. The reproductive system can be shewn to be susceptible to an extraordinary degree (though why we know not) to changed conditions of life; and this susceptibility leads both to beneficial and to evil results. A large collection of facts on this subject is given in chap. xviii. of vol. ii. of my 'Variation of Animals and Plants under Domestication,' I can here give only the briefest abstract ; and every one interested in the subject may consult the above work. Very slight changes increase the health, vigour and fertility of most or all organic beings, whilst other changes are known to render a large number of animals sterile. One of the most familiar cases, is that of tamed elephants not breeding in India ; though they often breed in Ava, where the females are allowed to roam about the forests to some extent, and are thus placed under more natural conditions. The case of various American monkeys, both sexes of which have been kept for many years together in their own countries, and yet have very rarely or never bred, is a more apposite instance, because of their relationship to man. It is remarkable how slight a change in the conditions often induces sterility in a wild animal when captured ; and this is the more strange as all our domesticated animals have

[45] On the close relationship of the Norfolk Islanders, see Sir W. Denison, 'Varieties of Vice-Regal Life,' vol. i., 1870, p. 410. For the Todas, see Col. Marshall's work, 1873, p. 110. For the Western Islands of Scotland, Dr. Mitchell, 'Edinburgh Medical Journal,' March to June, 1865.

become more fertile than they were in a state of nature; and some of them can resist the most unnatural conditions with undiminished fertility.[46] Certain groups of animals are much more liable than others to be affected by captivity; and generally all the species of the same group are affected in the same manner. But sometimes a single species in a group is rendered sterile, whilst the others are not so; on the other hand, a single species may retain its fertility whilst most of the others fail to breed. The males and females of some species when confined, or when allowed to live almost, but not quite free, in their native country, never unite; others thus circumstanced frequently unite but never produce offspring; others again produce some offspring, but fewer than in a state of nature; and as bearing on the above cases of man, it is important to remark that the young are apt to be weak and sickly, or malformed, and to perish at an early age.

Seeing how general is this law of the susceptibility of the reproductive system to changed conditions of life, and that it holds good with our nearest allies, the Quadrumana, I can hardly doubt that it applies to man in his primeval state. Hence if savages of any race are induced suddenly to change their habits of life, they become more or less sterile, and their young offspring suffer in health, in the same manner and from the same cause, as do the elephant and hunting-leopard in India, many monkeys in America, and a host of animals of all kinds, on removal from their natural conditions.

[46] For the evidence on this head, see 'Variation of Animals,' &c., vol. ii. p. 111.

We can see why it is that aborigines, who have long
inhabited islands, and who must have been long
exposed to nearly uniform conditions, should be
specially affected by any change in their habits, as
seems to be the case. Civilised races can certainly
resist changes of all kinds far better than savages;
and in this respect they resemble domesticated animals,
for though the latter sometimes suffer in health
(for instance European dogs in India), yet they are
rarely rendered sterile, though a few such instances
have been recorded.[47] The immunity of civilised races
and domesticated animals is probably due to their
having been subjected to a greater extent, and therefore having grown somewhat more accustomed, to
diversified or varying conditions, than the majority of
wild animals; and to their having formerly im-
migrated or been carried from country to country, and
to different families or sub-races having inter-crossed.
It appears that a cross with civilised races at once
gives to an aboriginal race an immunity from the evil
consequences of changed conditions. Thus the crossed
offspring from the Tahitians and English, when
settled in Pitcairn Island, increased so rapidly that
the Island was soon overstocked; and in June 1856
they were removed to Norfolk Island. They then
consisted of 60 married persons and 134 children,
making a total of 194. Here they likewise increased
so rapidly, that although sixteen of them returned to
Pitcairn Island in 1859, they numbered in January
1868, 300 souls; the males and females being in
exactly equal numbers. What a contrast does this
case present with that of the Tasmanians; the

[47] 'Variation of Animals,' &c., vol. ii. p. 16.

Norfolk Islanders *increased* in only twelve and a half years from 194 to 300; whereas the Tasmanians *decreased* during fifteen years from 120 to 46, of which latter number only ten were children.[48]

So again in the interval between the census of 1866 and 1872 the natives of full blood in the Sandwich Islands decreased by 8081, whilst the half-castes, who are believed to be healthier, increased by 847; but I do not know whether the latter number includes the offspring from the half-castes, or only the half-castes of the first generation.

The cases which I have here given all relate to aborigines, who have been subjected to new conditions as the result of the immigration of civilised men. But sterility and ill-health would probably follow, if savages were compelled by any cause, such as the inroad of a conquering tribe, to desert their homes and to change their habits. It is an interesting circumstance that the chief check to wild animals becoming domesticated, which implies the power of their breeding freely when first captured, and one chief check to wild men, when brought into contact with civilisation, surviving to form a civilised race, is the same, namely, sterility from changed conditions of life.

Finally, although the gradual decrease and ultimate extinction of the races of man is a highly complex problem, depending on many causes which differ in different places and at different times; it is the same problem as that presented by the extinction of one of

---

[48] These details are taken from 'The Mutineers of the "Bounty,"' by Lady Belcher, 1870; and from 'Pitcairn Island,' ordered to be printed by the House of Commons, May 29th, 1863. The following statements about the Sandwich Islanders are from the 'Honolulu Gazette,' and from Mr. Coan.

the higher animals—of the fossil horse, for instance, which disappeared from South America, soon afterwards to be replaced, within the same districts, by countless troups of the Spanish horse. The New Zealander seems conscious of this parallelism, for he compares his future fate with that of the native rat now almost exterminated by the European rat. Though the difficulty is great to our imagination, and really great, if we wish to ascertain the precise causes and their manner of action, it ought not to be so to our reason, as long as we keep steadily in mind that the increase of each species and each race is constantly checked in various ways; so that if any new check, even a slight one, be superadded, the race will surely decrease in number; and decreasing numbers will sooner or later lead to extinction; the end, in most cases, being promptly determined by the inroads of conquering tribes.

On the Formation of the Races of Man.—In some cases the crossing of distinct races has led to the formation of a new race. The singular fact that the Europeans and Hindoos, who belong to the same Aryan stock, and speak a language fundamentally the same, differ widely in appearance, whilst Europeans differ but little from Jews, who belong to the Semitic stock, and speak quite another language, has been accounted for by Broca,[49] through certain Aryan branches having been largely crossed by indigenous tribes during their wide diffusion. When two races in close contact cross, the first result is a heterogeneous mixture: thus Mr. Hunter, in describing the Santali

[49] 'On Anthropology,' translation 'Anthropolog. Review,' Jan. 1868, p. 38.

or hill-tribes of India, says that hundreds of imperceptible gradations may be traced "from the black, squat
"tribes of the mountains to the tall olive-coloured
"Brahman, with his intellectual brow, calm eyes, and
"high but narrow head;" so that it is necessary in
courts of justice to ask the witnesses whether they
are Santalis or Hindoos.[50] Whether a heterogeneous
people, such as the inhabitants of some of the Polynesian islands, formed by the crossing of two distinct
races, with few or no pure members left, would ever
become homogeneous, is not known from direct evidence. But as with our domesticated animals, a cross-
breed can certainly be fixed and made uniform by
careful selection[51] in the course of a few generations,
we may infer that the free intercrossing of a heterogeneous mixture during a long descent would supply
the place of selection, and overcome any tendency to
reversion; so that the crossed race would ultimately
become homogeneous, though it might not partake in
an equal degree of the characters of the two parent-
races.

Of all the differences between the races of man, the
colour of the skin is the most conspicuous and one
of the best marked. It was formerly thought that
differences of this kind could be accounted for by
long exposure to different climates; but Pallas first
shewed that this is not tenable, and he has since been
followed by almost all anthropologists.[52] This view

[50] 'The Annals of Rural
Bengal,' 1868, p. 134.
[51] 'The Variation of Animals
and Plants under Domestication,' vol. ii. p. 95.
[52] Pallas, 'Act. Acad. St.
Petersburg,' 1780, part ii. p. 69.

He was followed by Rudolphi,
in his 'Beyträge zur Anthropologie,' 1812. An excellent summary of the evidence is given
by Godron, 'De l'Espèce,' 1859,
vol. ii. p. 246, &c.

has been rejected chiefly because the distribution of the variously coloured races, most of whom must have long inhabited their present homes, does not coincide with corresponding differences of climate.   Some little weight may be given to such cases as that of the Dutch families, who, as we hear on excellent authority,[53] have not undergone the least change of colour after residing for three centuries in South Africa. An argument on the same side may likewise be drawn from the uniform appearance in various parts of the world of gipsies and Jews, though the uniformity of the latter has been somewhat exaggerated.[54]   A very damp or a very dry atmosphere has been supposed to be more influential in modifying the colour of the skin than mere heat; but as D'Orbigny in South America, and Livingstone in Africa, arrived at diametrically opposite conclusions with respect to dampness and dryness, any conclusion on this head must be considered as very doubtful.[55]

Various facts, which I have given elsewhere, prove that the colour of the skin and hair is sometimes correlated in a surprising manner with a complete immunity from the action of certain vegetable poisons, and from the attacks of certain parasites.   Hence it occurred to me, that negroes and other dark races might have acquired their dark tints by the darker individuals escaping from the deadly influence of the miasma of their native countries, during a long series of generations.

[53] Sir Andrew Smith, as quoted by Knox, 'Races of Man' 1850, p. 473.

[54] See De Quatrefages on this head, 'Revue des Cours Scientifiques,' Oct. 17, 1868, p. 731.

[55] Livingstone's 'Travels and Researches in S. Africa,' 1857, pp. 338, 339.   D'Orbigny, as quoted by Godron, 'De l'Espèce,' vol. ii. p. 266.

I afterwards found that this same idea had long ago occurred to Dr. Wells.[56] It has long been known that negroes, and even mulattoes, are almost completely exempt from the yellow-fever, so destructive in tropical America.[57] They likewise escape to a large extent the fatal intermittent fevers, that prevail along at least 2600 miles of the shores of Africa, and which annually cause one-fifth of the white settlers to die, and another fifth to return home invalided.[58] This immunity in the negro seems to be partly inherent, depending on some unknown peculiarity of constitution, and partly the result of acclimatisation. Pouchet[59] states that the negro regiments recruited near the Soudan, and borrowed from the Viceroy of Egypt for the Mexican war, escaped the yellow-fever almost equally with the negroes originally brought from various parts of Africa and accustomed to the climate of the West Indies. That acclimatisation plays a part, is shewn by the many cases in which negroes have become somewhat liable to tropical fevers, after having resided for some time in a colder climate.[60] The nature of the climate under which the white races have long resided, likewise

[56] See a paper read before the Royal Soc. in 1813, and published in his Essays in 1818. I have given an account of Dr. Wells' views in the Historical Sketch (p. xvi.) to my 'Origin of Species.' Various cases of colour correlated with constitutional peculiarities are given in my 'Variation of Animals under Domestication,' vol. ii. pp. 227, 335.

[57] See, for instance, Nott and Gliddon, 'Types of Mankind,' p. 68.

[58] Major Tulloch, in a paper read before the Statistical Society, April 20th, 1840, and given in the 'Athenæum,' 1840, p. 353.

[59] 'The Plurality of the Human Race' (translat.), 1864, p. 60.

[60] Quatrefages, 'Unité de l'Espèce Humaine,' 1861, p. 205. Waitz, 'Introduct. to Anthropology,' translat. vol. i. 1863, p. 124. Livingstone gives analogous cases in his 'Travels.'

has some influence on them; for during the fearful epidemic of yellow fever in Demerara during 1837, Dr. Blair found that the death-rate of the immigrants was proportional to the latitude of the country whence they had come. With the negro the immunity, as far as it is the result of acclimatisation, implies exposure during a prodigious length of time; for the aborigines of tropical America who have resided there from time immemorial, are not exempt from yellow fever; and the Rev. H. B. Tristram states, that there are districts in Northern Africa which the native inhabitants are compelled annually to leave, though the negroes can remain with safety.

That the immunity of the negro is in any degree correlated with the colour of his skin is a mere conjecture: it may be correlated with some difference in his blood, nervous system, or other tissues. Nevertheless, from the facts above alluded to, and from some connection apparently existing between complexion and a tendency to consumption, the conjecture seemed to me not improbable. Consequently I endeavoured, with but little success,[61] to ascertain how far it holds good.

[61] In the spring of 1862 I obtained permission from the Director-General of the Medical department of the Army, to transmit to the surgeons of the various regiments on foreign service a blank table, with the following appended remarks, but I have received no returns. "As several well-marked cases "have been recorded with our "domestic animals of a relation "between the colour of the "dermal appendages and the "constitution; and it being "notorious that there is some "limited degree of relation "between the colour of the "races of man and the climate "inhabited by them; the fol-"lowing investigation seems "worth consideration. Namely, "whether there is any relation "in Europeans between the "colour of their hair, and their "liability to the diseases of "tropical countries. If the "surgeons of the several regi-"ments, when stationed in "unhealthy tropical districts,

The late Dr. Daniell, who had long lived on the West Coast of Africa, told me that he did not believe in any such relation. He was himself unusually fair, and had withstood the climate in a wonderful manner. When he first arrived as a boy on the coast, an old and experienced negro chief predicted from his appearance that this would prove the case. Dr. Nicholson, of Antigua, after having attended to this subject, writes to me that dark-coloured Europeans escape the yellow fever more than those that are light-coloured. Mr. J. M. Harris altogether denies that Europeans with dark hair withstand a hot climate better than other men: on the contrary, experience has taught him in making a selection of men for service on the coast of Africa, to choose those with red hair.[62] As far, therefore, as

"would be so good as first to "count, as a standard of com- "parison, how many men, in "the force whence the sick are "drawn, have dark and light- "coloured hair, and hair of "intermediate or doubtful tints; "and if a similar account were "kept by the same medical "gentlemen, of all the men who "suffered from malarious and "yellow fevers, or from dysen- "tery, it would soon be apparent, "after some thousand cases had "been tabulated, whether there "exists any relation between "the colour of the hair and con- "stitutional liability to tropical "diseases. Perhaps no such "relation would be discovered, "but the investigation is well "worth making. In case any "positive result were obtained, "it might be of some practical "use in selecting men for any "particular service. Theoreti- "cally the result would be of "high interest, as indicating "one means by which a race of "men inhabiting from a remote "period an unhealthy tropical "climate, might have become "dark-coloured by the better "preservation of dark-haired or "dark-complexioned individuals "during a long succession of "generations."

[62] 'Anthropological Review,' Jan. 1866, p. xxi. Dr. Sharpe also says, with respect to India "('Man a Special Creation,' 1873, "p. 118), that it has been "noticed by some medical "officers that Europeans with "light hair and florid com- "plexions suffer less from dis- "eases of tropical countries than "persons with dark hair and "sallow complexions; and, so "far as I know, there appear to

these slight indications go, there seems no foundation for the hypothesis, that blackness has resulted from the darker and darker individuals having survived better during long exposure to fever-generating miasma.

Dr. Sharpe remarks,[63] that a tropical sun, which burns and blisters a white skin, does not injure a black one at all; and, as he adds, this is not due to habit in the individual, for children only six or eight months old are often carried about naked, and are not affected. I have been assured by a medical man, that some years ago during each summer, but not during the winter, his hands became marked with light brown patches, like, although larger than freckles, and that these patches were never affected by sun-burning, whilst the white parts of his skin have on several occasions been much inflamed and blistered. With the lower animals there is, also, a constitutional difference in liability to the action of the sun between those parts of the skin clothed with white hair and other parts.[64] Whether the saving of the skin from being thus burnt is of sufficient importance to account for a dark tint having been gradually acquired by man through natural selection, I am unable to judge. If it be so, we should have to assume that the natives of tropical America have lived there for a much shorter time than the

---

"be good grounds for this "remark." On the other hand, Mr. Heddle, of Sierra Leone, "who has had more clerks "killed under him than any "other man," by the climate of the West African Coast (W. Reade, ' African Sketch Book,'

vol. ii. p. 522), holds a directly opposite view, as does Capt. Burton.
    [63] 'Man a Special Creation,' 1873, p. 119.
    [64] 'Variation of Animals and Plants under Domestication,' vol. ii. pp. 336, 337.

negroes in Africa, or the Papuans in the southern parts
of the Malay archipelago, just as the lighter-coloured
Hindoos have resided in India for a shorter time than
the darker aborigines of the central and southern parts
of the peninsula.

Although with our present knowledge we cannot
account for the differences of colour in the races of man,
through any advantage thus gained, or from the direct
action of climate; yet we must not quite ignore the
latter agency, for there is good reason to believe that
some inherited effect is thus produced.[65]

We have seen in the second chapter that the conditions of life affect the development of the bodily frame
in a direct manner, and that the effects are transmitted.
Thus, as is generally admitted, the European settlers
in the United States undergo a slight but extraordinary
rapid change of appearance. Their bodies and limbs
become elongated; and I hear from Col. Bernys that
during the late war in the United States, good evidence
was afforded of this fact by the ridiculous appearance
presented by the German regiments, when dressed in
ready-made clothes manufactured for the American
market, and which were much too long for the men in
every way. There is, also, a considerable body of
evidence shewing that in the Southern States the

[65] See, for instance, Quatrefages ('Revue des Cours Scientifiques,' Oct. 10, 1868, p. 724)
on the effects of residence in
Abyssinia and Arabia, and other
analogous cases. Dr. Rolle
('Der Mensch, seine Abstam-
mung,' &c., 1865, s. 99) states,
on the authority of Khanikof,
that the greater number of
German families settled in
Georgia, have acquired in the
course of two generations dark
hair and eyes. Mr. D. Forbes
informs me that the Quichuas
in the Andes vary greatly in
colour, according to the position
of the valleys inhabited by
them.

house-slaves of the third generation present a markedly different appearance from the field-slaves.[66]

If, however, we look to the races of man as distributed over the world, we must infer that their characteristic differences cannot be accounted for by the direct action of different conditions of life, even after exposure to them for an enormous period of time. The Esquimaux live exclusively on animal food; they are clothed in thick fur, and are exposed to intense cold and to prolonged darkness; yet they do not differ in any extreme degree from the inhabitants of Southern China, who live entirely on vegetable food, and are exposed almost naked to a hot, glaring climate. The unclothed Fuegians live on the marine productions of their inhospitable shores; the Botocudos of Brazil wander about the hot forests of the interior and live chiefly on vegetable productions; yet these tribes resemble each other so closely that the Fuegians on board the "Beagle" were mistaken by some Brazilians for Botocudos. The Botocudos again, as well as the other inhabitants of tropical America, are wholly different from the Negroes who inhabit the opposite shores of the Atlantic, are exposed to a nearly similar climate, and follow nearly the same habits of life.

Nor can the differences between the races of man be accounted for by the inherited effects of the increased or decreased use of parts, except to a quite insignificant degree. Men who habitually live in canoes, may have their legs somewhat stunted; those who inhabit lofty regions may have their chests enlarged; and those who constantly use certain sense-organs may have the

[66] Harlan, 'Medical Researches,' p. 532. Quatrefages ('Unité de l'Espèce Humaine, 1861, p. 128) has collected much evidence on this head.

cavities in which they are lodged somewhat increased in size, and their features consequently a little modified. With civilised nations, the reduced size of the jaws from lessened use—the habitual play of different muscles serving to express different emotions—and the increased size of the brain from greater intellectual activity, have together produced a considerable effect on their general appearance when compared with savages.[67] Increased bodily stature, without any corresponding increase in the size of the brain, may (judging from the previously adduced case of rabbits), have given to some races an elongated skull of the dolichocephalic type.

Lastly, the little-understood principle of correlated development has sometimes come into action, as in the case of great muscular development and strongly projecting supra-orbital ridges. The colour of the skin and hair are plainly correlated, as is the texture of the hair with its colour in the Mandans of North America.[68] The colour also of the skin, and the odour emitted by it, are likewise in some manner connected. With the breeds of sheep the number of hairs within a given space and the number of the excretory pores are related.[69] If we may judge from the analogy of our domesticated animals, many modifications of

[67] See Prof. Schaaffhausen, translat. in 'Anthropological Review,' Oct. 1868, p. 429.

[68] Mr. Catlin states ('N. American Indians,' 3rd edit. 1842, vol. i. p. 49) that in the whole tribe of the Mandans, about one in ten or twelve of the members, of all ages and both sexes, have bright silvery grey hair, which is hereditary. Now this hair is as coarse and harsh as that of a horse's mane, whilst the hair of other colours is fine and soft.

[69] On the odour of the skin, Godron, 'Sur l'Espèce,' tom. ii. p. 217. On the pores in the skin, Dr. Wilckens, 'Die Aufgaben der Landwirth. Zootechnik,' 1869, s. 7.

structure in man probably come under this principle of correlated development.

We have now seen that the external characteristic differences between the races of man cannot be accounted for in a satisfactory manner by the direct action of the conditions of life, nor by the effects of the continued use of parts, nor through the principle of correlation. We are therefore led to enquire whether slight individual differences, to which man is eminently liable, may not have been preserved and augmented during a long series of generations through natural selection. But here we are at once met by the objection that beneficial variations alone can be thus preserved; and as far as we are enabled to judge, although always liable to err on this head, none of the differences between the races of man are of any direct or special service to him.   The intellectual and moral or social faculties must of course be excepted from this remark. The great variability of all the external differences between the races of man, likewise indicates that they cannot be of much importance; for if important, they would long ago have been either fixed and preserved, or eliminated.   In this respect man resembles those forms, called by naturalists protean or polymorphic, which have remained extremely variable, owing, as it seems, to such variations being of an indifferent nature, and to their having thus escaped the action of natural selection.

We have thus far been baffled in all our attempts to account for the differences between the races of man; but there remains one important agency, namely Sexual Selection, which appears to have acted power-

fully on man, as on many other animals. I do not
intend to assert that sexual selection will account for
all the differences between the races. An unexplained
residuum is left, about which we can only say, in our
ignorance, that as individuals are continually born
with, for instance, heads a little rounder or narrower,
and with noses a little longer or shorter, such slight
differences might become fixed and uniform, if the
unknown agencies which induced them were to act in
a more constant manner, aided by long-continued
intercrossing. Such variations come under the provisional class, alluded to in our second chapter, which
for the want of a better term are often called spontaneous. Nor do I pretend that the effects of sexual
selection can be indicated with scientific precision; but
it can be shewn that it would be an inexplicable fact
if man had not been modified by this agency, which
appears to have acted powerfully on innumerable
animals. It can further be shewn that the differences
between the races of man, as in colour, hairiness, form
of features, &c., are of a kind which might have been
expected to come under the influence of sexual selection.
But in order to treat this subject properly, I have
found it necessary to pass the whole animal kingdom
in review. I have therefore devoted to it the Second
Part of this work. At the close I shall return to man,
and, after attempting to shew how far he has been
modified through sexual selection, will give a brief
summary of the chapters in this First Part.

Note on the Resemblances and Differences in the Structure
    and the Development of the Brain in Man and Apes.   By
    Professor Huxley, F.R.S.

The controversy respecting the nature and the extent of the differences in the structure of the brain in man and the apes, which arose
some fifteen years ago, has not yet come to an end, though the
subject matter of the dispute is, at present, totally different from
what it was formerly.   It was originally asserted and re-asserted,
with singular pertinacity, that the brain of all the apes, even the
highest, differs from that of man, in the absence of such conspicuous
structures as the posterior lobes of the cerebral hemispheres, with
the posterior cornu of the lateral ventricle and the *hippocampus
minor*, contained in those lobes, which are so obvious in man.

But the truth that the three structures in question are as well
developed in apes' as in human brains, or even better ; and that it
is characteristic of all the *Primates* (if we exclude the Lemurs) to
have these parts well developed, stands at present on as secure a
basis as any proposition in comparative anatomy.   Moreover, it is
admitted by every one of the long series of anatomists who, of late
years, have paid special attention to the arrangement of the complicated sulci and gyri which appear upon the surface of the cerebral
hemispheres in man and the higher apes, that they are disposed
after the very same pattern in him, as in them.   Every principal
gyrus and sulcus of a chimpanzee's brain is clearly represented in
that of a man, so that the terminology which applies to the one
answers for the other.   On this point there is no difference of
opinion.   Some years since, Professor Bischoff published a memoir [70]
on the cerebral convolutions of man and apes ; and as the purpose
of my learned colleague was certainly not to diminish the value of
the differences between apes and men in this respect, I am glad to
make a citation from him.

" That the apes, and especially the orang, chimpanzee and gorilla,
" come very close to man in their organisation, much nearer. than
" to any other animal, is a well known fact, disputed by nobody.
" Looking at the matter from the point of view of organisation

---

[70] 'Die Grosshirn-Windungen des Menschen ; ' 'Abhandlungen
der K. Bayerischen Akademie,' Bd. x., 1868.

" alone, no one probably would ever have disputed the view of
" Linnæus, that man should be placed, merely as a peculiar species, at
" the head of the mammalia and of those apes. Both shew, in all
" their organs, so close an affinity, that the most exact anatomical
" investigation is needed in order to demonstrate those differences
" which really exist. So it is with the brains. The brains of man,
" the orang, the chimpanzee, the gorilla, in spite of all the important
" differences which they present, come very close to one another "
" (l. c. p. 101).

There remains, then, no dispute as to the resemblance in fundamental characters, between the ape's brain and man's; nor any as
to the wonderfully close similarity between the chimpanzee,
orang and man, in even the details of the arrangement of the gyri
and sulci of the cerebral hemispheres. Nor, turning to the differences between the brains of the highest apes and that of man, is
there any serious question as to the nature and extent of these
differences. It is admitted that the man's cerebral hemispheres
are absolutely and relatively larger than those of the orang and
chimpanzee; that his frontal lobes are less excavated by the
upward protrusion of the roof of the orbits; that his gyri and sulci
are, as a rule, less symmetrically disposed, and present a greater
number of secondary plications. And it is admitted that, as a rule,
in man, the temporo-occipital or " external perpendicular " fissure,
which is usually so strongly marked a feature of the ape's brain is
but faintly marked. But it also clear, that none of these differences
constitutes a sharp demarcation between the man's and the ape's
brain. In respect to the external perpendicular fissure of Gratiolet,
in the human brain for instance, Professor Turner remarks :[n]

" In some brains it appears simply as an indentation of the
" margin of the hemisphere, but, in others, it extends for some
" distance more or less transversely outwards. I saw it in the right
" hemisphere of a female brain pass more than two inches outwards;
" and on another specimen, also the right hemisphere, it proceeded
" for four-tenths of an inch outwards, and then extended down-
" wards, as far as the lower margin of the outer surface of the
" hemisphere. The imperfect definition of this fissure in the majority
" of human brains, as compared with its remarkable distinctness in
" the brain of most Quadrumana, is owing to the presence, in the

---

[n] 'Convolutions of the Human Cerebrum Topographically
Considered,' 1866, p. 12.

" former, of certain superficial, well marked, secondary convolutions
" which bridge it over and connect the parietal with the occipital
" lobe.   The closer the first of these bridging gyri lies to the longi-
" tudinal fissure, the shorter is the external parieto-occipital fissure."
(l. c. p. 12.)

The obliteration of the external perpendicular fissure of Gratiolet,
therefore, is not a constant character of the human brain.   On the
other hand, its full development is not a constant character of the
higher ape's brain.   For, in the chimpanzee, the more or less
extensive obliteration of the external perpendicular sulcus by
" bridging convolutions," on one side or the other, has been noted
over and over again by Prof. Rolleston, Mr. Marshall, M. Broca and
Professor Turner.   At the conclusion of a special paper on this
subject the latter writes : [72]

" The three specimens of the brain of a chimpanzee just described,
" prove, that the generalisation which Gratiolet has attempted to
" draw of the complete absence of the first connecting convolution
" and the concealment of the second, as essentially characteristic
" features in the brain of this animal, is by no means universally
" applicable.   In only one specimen did the brain, in these par-
" ticulars, follow the law which Gratiolet has expressed.   As
" regards the presence of the superior bridging convolution, I am
" inclined to think that it has existed in one hemisphere, at least,
" in a majority of the brains of this animal which have, up to this
" time, been figured or described.   The superficial position of the
" second bridging convolution is evidently less frequent, and has as
" yet, I believe, only been seen in the brain (A) recorded in this
" communication.   The asymmetrical arrangement in the convo-
" lutions of the two hemispheres, which previous observers have
" referred to in their descriptions, is also well illustrated in these
" specimens." (pp. 8, 9.)

Even were the presence of the temporo-occipital, or external perpendicular, sulcus, a mark of distinction between the higher apes
and man, the value of such a distinctive character would be rendered very doubtful by the structure of the brain in the Platyrhine
apes.   In fact, while the temporo-occipital is one of the most
constant of sulci in the Catarhine, or Old World, apes, it is never

---

[72] Notes more especially on
the bridging convolutions in the
Brain of the Chimpanzee, ' Proceedings of the Royal Society
of Edinburgh,' 1865-6.

very strongly developed in the New World apes; it is absent in the smaller Platyrhini; rudimentary in *Pithecia*;[73] and more or less obliterated by bridging convolutions in *Ateles*.

A character which is thus variable within the limits of a single group can have no great taxonomic value.

It is further established, that the degree of asymmetry of the convolution of the two sides in the human brain is subject to much individual variation; and that, in those individuals of the Bushman race who have been examined, the gyri and sulci of the two hemispheres are considerably less complicated and more symmetrical than in the European brain, while, in some individuals of the chimpanzee, their complexity and asymmetry become notable. This is particularly the case in the brain of a young male chimpanzee figured by M. Broca. ('L'ordre des Primates,' p. 165, fig. 11.)

Again, as respects the question of absolute size, it is established that the difference between the largest and the smallest healthy human brain is greater than the difference between the smallest healthy human brain and the largest chimpanzee's or orang's brain.

Moreover, there is one circumstance in which the orang's and chimpanzee's brains resemble man's, but in which they differ from the lower apes, and that is the presence of two corpora candicantia —the *Cynomorpha* having but one.

In view of these facts I do not hesitate in this year 1874, to repeat and insist upon the proposition which I enunciated in 1863:[74]

"So far as cerebral structure goes, therefore, it is clear that man "differs less from the chimpanzee or the orang, than these do even "from the monkeys, and that the difference between the brain of "the chimpanzee and of man is almost insignificant when com-"pared with that between the chimpanzee brain and that of a "Lemur."

In the paper to which I have referred, Professor Bischoff does not deny the second part of this statement, but he first makes the irrelevant remark that it is not wonderful if the brains of an orang and a Lemur are very different; and secondly, goes on to assert that, "If we successively compare the brain of a man with that of

---

[73] Flower 'On the Anatomy of *Pithecia Monachus*,' 'Proceedings of the Zoological Society,' 1862.

[74] 'Man's Place in Nature,' p. 102.

" an orang; the brain of this with that of a chimpanzee; of this
" with that of a gorilla, and so on of a *Hylobates, Semnopithecus,*
" *Cynocephalus, Cercopithecus, Macacus, Cebus, Callithrix, Lemur,*
" *Stenops, Hapale,* we shall not meet with a greater, or even as
" great a, break in the degree of development of the convolutions,
" as we find between the brain of a man and that of an orang or
" chimpanzee."

To which I reply, firstly, that whether this assertion be true or
false, it has nothing whatever to do with the proposition enunciated
in 'Man's Place in Nature,' which refers not to the development of
the convolutions alone, but to the structure of the whole brain.   If
Professor Bischoff had taken the trouble to refer to p. 96 of the
work he criticises, in fact, he would have found the following
passage: "And it is a remarkable circumstance that though, so far
" as our present knowledge extends, there *is* one true structural
" break in the series of forms of Simian brains, this hiatus does not
" lie between man and the manlike apes, but between the lower and
" the lowest Simians, or in other words, between the Old and New
" World apes and monkeys and the Lemurs.   Every Lemur which
" has yet been examined, in fact, has its cerebellum partially visible
" from above; and its posterior lobe, with the contained posterior
" cornu and hippocampus minor, more or less rudimentary.   Every
" marmoset, American monkey, Old World monkey, baboon, or
" manlike ape, on the contrary, has its cerebellum entirely hidden,
" posteriorly, by the cerebral lobes, and possesses a large posterior
" cornu with a well-developed hippocampus minor."

This statement was a strictly accurate account of what was
known when it was made; and it does not appear to me to be more
than apparently weakened by the subsequent discovery of the
relatively small development of the posterior lobes in the Siamang
and in the Howling monkey.   Notwithstanding the exceptional
brevity of the posterior lobes in these two species, no one will
pretend that their brains, in the slightest degree, approach those of
the Lemurs.   And if, instead of putting *Hapale* out of its natural
place, as Professor Bischoff most unaccountably does, we write the
series of animals he has chosen to mention as follows: *Homo,
Pithecus, Troglodytes, Hylobates, Semnopithecus, Cynocephalus,
Cercopithecus, Macacus, Cebus, Callithrix, Hapale, Lemur, Stenops,*
I venture to reaffirm that the great break in this series lies between
Hapale and *Lemur,* and that this break is considerably greater than
that between any other two terms of that series.   Professor Bischoff

ignores the fact that long before he wrote, Gratiolet had suggested the separation of the Lemurs from the other *Primates* on the very ground of the difference in their cerebral characters; and that Professor Flower had made the following observations in the course of his description of the brain of the Javan Loris : [75]

"And it is especially remarkable that, in the development of the "posterior lobes, there is no approximation to the Lemurine, short "hemisphered brain, in those monkeys which are commonly sup- "posed to approach this family in other respects, viz., the lower "members of the Platyrhine group."

So far as the structure of the adult brain is concerned, then, the very considerable additions to our knowledge, which have been made by the researches of so many investigators, during the past ten years, fully justify the statement which I made in 1863. But it has been said, that, admitting the similarity between the adult brains of man and apes, they are nevertheless, in reality, widely different, because they exhibit fundamental differences in the mode of their development. No one would be more ready than I to admit the force of this argument, if such fundamental differences of develop- ment really exist. But I deny that they do exist. On the contrary, there is a fundamental agreement in the development of the brain in men and apes.

Gratiolet originated the statement that there is a fundamental difference in the development of the brains of apes and that of man —consisting in this ; that, in the apes, the sulci which first make their appearance are situated on the posterior region of the cerebral hemispheres, while, in the human fœtus, the sulci first become visible on the frontal lobes.[76]

This general statement is based upon two observations, the one of a Gibbon almost ready to be born, in which the posterior gyri were " well developed," while those of the frontal lobes were " hardly

---

[75] ' Transactions of the Zoolog- ical Society,' vol. v. 1862.

[76] " Chez tous les singes, les "plis postérieurs se développent " les premiers; les plis antérieurs " se développent plus tard, aussi "la vertèbre occipitale et la parié- "tale sont-elles relativement très- "grandes chez le fœtus. L'Hom- "me présente une exception re- " marquable quant à l'époque de

"l'apparition des plis frontaux, "qui sont les premiers indiqués; "mais le développement général "du lobe frontal, envisagé seule- "ment par rapport à son volume, "suit les mêmes lois que dans "les singes :" Gratiolet, ' Mé- moire sur les plis cérébers,' d3 l'Homme et des Primataux p. 39, Tab. iv. fig. 3.

"indicated "[77] (l. c. p. 39), and the other of a human fœtus at the
22nd or 23rd week of uterogestation, in which Gratiolet notes that
the insula was uncovered, but that nevertheless "des incisures
"sèment de lobe antérieur, une scissure peu profonde indique la
"séparation du lobe occipital, trés-réduit, d'ailleurs dès cette époque.
"Le reste de la surface cérébrale est encore absolument lisse."

Three views of this brain are given in Plate II. figs. 1, 2, 3, of
the work cited, shewing the upper, lateral and inferior views of the
hemispheres, but not the inner view. It is worthy of note that the
figure by no means bears out Gratiolet's description, inasmuch as
the fissure (antero-temporal) on the posterior half of the face of the
hemisphere is more marked than any of those vaguely indicated in
the anterior half. If the figure is correct, it in no way justifies
Gratiolet's conclusion : " Il y a donc entre ces cerveaux [those of a
" Callithrix and of a Gibbon] et celui du fœtus humain une différence
"fondamental. Chez celui-ci, longtemps avant que les plis tempo-
" raux apparaissent, les plis frontaux *essayent* d'exister."

Since Gratiolet's time, however, the development of the gyri and
sulci of the brain has been made the subject of renewed investigation
by Schmidt, Bischoff, Pansch,[78] and more particularly by Ecker,[79]

---

[77] Gratiolet's words are (l. c.
p. 39): "Dans le fœtus dont il
"s'agit les plis cérébraux pos-
"térieurs sont bien développés,
"tandis que les plis du lobe
"frontal sont à peine indiqués."
The figure, however (Pl. iv. fig.
3), shews the fissure of Rolando,
and one of the frontal sulci,
plainly enough. Nevertheless,
M. Alix, in his 'Notice sur les
travaux anthropologiques de
Gratiolet' (Mém. de la Société
d'Anthropologie de Paris,' 1868,
page 32), writes thus : " Gratio-
"let a eu entre les mains le
"cerveau d'un fœtus de Gibbon,
"singe éminemment supérieur,
"et tellement rapproché de
"l'orang, que des naturalistes
"très-compétents l'ont rangé
"parmi les anthropoïdes. M.
"Huxley, par exemple, n'hésite
"pas sur ce point. Eh bien,

"c'est sur le cerveau d'un fœtus
"de Gibbon que Gratiolet a vu
"*les circonvolutions du lobe
"temporo-sphénoidal déjà déve-
"loppées lorsqu'il n'existent pas
"encore de plis sur le lobe
"frontal.* Il était donc bien
"autorisé à dire que, chez
"l'homme les circonvolutions
"apparaissent d'*a* en ω, tandis
"que chez les singes elles se
"développent d'ω en *a*."

[78] 'Ueber die typische Anord-
nung der Furchen und Wind-
ungen auf den Grosshirn-Hemi-
sphären des Menschen und der
Affen.' ' Archiv für Anthropologie,' iii., 1868.

[79] 'Zur Entwickelungs Geschichte der Furchen und Wind-
ungen der Grosshirn-Hemisphä-
ren im Fœtus des Menschen.'
'Archiv für Anthropologie,' iii.,
1868.

whose work is not only the latest, but by far the most complete, memoir on the subject.

The final results of their inquiries may be summed up as follows :—

1. In the human fœtus, the sylvian fissure is formed in the course of the third month of uterogestation. In this, and in the fourth month, the cerebral hemispheres are smooth and rounded (with the exception of the sylvian depression), and they project backwards far beyond the cerebellum.

2. The sulci, properly so called, begin to appear in the interval between the end of the fourth and the beginning of the sixth month of fœtal life, but Ecker is careful to point out that, not only the time, but the order, of their appearance is subject to considerable individual variation. In no case, however, are either the frontal or the temporal sulci the earliest.

The first which appears, in fact, lies on the inner face of the hemisphere (whence doubtless Gratiolet, who does not seem to have examined that face in his fœtus, overlooked it), and is either the internal perpendicular (occipito-parietal), or the calcarine sulcus, these two being close together and eventually running into one another. As a rule the occipito-parietal is the earlier of the two.

3. At the latter part of this period, another sulcus, the " posterio-parietal," or " Fissure of Rolando " is developed, and it is followed, in the course of the sixth month, by the other principal sulci of the frontal, parietal, temporal and occipital lobes. There is, however, no clear evidence that one of these constantly appears before the other; and it is remarkable that, in the brain at the period described and figured by Ecker (l. c. p. 212–13, Taf. II. figs. 1, 2, 3, 4), the antero-temporal sulcus (scissure parallèle) so characteristic of the ape's brain, is as well, if not better developed than the fissure of Rolando, and is much more marked than the proper frontal sulci.

Taking the facts as they now stand, it appears to me that the order of the appearance of the sulci and gyri in the fœtal human brain is in perfect harmony with the general doctrine of evolution, and with the view that man has been evolved from some ape-like form ; though there can be no doubt that that form was, in many respects, different from any member of the Primates now living.

Von Baer taught us, half a century ago, that, in the course of their development, allied animals put on at first, the characters of the greater groups to which they belong, and, by degrees, assume those which restrict them within the limits of their family, genus, and species; and he proved, at the same time, that no developmental stage of a higher animal is precisely similar to the adult condition of any lower animal. It is quite correct to say that a frog passes through the condition of a fish, inasmuch as at one period of its life the tadpole has all the characters of a fish; and if it went no further, would have to be grouped among fishes. But it is equally true that a tadpole is very different from any known fish.

In like manner, the brain of a human fœtus, at the fifth month, may correctly be said to be, not only the brain of an ape, but that of an Arctopithecine or marmoset-like ape; for its hemispheres, with their great posterior lobster, and with no sulci but the sylvian and the calcarine, present the characteristics found only in the group of the Arctopithecine *Primates*. But it is equally true, as Gratiolet remarks, that, in its widely open sylvian fissure, it differs from the brain of any actual marmoset. No doubt it would be much more similar to the brain of an advanced fœtus of a marmoset. But we know nothing whatever of the development of the brain in the marmosets. In the Platyrhini proper, the only observation with which I am acquainted is due to Pansch, who found in the brain of a fœtal *Cebus Apella*, in addition to the sylvian fissure and the deep calcarine fissure, only a very shallow antero-temporal fissure (*scissure parallèle* of Gratiolet).

Now this fact, taken together with the circumstance that the antero-temporal sulcus is present in such Platyrhini as the Saimiri, which present mere traces of sulci on the anterior half of the exterior of the cerebral hemispheres, or none at all, undoubtedly, so far as it goes, affords fair evidence in favour of Gratiolet's hypothesis, that the posterior sulci appear before the anterior, in the brains of the *Platyrhini*. But, it by no means follows, that the rule which may hold good for the *Platyrhini* extends to the *Catarhini*. We have no information whatever respecting the development of the brain in the *Cynomorpha*; and, as regards the *Anthropomorpha*, nothing but the account of the brain of the Gibbon, near birth, already referred to. At the present moment there is not a shadow of evidence to shew that the sulci of a chimpanzee's, or orang's, brain do not appear in the same order as a man's.

Gratiolet opens his preface with the aphorism: "Il est dangereux "dans les sciences de conclure trop vite." I fear he must have forgotten this sound maxim by the time he had reached the discussion of the differences between men and apes, in the body of his work. No doubt, the excellent author of one of the most remarkable contributions to the just understanding of the mammalian brain which has ever been made, would have been the first to admit the insufficiency of his data had he lived to profit by the advance of inquiry. The misfortune is that his conclusions have been employed by persons incompetent to appreciate their foundation, as arguments in favour of obscurantism.[80]

But it is important to remark that, whether Gratiolet was right or wrong in his hypothesis respecting the relative order of appearance of the temporal and frontal sulci, the fact remains; that, before either temporal or frontal sulci, appear, the fœtal brain of man presents characters which are found only in the lowest group of the *Primates* (leaving out the Lemurs); and that this is exactly what we should expect to be the case, if man has resulted from the gradual modification of the same form as that from which the other *Primates* have sprung.

[80] For example, M. l'Abbé Lecomte in his terrible pamphlet 'Le Darwinisme et l'origine de l'Homme,' 1873.

Part II.

SEXUAL SELECTION.

———

CHAPTER VIII.

Principles of Sexual Selection.

Secondary sexual characters—Sexual selection—Manner of action—
   Excess of males—Polygamy—The male alone generally modified
   through sexual selection—Eagerness of the male—Variability of
   the male—Choice exerted by the female—Sexual compared with
   natural selection—Inheritance, at corresponding periods of life, at
   corresponding seasons of the year, and as limited by sex—Relations between the several forms of inheritance—Causes why one
   sex and the young are not modified through sexual selection—
   Supplement on the proportional numbers of the two sexes
   throughout the animal kingdom—The proportion of the sexes in
   relation to natural selection.

With animals which have their sexes separated, the
males necessarily differ from the females in their
organs of reproduction; and these are the primary
sexual characters. But the sexes often differ in what
Hunter has called secondary sexual characters, which
are not directly connected with the act of reproduction; for instance, the male possesses certain organs of
sense or locomotion, of which the female is quite
destitute, or has them more highly-developed, in order
that he may readily find or reach her; or again the

male has special organs of prehension for holding her securely. These latter organs, of infinitely diversified kinds, graduate into those which are commonly ranked as primary, and in some cases can hardly be distinguished from them; we see instances of this in the complex appendages at the apex of the abdomen in male insects. Unless indeed we confine the term "primary" to the reproductive glands, it is scarcely possible to decide which ought to be called primary and which secondary.

The female often differs from the male in having organs for the nourishment or protection of her young, such as the mammary glands of mammals, and the abdominal sacks of the marsupials. In some few cases also the male possesses similar organs, which are wanting in the female, such as the receptacles for the ova in certain male fishes, and those temporarily developed in certain male frogs. The females of most bees are provided with a special apparatus for collecting and carrying pollen, and their ovipositor is modified into a sting for the defence of the larvæ and the community. Many similar cases could be given, but they do not here concern us. There are, however, other sexual differences quite unconnected with the primary reproductive organs, and it is with these that we are more especially concerned—such as the greater size, strength, and pugnacity of the male, his weapons of offence or means of defence against rivals, his gaudy colouring and various ornaments, his power of song, and other such characters.

Besides the primary and secondary sexual differences, such as the foregoing, the males and females of some animals differ in structures related to different habits

of life, and not at all, or only indirectly, to the reproductive functions. Thus the females of certain flies
(Culicidæ and Tabanidæ) are blood-suckers, whilst the
males, living on flowers, have mouths destitute of
mandibles.[1] The males of certain moths and of some
crustaceans (e.g. Tanais) have imperfect, closed mouths,
and cannot feed. The complemental males of certain
Cirripedes live like epiphytic plants either on the
female or the hermaphrodite form, and are destitute
of a mouth and of prehensile limbs. In these cases it
is the male which has been modified, and has lost
certain important organs, which the females possess.
In other cases it is the female which has lost such
parts; for instance, the female glow-worm is destitute
of wings, as also are many female moths, some of
which never leave their cocoons. Many female
parasitic crustaceans have lost their natatory legs. In
some weevil-beetles (Curculionidæ) there is a great
difference between the male and female in the length
of the rostrum or snout;[2] but the meaning of this and
of many analogous differences, is not at all understood.
Differences of structure between the two sexes in
relation to different habits of life are generally confined to the lower animals; but with some few birds
the beak of the male differs from that of the female. In
the Huia of New Zealand the difference is wonderfully
great, and we hear from Dr. Buller[3] that the male
uses his strong beak in chiselling the larvæ of insects
out of decayed wood, whilst the female probes the

[1] Westwood, 'Modern Class.
of Insects,' vol. ii. 1840, p. 541.
For the statement about Tanais,
mentioned below, I am indebted
to Fritz Müller.

[2] Kirby and Spence, 'Introduction to Entomology,' vol. iii.
1826, p. 309.
[3] 'Birds of New Zealand,
1872, p. 66.

softer parts with her far longer, much curved and pliant beak: and thus they mutually aid each other. In most cases, differences of structure between the sexes are more or less directly connected with the propagation of the species: thus a female, which has to nourish a multitude of ova, requires more food than the male, and consequently requires special means for procuring it. A male animal, which lives for a very short time, might lose its organs for procuring food through disuse, without detriment; but he would retain his locomotive organs in a perfect state, so that he might reach the female. The female, on the other hand, might safely lose her organs for flying, swimming, or walking, if she gradually acquired habits which rendered such powers useless.

We are, however, here concerned only with sexual selection. This depends on the advantage which certain individuals have over others of the same sex and species solely in respect of reproduction. When, as in the cases above mentioned, the two sexes differ in structure in relation to different habits of life, they have no doubt been modified through natural selection, and by inheritance limited to one and the same sex. So again the primary sexual organs, and those for nourishing or protecting the young, come under the same influence; for those individuals which generated or nourished their offspring best, would leave, *cæteris paribus*, the greatest number to inherit their superiority; whilst those which generated or nourished their offspring badly, would leave but few to inherit their weaker powers. As the male has to find the female, he requires organs of sense and locomotion, but if these organs are necessary for the other purposes of life, as is generally the case, they will have been developed through natural selection. When the male has found the female, he sometimes absolutely requires prehensile organs to hold her; thus Dr. Wallace informs me that the males of certain moths cannot unite with the females if their tarsi or feet are broken. The males of many oceanic crustaceans, when adult, have their legs and antennæ modified in an extraordinary manner for the prehension of the female; hence we may suspect that it is because these animals are washed about by the waves of the open sea, that they require these organs in order to propagate their kind, and if so, their development has been the result of ordinary or natural selection. Some animals extremely low in the scale have been modified for this same purpose; thus the males of certain parasitic worms, when fully grown, have the lower surface of the terminal part of their bodies roughened like a rasp, and with this they coil round and permanently hold the females.[4]

When the two sexes follow exactly the same habits of life, and the male has the sensory or locomotive organs more highly developed than those of the female, it may be that the perfection of these is indispensable

[4] M. Perrier advances this case ('Revue Scientifique,' Feb. 1, 1873, p. 865) as one fatal to the belief in sexual selection, inasmuch as he supposes that I attribute all the differences between the sexes to sexual selection. This distinguished naturalist, therefore, like so many other Frenchmen, has not taken the trouble to understand even the first principles of sexual selection. An English naturalist insists that the claspers of certain male animals could not have been developed through the choice of the female! Had I not met with this remark, I should not have thought it possible for any one to have read this chapter and to have imagined that I maintain that the choice of the female had anything to do with the development of the prehensile organs in the male.

to the male for finding the female; but in the vast majority of cases, they serve only to give one male an advantage over another, for with sufficient time, the less well-endowed males would succeed in pairing with the females; and judging from the structure of the female, they would be in all other respects equally well adapted for their ordinary habits of life. Since in such cases the males have acquired their present structure, not from being better fitted to survive in the struggle for existence, but from having gained an advantage over other males, and from having transmitted this advantage to their male offspring alone, sexual selection must here have come into action. It was the importance of this distinction which led me to designate this form of selection as Sexual Selection. So again, if the chief service rendered to the male by his prehensile organs is to prevent the escape of the female before the arrival of other males, or when assaulted by them, these organs will have been perfected through sexual selection, that is by the advantage acquired by certain individuals over their rivals. But in most cases of this kind it is impossible to distinguish between the effects of natural and sexual selection. Whole chapters could be filled with details on the differences between the sexes in their sensory, locomotive, and prehensile organs. As, however, these structures are not more interesting than others adapted for the ordinary purposes of life I shall pass them over almost entirely, giving only a few instances under each class.

There are many other structures and instincts which must have been developed through sexual selection—such as the weapons of offence and the means of defence of the males for fighting with and driving away their rivals—their courage and pugnacity—their various ornaments—their contrivances for producing vocal or instrumental music—and their glands for emitting odours, most of these latter structures serving only to allure or excite the female.   It is clear that these characters are the result of sexual and not of ordinary selection, since unarmed, unornamented, or unattractive males would succeed equally well in the battle for life and in leaving a numerous progeny, but for the presence of better endowed males. We may infer that this would be the case, because the females, which are unarmed and unornamented, are able to survive and procreate their kind.   Secondary sexual characters of the kind just referred to, will be fully discussed in the following chapters, as being in many respects interesting, but especially as depending on the will, choice, and rivalry of the individuals of either sex.   When we behold two males fighting for the possession of the female, or several male birds displaying their gorgeous plumage, and performing strange antics before an assembled body of females, we cannot doubt that, though led by instinct, they know what they are about, and consciously exert their mental and bodily powers.

Just as man can improve the breed of his game-cocks by the selection of those birds which are victorious in the cockpit, so it appears that the strongest and most vigorous males, or those provided with the best weapons, have prevailed under nature, and have led to the improvement of the natural breed or species.   A slight degree of variability leading to some advantage, however slight, in reiterated deadly contests would suffice for the work of sexual selection; and it is certain that secondary sexual characters are eminently variable. Just as man can give beauty, according to his standard of taste, to his male poultry, or more strictly can modify the beauty originally acquired by the parent species, can give to the Sebright bantam a new and elegant plumage, an erect and peculiar carriage—so it appears that female birds in a state of nature, have by a long selection of the more attractive males, added to their beauty or other attractive qualities. No doubt this implies powers of discrimination and taste on the part of the female which will at first appear extremely improbable; but by the facts to be adduced hereafter, I hope to be able to shew that the females actually have these powers. When, however, it is said that the lower animals have a sense of beauty, it must not be supposed that such sense is comparable with that of a cultivated man, with his multiform and complex associated ideas. A more just comparison would be between the taste for the beautiful in animals, and that in the lowest savages, who admire and deck themselves with any brilliant, glittering, or curious object.

From our ignorance on several points, the precise manner in which sexual selection acts is somewhat uncertain. Nevertheless if those naturalists who already believe in the mutability of species, will read the following chapters, they will, I think, agree with me, that sexual selection has played an important part in the history of the organic world. It is certain that amongst almost all animals there is a struggle between the males for the possession of the female. This fact is so notorious that it would be superfluous to give instances. Hence the females have the opportunity of selecting one out of several males, on the supposition that their mental capacity suffices for the exertion of a choice. In many cases special circumstances tend to make the struggle between the males particularly severe. Thus the males of our migratory birds generally arrive at their places of breeding before the females, so that many males are ready to contend for each female. I am informed by Mr. Jenner Weir, that the bird-catchers assert that this is invariably the case with the nightingale and blackcap, and with respect to the latter he can himself confirm the statement.

Mr. Swaysland of Brighton has been in the habit, during the last forty years, of catching our migratory birds on their first arrival, and he has never known the females of any species to arrive before their males. During one spring he shot thirty-nine males of Ray's wagtail (*Budytes Raii*) before he saw a single female. Mr. Gould has ascertained by the dissection of those snipes which arrive the first in this country, that the males come before the females. And the like holds good with most of the migratory birds of the United States.[5] The majority of the male salmon in our rivers, on coming up from the sea, are ready to breed before the females. So it appears to be with frogs and toads. Throughout the great class of insects the males almost always are the first to emerge from the pupal state, so that they generally abound for a time before any females can be seen.[6] The cause of

[5] J. A. Allen, on the 'Mammals and Winter Birds of Florida,' Bull. Comp. Zoology, Harvard College, p. 268.

[6] Even with those plants in which the sexes are separate, the male flowers are generally mature before the female. As first shewn by C. K. Sprengel, many hermaphrodite plants are dichogamous; that is, their male and female organs are not ready at the same time, so that they cannot be self-fertilised. Now in such flowers, the pollen is in general matured before the stigma, though there are exceptional cases in which the female organs are beforehand.

this difference between the males and females in their periods of arrival and maturity is sufficiently obvious. Those males which annually first migrated into any country, or which in the spring were first ready to breed, or were the most eager, would leave the largest number of offspring; and these would tend to inherit similar instincts and constitutions. It must be borne in mind that it would have been impossible to change very materially the time of sexual maturity in the females, without at the same time interfering with the period of the production of the young—a period which must be determined by the seasons of the year. On the whole there can be no doubt that with almost all animals, in which the sexes are separate, there is a constantly recurrent struggle between the males for the possession of the females.

Our difficulty in regard to sexual selection lies in understanding how it is that the males which conquer other males, or those which prove the most attractive to the females, leave a greater number of offspring to inherit their superiority than their beaten and less attractive rivals. Unless this result does follow, the characters which give to certain males an advantage over others, could not be perfected and augmented through sexual selection. When the sexes exist in exactly equal numbers, the worst-endowed males will (except where polygamy prevails), ultimately find females, and leave as many offspring, as well fitted for their general habits of life, as the best-endowed males. From various facts and considerations, I formerly inferred that with most animals, in which secondary sexual characters are well developed, the males considerably exceeded the females in number; but this is not by any means always true. If the males were to the females as two to one, or as three to two, or even in a somewhat lower ratio, the whole affair would be simple ; for the better-armed or more attractive males would leave the largest number of offspring. But after investigating, as far as possible, the numerical proportion of the sexes, I do not believe that any great inequality in number commonly exists. In most cases sexual selection appears to have been effective in the following manner.

Let us take any species, a bird for instance, and divide the females inhabiting a district into two equal bodies, the one consisting of the more vigorous and better-nourished individuals, and the other of the less vigorous and healthy. The former, there can be little doubt, would be ready to breed in the spring before the others; and this is the opinion of Mr. Jenner Weir, who has carefully attended to the habits of birds during many years. There can also be no doubt that the most vigorous, best-nourished and earliest breeders would on an average succeed in rearing the largest number of fine offspring.[7] The males, as we have seen, are generally ready to breed before the females ; the strongest, and with some species the best armed of the males, drive away the weaker ; and the former would then unite with the more vigorous and better-nourished females, because they are the first

[7] Here is excellent evidence on the character of the offspring from an experienced ornithologist. Mr. J. A. Allen, in speaking ('Mammals and Winter Birds of E. Florida,' p. 229) of the later broods, after the accidental destruction of the first, says, that these "are found to "be smaller and paler-coloured "than those hatched earlier in "the season. In cases where "several broods are reared each "year, as a general rule the "birds of the earlier broods seem "in all respects the most perfect "and vigorous."

to breed.[8] Such vigorous pairs would surely rear a larger number of offspring than the retarded females, which would be compelled to unite with the conquered and less powerful males, supposing the sexes to be numerically equal; and this is all that is wanted to add, in the course of successive generations, to the size, strength and courage of the males, or to improve their weapons.

But in very many cases the males which conquer their rivals, do not obtain possession of the females, independently of the choice of the latter. The courtship of animals is by no means so simple and short an affair as might be thought. The females are most excited by, or prefer pairing with, the more ornamented males, or those which are the best songsters, or play the best antics; but it is obviously probable that they would at the same time prefer the more vigorous and lively males, and this has in some cases been confirmed by actual observation.[9] Thus the more vigorous females, which are the first to breed, will have the choice of many males; and though they may not always select the strongest or best armed, they will select those which are vigorous and well armed, and in other respects the most attractive. Both sexes, therefore, of such early pairs would as above explained, have an advantage over others in rearing offspring;

[8] Hermann Müller has come to this same conclusion with respect to those female bees which are the first to emerge from the pupa each year. See his remarkable essay, 'Anwendung den Darwin'schen Lehre auf Bienen,' 'Verh. d. V. Jahrg.' xxix. p. 45.

[9] With respect to poultry, I have received information, hereafter to be given, to this effect. Even with birds, such as pigeons, which pair for life, the female, as I hear from Mr. Jenner Weir, will desert her mate if he is injured or grows weak.

and this apparently has sufficed during a long course of generations to add not only to the strength and fighting powers of the males, but likewise to their various ornaments or other attractions.

In the converse and much rarer case of the males selecting particular females, it is plain that those which were the most vigorous and had conquered others, would have the freest choice; and it is almost certain that they would select vigorous as well as attractive females. Such pairs would have an advantage in rearing offspring, more especially if the male had the power to defend the female during the pairing-season as occurs with some of the higher animals, or aided her in providing for the young. The same principles would apply if each sex preferred and selected certain individuals of the opposite sex; supposing that they selected not only the more attractive, but likewise the more vigorous individuals.

Numerical Proportion of the Two Sexes.—I have remarked that sexual selection would be a simple affair if the males were considerably more numerous than the females. Hence I was led to investigate, as far as I could, the proportions between the two sexes of as many animals as possible; but the materials are scanty. I will here give only a brief abstract of the results, retaining the details for a supplementary discussion, so as not to interfere with the course of my argument. Domesticated animals alone afford the means of ascertaining the proportional numbers at birth; but no records have been specially kept for this purpose. By indirect means, however, I have collected a considerable body of statistics, from which it appears that with most of our domestic animals the sexes are nearly equal at birth. Thus 25,560 births of race-horses have been recorded during twenty-one years, and the male births were to the female births as 99·7 to 100. In greyhounds the inequality is greater than with any other animal, for out of 6878 births during twelve years, the male births were to the female as 110·1 to 100. It is, however, in some degree doubtful whether it is safe to infer that the proportion would be the same under natural conditions as under domestication ; for slight and unknown differences in the conditions affect the proportion of the sexes. Thus with mankind, the male births in England are as 104·5, in Russia as 108·9, and with the Jews of Livonia as 120, to 100 female births. But I shall recur to this curious point of the excess of male births in the supplement to this chapter. At the Cape of Good Hope, however, male children of European extraction have been born during several years in the proportion of between 90 and 99 to 100 female children.

For our present purpose we are concerned with the proportion of the sexes, not only at birth, but also at maturity, and this adds another element of doubt; for it is a well-ascertained fact that with man the number of males dying before or during birth, and during the first few years of infancy, is considerably larger than that of females. So it almost certainly is with male lambs, and probably with some other animals. The males of some species kill one another by fighting ; or they drive one another about until they become greatly emaciated. They must also be often exposed to various dangers, whilst wandering about in eager search for the females. In many kinds of fish the males are much smaller than the females, and they are believed often to be devoured by the latter, or by other fishes. The females of some birds appear to die earlier than the males; they are also liable to be destroyed on their nests, or whilst in charge of their young. With insects the female larvæ are often larger than those of the males, and would consequently be more likely to be devoured. In some cases the mature females are less active and less rapid in their movements than the males, and could not escape so well from danger. Hence, with animals in a state of nature, we must rely on mere estimation, in order to judge of the proportions of the sexes at maturity; and this is but little trustworthy, except when the inequality is strongly marked. Nevertheless, as far as a judgment can be formed, we may conclude from the facts given in the supplement, that the males of some few mammals, of many birds, of some fish and insects, are considerably more numerous than the females.

The proportion between the sexes fluctuates slightly during successive years: thus with race-horses, for every 100 mares born the stallions varied from 107·1 in one year to 92·6 in another year, and with grey-hounds from 116·3 to 95·3. But had larger numbers been tabulated throughout an area more extensive than England, these fluctuations would probably have disappeared; and such as they are, would hardly suffice to lead to effective sexual selection in a state of nature. Nevertheless, in the cases of some few wild animals, as shewn in the supplement, the proportions seem to fluctuate either during different seasons or in different localities in a sufficient degree to lead to such selection. For it should be observed that any advantage, gained during certain years or in certain localities by those males which were able to conquer their rivals, or were the most attractive to the females, would probably be transmitted to the offspring, and would not subsequently be eliminated. During the succeeding seasons, when, from the equality of the sexes, every male was able to procure a female, the stronger or more attractive males previously produced would still have at least as good a chance of leaving offspring as the weaker or less attractive.

Polygamy.—The practice of polygamy leads to the same results as would follow from an actual inequality in the number of the sexes; for if each male secures two or more females, many males cannot pair; and the latter assuredly will be the weaker or less attractive individuals. Many mammals and some few birds are polygamous, but with animals belonging to the lower classes I have found no evidence of this habit. The intellectual powers of such animals are, perhaps, not sufficient to lead them to collect and guard a harem of females. That some relation exists between polygamy and the development of secondary sexual characters, appears nearly certain; and this supports the view that a numerical preponderance of males would be eminently favourable to the action of sexual selection. Nevertheless many animals, which are strictly monogamous, especially birds, display strongly-marked secondary sexual characters; whilst some few animals, which are polygamous, do not have such characters.

We will first briefly run through the mammals, and then turn to birds. The gorilla seems to be polygamous, and the male differs considerably from the female ; so it is with some baboons, which live in herds containing twice as many adult females as males. In South America the *Mycetes caraya* presents well-marked sexual differences, in colour, beard, and vocal organs ; and the male generally lives with two or three wives: the male of the *Cebus capucinus* differs somewhat from the female, and appears to be polygamous.[10] Little is known on this head with respect to most other monkeys, but some species are strictly monogamous. The ruminants are eminently polygamous, and they present sexual differences more frequently than almost any other group of mammals ; this holds good, especially in their weapons, but also in other characters. Most deer, cattle, and sheep are polygamous ; as are most antelopes, though some are monogamous. Sir Andrew Smith, in speaking of the antelopes of South Africa, says that in herds of about a dozen there was rarely more than one mature male. The Asiatic *Antilope saiga* appears to be the most inordinate polygamist in the world ; for Pallas [11] states that the male drives away all rivals, and collects a herd of about a hundred females and kids together ; the female is hornless and has softer hair, but does not otherwise differ much from the male. The wild horse of the Falkland Islands and of the Western States of N. America is polygamous,

---

[10] On the Gorilla, Savage and Wyman, 'Boston Journal of Nat. Hist.' vol. v. 1845–47, p. 423. On Cynocephalus, Brehm, 'Illust. Thierleben,' B. i. 1864, s. 77. On Mycetes, Rengger, 'Natur-gesch.: Säugethiere von Para-guay,' 1830, ss. 14, 20. Cebus, Brehm, ibid. s. 108.

[11] Pallas, 'Spicilegia Zoolog.,

Fasc.' xii. 1777, p. 29. Sir Andrew Smith, 'Illustrations of the Zoology of S. Africa,' 1849, pl. 29, on the Kobus. Owen, in his 'Anatomy of Vertebrates' (vol. iii. 1868, p. 633) gives a table shewing incidentally which species of antelopes are grega-rious.

but, except in his greater size and in the proportions
of his body, differs but little from the mare. The wild
boar presents well-marked sexual characters, in his
great tusks and some other points. In Europe and in
India he leads a solitary life, except during the breeding-season; but as is believed by Sir W. Elliot, who
has had many opportunities in India of observing this
animal, he consorts at this season with several females.
Whether this holds good in Europe is doubtful, but it
is supported by some evidence. The adult male Indian
elephant, like the boar, passes much of his time in solitude; but as Dr. Campbell states, when with others,
"it is rare to find more than one male with a whole
"herd of females;" the larger males expelling or
killing the smaller and weaker ones. The male differs
from the female in his immense tusks, greater size,
strength, and endurance; so great is the difference in
these respects, that the males when caught are valued
at one-fifth more than the females.[12] The sexes of
other pachydermatous animals differ very little or not
at all, and, as far as known, they are not polygamists.
Nor have I heard of any species in the Orders of
Cheiroptera, Edentata, Insectivora and Rodents being
polygamous, excepting that amongst the Rodents, the
common rat, according to some rat-catchers, lives with
several females. Nevertheless the two sexes of some
sloths (Edentata) differ in the character and colour of
certain patches of hair on their shoulders.[13] And
many kinds of bats (Cheiroptera) present well-marked
sexual differences, chiefly in the males possessing

[12] Dr. Campbell, in 'Proc.
Zoolog. Soc.' 1869, p. 138. See
also an interesting paper, by
Lieut. Johnstone, in 'Proc.
Asiatic Soc. ot Bengal,' May,
1868.

[13] Dr. Gray, in 'Annals and
Mag. of Nat. Hist.' 1871, p. 302.

odoriferous glands and pouches, and by their being of a lighter colour.[14] In the great order of Rodents, as far as I can learn, the sexes rarely differ, and when they do so, it is but slightly in the tint of the fur.

As I hear from Sir Andrew Smith, the lion in South Africa sometimes lives with a single female, but generally with more, and, in one case, was found with as many as five females; so that he is polygamous. As far as I can discover, he is the only polygamist amongst all the terrestrial Carnivora, and he alone presents well-marked sexual characters. If, however, we turn to the marine Carnivora, as we shall hereafter see, the case is widely different; for many species of seals offer extraordinary sexual differences, and they are eminently polygamous. Thus, according to Péron, the male sea-elephant of the Southern Ocean always possesses several females, and the sea-lion of Forster is said to be surrounded by from twenty to thirty females. In the North, the male sea-bear of Steller is accompanied by even a greater number of females. It is an interesting fact, as Dr. Gill remarks,[15] that in the monogamous species, "or those living in small com-"munities, there is little difference in size between the "males and females; in the social species, or rather "those of which the males have harems, the males are "vastly larger than the females."

Amongst birds, many species, the sexes of which differ greatly from each other, are certainly monogamous. In great Britain we see well-marked sexual differences, for instance, in the wild-duck which pairs

[14] See Dr. Dobson's excellent paper in 'Proc. Zoolog. Soc.' 1873, p. 241.

[15] The Eared Seals, 'American Naturalist,' vol. iv., Jan. 1871.

with a single female, the common blackbird, and the
bullfinch which is said to pair for life. I am informed
by Mr. Wallace that the like is true of the Chatterers
or Cotingidæ of South America, and of many other
birds. In several groups I have not been able to
discover whether the species are polygamous or monogamous. Lesson says that birds of paradise, so remarkable for their sexual differences, are polygamous,
but Mr. Wallace doubts whether he had sufficient
evidence. Mr. Salvin tells me he has been led to
believe that humming-birds are polygamous. The
male widow-bird, remarkable for his caudal plumes,
certainly seems to be a polygamist.[16] I have been
assured by Mr. Jenner Weir and by others, that it is
somewhat common for three starlings to frequent the
same nest; but whether this is a case of polygamy or
polyandry has not been ascertained.

The Gallinaceæ exhibit almost as strongly marked
sexual differences as birds of paradise or humming-
birds, and many of the species are, as is well known,
polygamous; others being strictly monogamous.
What a contrast is presented between the sexes of the
polygamous peacock or pheasant, and the monogamous
guinea-fowl or partridge! Many similar cases could
be given, as in the grouse tribe, in which the males of
the polygamous capercailzie and black-cock differ
greatly from the females; whilst the sexes of the
monogamous red grouse and ptarmigan differ very

[16] 'The Ibis,' vol. iii. 1861 p.
133, on the Progne Widow-
bird. See also on the *Vidua
axillaris*, ibid. vol. ii. 1860, p.
211. On the polygamy of the
Capercailzie and Great Bustard,
see L. Lloyd, 'Game Birds of
Sweden,' 1867, p. 19, and 182.
Montagu and Selby speak of
the Black Grouse as polygamous
and of the Red Grouse as monogamous.

little. In the Cursores, except amongst the bustards, few species offer strongly-marked sexual differences, and the great bustard (*Otis tarda*) is said to be polygamous. With the Grallatores, extremely few species differ sexually, but the ruff (*Machetes pugnax*) affords a marked exception, and this species is believed by Montagu to be a polygamist. Hence it appears that amongst birds there often exists a close relation between polygamy and the development of strongly-marked sexual differences. I asked Mr. Bartlett, of the Zoological Gardens, who has had very large experience with birds, whether the male tragopan (one of the Gallinaceæ) was polygamous, and I was struck by his answering, " I do not know, but should think so " from his splendid colours."

It deserves notice that the instinct of pairing with a single female is easily lost under domestication. The wild-duck is strictly monogamous, the domestic-duck highly polygamous. The Rev. W. D. Fox informs me that out of some half-tamed wild-ducks, on a large pond in his neighbourhood, so many mallards were shot by the gamekeeper that only one was left for every seven or eight females; yet unusually large broods were reared. The guinea-fowl is strictly monogamous; but Mr. Fox finds that his birds succeed best when he keeps one cock to two or three hens. Canary-birds pair in a state of nature, but the breeders in England successfully put one male to four or five females. I have noticed these cases, as rendering it probable that wild monogamous species might readily become either temporarily or permanently polygamous.

Too little is known of the habits of reptiles and fishes to enable us to speak of their marriage arrangements. The stickle-back (Gasterosteus), however, is said to be a polygamist;[17] and the male during the breeding season differs conspicuously from the female.

To sum up on the means through which, as far as we can judge, sexual selection has led to the development of secondary sexual characters. It has been shewn that the largest number of vigorous offspring will be reared from the pairing of the strongest and best-armed males, victorious in contests over other males, with the most vigorous and best-nourished females, which are the first to breed in the spring. If such females select the more attractive, and at the same time vigorous males, they will rear a larger number of offspring than the retarded females, which must pair with the less vigorous and less attractive males. So it will be if the more vigorous males select the more attractive and at the same time healthy and vigorous females; and this will especially hold good if the male defends the female, and aids in providing food for the young. The advantage thus gained by the more vigorous pairs in rearing a larger number of offspring has apparently sufficed to render sexual selection efficient. But a large numerical preponderance of males over females will be still more efficient; whether the preponderance is only occasional and local, or permanent; whether it occurs at birth, or afterwards from the greater destruction of the females; or whether it indirectly follows from the practice of polygamy.

The Male generally more modified than the Female.—
Throughout the animal kingdom, when the sexes differ

[17] Noel Humphreys, ' River Gardens,' 1857.

in external appearance, it is, with rare exceptions, the
male which has been the more modified; for, generally,
the female retains a closer resemblance to the young of
her own species, and to other adult members of the
same group. The cause of this seems to lie in the
males of almost all animals having stronger passions
than the females. Hence it is the males that fight
together and sedulously display their charms before
the females; and the victors transmit their superiority
to their male offspring. Why both sexes do not thus
acquire the characters of their fathers, will be considered hereafter. That the males of all mammals
eagerly pursue the females is notorious to every one.
So it is with birds; but many cock birds do not so
much pursue the hen, as display their plumage, perform strange antics, and pour forth their song in her
presence. The male in the few fish observed seems
much more eager than the female; and the same is
true of alligators, and apparently of Batrachians.
Throughout the enormous class of insects, as Kirby
remarks,[18] "the law is, that the male shall seek the
"female." Two good authorities, Mr. Blackwall and
Mr. C. Spence Bate, tell me that the males of spiders
and crustaceans are more active and more erratic in
their habits than the females. When the organs of
sense or locomotion are present in the one sex of insects
and crustaceans and absent in the other, or when, as is
frequently the case, they are more highly developed in
the one than in the other, it is, as far as I can discover,
almost invariably the male which retains such organs,
or has them most developed; and this shews that the

[18] Kirby and Spence, 'Introduction to Entomology, vol. iii.
1826, p. 342.

male is the more active member in the courtship of the sexes.[19]

The female, on the other hand, with the rarest exceptions, is less eager than the male. As the illustrious Hunter[20] long ago observed, she generally "requires to be courted;" she is coy, and may often be seen endeavouring for a long time to escape from the male. Every observer of the habits of animals will be able to call to mind instances of this kind. It is shown by various facts, given hereafter, and by the results fairly attributable to sexual selection, that the female, though comparatively passive, generally exerts some choice and accepts one male in preference to others. Or she may accept, as appearances would sometimes lead us to believe, not the male which is the most attractive to her, but the one which is the least distasteful. The exertion of some choice on the part of the female seems a law almost as general as the eagerness of the male.

We are naturally led to enquire why the male, in so many and such distinct classes, has become more eager than the female, so that he searches for her, and plays the more active part in courtship. It would be no advantage and some loss of power if each sex searched

[19] One parasitic Hymenopterous insect (Westwood, 'Modern Class. of Insects,' vol. ii. p. 160) forms an exception to the rule, as the male has rudimentary wings, and never quits the cell in which it is born, whilst the female has well-developed wings. Audouin believes that the females of this species are impregnated by the males which are born in the same cells with them; but it is much more probable that the females visit other cells, so that close interbreeding is thus avoided. We shall hereafter meet in various classes, with a few exceptional cases, in which the female, instead of the male, is the seeker and wooer.

[20] 'Essays and Observations,' edited by Owen, vol. i. 1861, p. 194.

for the other; but why should the male almost always
be the seeker? The ovules of plants after fertilisation
have to be nourished for a time; hence the pollen is
necessarily brought to the female organs—being placed
on the stigma, by means of insects or the wind, or by
the spontaneous movements of the stamens; and in
the Algæ, &c., by the locomotive power of the anthero-
zooids. With lowly-organised aquatic animals, permanently affixed to the same spot and having their
sexes separate, the male element is invariably brought
to the female; and of this we can see the reason, for
even if the ova were detached before fertilisation, and
did not require subsequent nourishment or protection,
there would yet be greater difficulty in transporting
them than the male element, because, being larger than
the latter, they are produced in far smaller numbers.
So that many of the lower animals are, in this
respect, analogous with plants.[21] The males of affixed
and aquatic animals having been led to emit their
fertilising element in this way, it is natural that any
of their descendants, which rose in the scale and
became locomotive, should retain the same habit; and
they would approach the female as closely as possible,
in order not to risk the loss of the fertilising element
in a long passage of it through the water. With some
few of the lower animals, the females alone are fixed,
and the males of these must be the seekers. But it is
difficult to understand why the males of species, of
which the progenitors were primordially free, should
invariably have acquired the habit of approaching the

[21] Prof. Sachs ('Lehrbuch der Botanik,' 1870, s. 633) in speak-
ing of the male and female reproductive cells, remarks, "verhält sich die eine bei der Vereinigung activ, . . . die andere erscheint bei der Vereinigung passiv."

females, instead of being approached by them. But in all cases, in order that the males should seek efficiently, it would be necessary that they should be endowed with strong passions ; and the acquirement of such passions would naturally follow from the more eager leaving a larger number of offspring than the less eager.

The great eagerness of the males has thus indirectly led to their much more frequently developing secondary sexual characters than the females. But the development of such characters would be much aided, if the males were more liable to vary than the females—as I concluded they were—after a long study of domesticated animals. Von Nathusius, who has had very wide experience, is strongly of the same opinion.[22] Good evidence also in favour of this conclusion can be produced by a comparison of the two sexes in mankind. During the Novara Expedition[23] a vast number of measurements was made of various parts of the body in different races, and the men were found in almost every case to present a greater range of variation than the women ; but I shall have to recur to this subject in a future chapter. Mr. J. Wood,[24] who has carefully attended to the variation of the muscles in man, puts in italics the conclusion that " the greatest number of " abnormalities in each subject is found in the males." He had previously remarked that " altogether in 102

[22] 'Vortrage über Viehzucht,' 1872, p. 63.

[23] 'Reise der Novara : Anthropolog. Theil,' 1867, ss. 216–269. The results were calculated by Dr. Weisbach from measurements made by Drs. K. Scherzer and Schwarz. On the greater variability of the males of domesticated animals, see my 'Variation of Animals and Plants under Domestication,' vol. ii. 1868, p. 75.

[24] 'Proceedings Royal Soc.' vol. xvi. July 1868, pp. 519 and 524.

" subjects, the varieties of redundancy were found to
" be half as many again as in females, contrasting
" widely with the greater frequency of deficiency in
" females before described." Professor Macalister likewise remarks [25] that variations in the muscles " are
" probably more common in males than females."
Certain muscles which are not normally present in
mankind are also more frequently developed in the
male than in the female sex, although exceptions to
this rule are said to occur. Dr. Burt Wilder [26] has
tabulated the cases of 152 individuals with supernumerary digits, of which 86 were males, and 39, or less
than half, females, the remaining 27 being of unknown
sex. It should not, however, be overlooked that women
would more frequently endeavour to conceal a deformity
of this kind than men. Again, Dr. L. Meyer asserts
that the ears of man are more variable in form than
those of a woman.[27] Lastly the temperature is more
variable in man than in woman.[28]

The cause of the greater general variability in the
male sex, than in the female is unknown, except in so
far as secondary sexual characters are extraordinarily
variable, and are usually confined to the males ; and, as
we shall presently see, this fact is, to a certain extent,
intelligible. Through the action of sexual and natural
selection male animals have been rendered in very
many instances widely different from their females ;
but independently of selection the two sexes, from

[25] 'Proc. Royal Irish Academy,' vol. x. 1868, p. 123.

[26] 'Massachusetts Medical
Soc.' vol. ii. No. 3, 1868, p. 9.

[27] 'Archiv für Path. Anat.
und Phys.' 1871, p. 488.

[28] The conclusions recently
arrived at by Dr. J. Stockton
Hough, on the temperature of
man, are given in the 'Pop.
Science Review,' Jan. 1st, 1874,
p. 97.

differing constitutionally, tend to vary in a somewhat different manner. The female has to expend much organic matter in the formation of her ova, whereas the male expends much force in fierce contests with his rivals, in wandering about in search of the female, in exerting his voice, pouring out odoriferous secretions, &c.: and this expenditure is generally concentrated within a short period. The great vigour of the male during the season of love seems often to intensify his colours, independently of any marked difference from the female.[29] In mankind, and even as low down in the organic scale as in the Lepidoptera, the temperature of the body is higher in the male than in the female, accompanied in the case of man by a slower pulse.[30] On the whole the expenditure of matter and force by the two sexes is probably nearly equal, though effected in very different ways and at different rates.

From the causes just specified the two sexes can hardly fail to differ somewhat in constitution, at least during the breeding season; and, although they may be subjected to exactly the same conditions, they will tend to vary in a different manner. If such variations are of no service to either sex, they will not be accumulated and increased by sexual or natural selection.

[29] Prof. Mantegazza is inclined to believe ('Lettera a Carlo Darwin,' 'Archivio per l'Anthropologia,' 1871, p. 306) that the bright colours, common in so many male animals, are due to the presence and retention by them of the spermatic fluid; but this can hardly be the case; for many male birds, for instance young pheasants, become brightly coloured in the autumn of their first year.

[30] For mankind, see Dr. J. Stockton Hough, whose conclusions are given in the 'Pop. Science Review,' 1874, p. 97. See Girard's observations on the Lepidoptera, as given in the 'Zoological Record,' 1869, p. 347.

Nevertheless, they may become permanent if the exciting cause acts permanently; and in accordance with a frequent form of inheritance they may be transmitted to that sex alone in which they first appeared. In this case the two sexes will come to present permanent, yet unimportant, differences of character. For instance, Mr. Allen shews that with a large number of birds inhabiting the northern and southern United States, the specimens from the south are darker-coloured than those from the north; and this seems to be the direct result of the difference in temperature, light, &c., between the two regions. Now, in some few cases, the two sexes of the same species appear to have been differently affected; in the *Agelæus phœniceus* the males have had their colours greatly intensified in the south; whereas with *Cardinalis virginianus* it is the females which have been thus affected; with *Quiscalus major* the females have been rendered extremely variable in tint, whilst the males remain nearly uniform.[31]

A few exceptional cases occur in various classes of animals, in which the females instead of the males have acquired well pronounced secondary sexual characters, such as brighter colours, greater size, strength, or pugnacity. With birds there has sometimes been a complete transposition of the ordinary characters proper to each sex; the females having become the more eager in courtship, the males remaining comparatively passive, but apparently selecting the more attractive females, as we may infer from the results. Certain hen birds have thus been rendered more highly coloured or otherwise ornamented, as well as more

[31] 'Mammals and Birds of E. Florida,' pp. 234, 280, 295.

powerful and pugnacious than the cocks; these characters being transmitted to the female offspring alone.

It may be suggested that in some cases a double process of selection has been carried on; that the males have selected the more attractive females, and the latter the more attractive males. This process, however, though it might lead to the modification of both sexes, would not make the one sex different from the other, unless indeed their tastes for the beautiful differed; but this is a supposition too improbable to be worth considering in the case of any animal, excepting man. There are, however, many animals in which the sexes resemble each other, both being furnished with the same ornaments, which analogy would lead us to attribute to the agency of sexual selection. In such cases it may be suggested with more plausibility, that there has been a double or mutual process of sexual selection; the more vigorous and precocious females selecting the more attractive and vigorous males, the latter rejecting all except the more attractive females. But from what we know of the habits of animals, this view is hardly probable, for the male is generally eager to pair with any female. It is more probable that the ornaments common to both sexes were acquired by one sex, generally the male, and then transmitted to the offspring of both sexes. If, indeed, during a lengthened period the males of any species were greatly to exceed the females in number, and then during another lengthened period, but under different conditions, the reverse were to occur, a double, but not simultaneous, process of sexual selection might easily be carried on, by which the two sexes might be rendered widely different.

We shall hereafter see that many animals exist, of which neither sex is brilliantly coloured or provided with special ornaments, and yet the members of both sexes or of one alone have probably acquired simple colours, such as white or black, through sexual selection. The absence of bright tints or other ornaments may be the result of variations of the right kind never having occurred, or of the animals themselves having preferred plain black or white. Obscure tints have often been developed through natural selection for the sake of protection, and the acquirement through sexual selection of conspicuous colours, appears to have been sometimes checked from the danger thus incurred. But in other cases the males during long ages may have struggled together for the possession of the females, and yet no effect will have been produced, unless a larger number of offspring were left by the more successful males to inherit their superiority, than by the less successful : and this, as previously shewn, depends on many complex contingencies.

Sexual selection acts in a less rigorous manner than natural selection. The latter produces its effects by the life or death at all ages of the more or less successful individuals. Death, indeed, not rarely ensues from the conflicts of rival males. But generally the less successful male merely fails to obtain a female, or obtains a retarded and less vigorous female later in the season, or, if polygamous, obtains fewer females ; so that they leave fewer, less vigorous, or no offspring. In regard to structures acquired through ordinary or natural selection, there is in most cases, as long as the conditions of life remain the same, a limit to the amount of advantageous modification in relation to certain special purposes; but in regard to structures adapted to make one male victorious over another, either in fighting or in charming the female, there is no definite limit to the amount of advantageous modification; so that as long as the proper variations arise the work of sexual selection will go on. This circumstance may partly account for the frequent and extraordinary amount of variability presented by secondary sexual characters. Nevertheless, natural selection will determine that such characters shall not be acquired by the victorious males, if they would be highly injurious, either by expending too much of their vital powers, or by exposing them to any great danger. The development, however, of certain structures—of the horns, for instance, in certain stags—has been carried to a wonderful extreme; and in some cases to an extreme which, as far as the general conditions of life are concerned, must be slightly injurious to the male. From this fact we learn that the advantages which favoured males derive from conquering other males in battle or courtship, and thus leaving a numerous progeny, are in the long run greater than those derived from rather more perfect adaptation to their conditions of life. We shall further see, and it could never have been anticipated, that the power to charm the female has sometimes been more important than the power to conquer other males in battle.

LAWS OF INHERITANCE.

In order to understand how sexual selection has acted on many animals of many classes, and in the course of ages has produced a conspicuous result, it is necessary to bear in mind the laws of inheritance, as far as they are known. Two distinct elements are included under the term "inheritance"—the transmission, and the development of characters; but as these generally go together, the distinction is often overlooked. We see this distinction in those characters which are transmitted through the early years of life, but are developed only at maturity or during old age. We see the same distinction more clearly with secondary sexual characters, for these are transmitted through both sexes, though developed in one alone. That they are present in both sexes, is manifest when two species, having strongly-marked sexual characters, are crossed, for each transmits the characters proper to its own male and female sex to the hybrid offspring of either sex. The same fact is likewise manifest, when characters proper to the male are occasionally developed in the female when she grows old or becomes diseased, as, for instance, when the common hen assumes the flowing tail-feathers, hackles, comb, spurs, voice, and even pugnacity of the cock. Conversely, the same thing is evident, more or less plainly, with castrated males. Again, independently of old age or disease, characters are occasionally transferred from the male to the female, as when, in certain breeds of the fowl, spurs regularly appear in the young and healthy females. But in truth they are simply developed in the female; for in every breed each detail in the structure of the spur is transmitted through the female to her male offspring. Many cases will hereafter be given, where the female exhibits, more or less perfectly, characters proper to the male, in whom they must have been first developed, and then transferred to the female. The converse case of the first development of characters in the female and of transference to the male, is less frequent; it will therefore be well to give one striking instance. With bees the pollen-collecting apparatus is used by the female alone for gathering pollen for the larvæ, yet in most of the species it is partially developed in the males to whom it is quite useless, and it is perfectly developed in the males of Bombus or the humble-bee.[32] As not a single other Hymenopterous insect, not even the wasp, which is closely allied to the bee, is provided with a pollen-collecting apparatus, we have no grounds for supposing that male bees primordially collected pollen as well as the females; although we have some reason to suspect that male mammals primordially suckled their young as well as the females. Lastly, in all cases of reversion, characters are transmitted through two, three, or many more generations, and are then developed under certain unknown favourable conditions. This important distinction between transmission and development will be best kept in mind by the aid of the hypothesis of pangenesis. According to this hypothesis, every unit or cell of the body throws off gemmules or undeveloped atoms, which are transmitted to the offspring of both sexes, and are multiplied by self-division. They may remain undeveloped during the early years of life or during successive generations; and their development into units or cells, like those from which they were derived, depends on their affinity for, and union with other units or cells previously developed in the due order of growth.

[32] H. Müller, 'Anwendung der Darwin'schen Lehre,' &c. Verh. d. n. V. Jahrg. xxix. p. 42.

Inheritance at corresponding Periods of Life.—This tendency is well established. A new character, appearing in a young animal, whether it lasts throughout life or is only transient, will, in general, reappear in the offspring at the same age and last for the same time. If, on the other hand, a new character appears at maturity, or even during old age, it tends to reappear in the offspring at the same advanced age. When deviations from this rule occur, the transmitted characters much oftener appear before, than after the corresponding age. As I have dwelt on this subject sufficiently in another work,[33] I will here merely give two or three instances, for the sake of recalling the subject to the reader's mind. In several breeds of the Fowl, the down-covered chickens, the young birds in their first true plumage, and the adults differ greatly from one another, as well as from their common parent-form, the *Gallus bankiva;* and these characters are faithfully transmitted by each breed to their offspring at the corresponding periods of life. For instance, the chickens of spangled Hamburgs, whilst covered with down, have a few dark spots on the head and rump, but are not striped longitudinally, as in many other breeds; in their first true plumage, "they are beautifully pencilled," that is each feather is transversely marked by numerous dark bars; but in their second plumage the feathers all become spangled or tipped with a dark round spot.[34] Hence in this breed

[33] 'The Variation of Animals and Plants under Domestication,' vol. ii. 1868, p. 75. In the last chapter but one, the provisional hypothesis of pangenesis, above alluded to, is fully explained.

[34] These facts are given on the high authority of a great breeder, Mr. Teebay; see Tegetmeier's 'Poultry Book,' 1868, p. 158. On the characters of chickens of different breeds, and on the

variations have occurred at, and been transmitted to, three distinct periods of life. The Pigeon offers a more remarkable case, because the aboriginal parent species does not undergo any change of plumage with advancing age, excepting that at maturity the breast becomes more iridescent; yet there are breeds which do not acquire their characteristic colours until they have moulted two, three, or four times; and these modifications of plumage are regularly transmitted.

Inheritance at corresponding Seasons of the Year.—
With animals in a state of nature, innumerable instances occur of characters appearing periodically at different seasons. We see this in the horns of the stag, and in the fur of arctic animals which becomes thick and white during the winter. Many birds acquire bright colours and other decorations during the breeding-season alone. Pallas states,[35] that in Siberia domestic cattle and horses become lighter-coloured during the winter; and I have myself observed, and heard of similar strongly marked changes of colour, that is, from brownish cream-colour or reddish-brown to a perfect white, in several ponies in England. Although I do not know that this tendency to change the colour of the coat during different seasons is transmitted, yet it probably is so, as all shades of colour are strongly inherited by the horse. Nor is

breeds of the pigeon, alluded to in the following paragraph, see 'Variation of Animals,' &c., vol. i. pp. 160, 249; vol. ii. p. 77.

[35] 'Novæ species Quadrupedum e Glirium ordine,' 1778, p. 7. On the transmission of colour by the horse, see 'Variation of Animals, &c., under Domestication,' vol. i. p. 51. Also vol. ii. p. 71, for a general discussion on 'Inheritance as limited by Sex.'

this form of inheritance, as limited by the seasons, more remarkable than its limitation by age or sex.

Inheritance as Limited by Sex.—The equal transmission of characters to both sexes is the commonest form of inheritance, at least with those animals which do not present strongly-marked sexual differences, and indeed with many of these. But characters are somewhat commonly transferred exclusively to that sex, in which they first appear. Ample evidence on this head has been advanced in my work on 'Variation under Domestication,' but a few instances may here be given. There are breeds of the sheep and goat, in which the horns of the male differ greatly in shape from those of the female; and these differences, acquired under domestication, are regularly transmitted to the same sex. As a rule, it is the females alone in cats which are tortoise-shell, the corresponding colour in the males being rusty-red. With most breeds of the fowl, the characters proper to each sex are transmitted to the same sex alone. So general is this form of transmission that it is an anomaly when variations in certain breeds are transmitted equally to both sexes. There are also certain sub-breeds of the fowl in which the males can hardly be distinguished from one another, whilst the females differ considerably in colour. The sexes of the pigeon in the parent-species do not differ in any external character; nevertheless, in certain domesticated breeds the male is coloured differently from the female.[36] The wattle in the English Carrier

[36] Dr. Chapuis, 'Le Pigeon Voyageur Belge,' 1865, p. 87. Boitard et Corbié, 'Les Pigeons de Volière,' &c., 1824, p. 173. See, also, on similar differences in certain breeds at Modena, 'Le variazioni dei Colombi domestici,' del Paolo Bonizzi, 1873.

pigeon, and the crop in the Pouter, are more highly developed in the male than in the female; and although these characters have been gained through long-continued selection by man, the slight differences between the sexes are wholly due to the form of inheritance which has prevailed; for they have arisen, not from, but rather in opposition to, the wish of the breeder.

Most of our domestic races have been formed by the accumulation of many slight variations; and as some of the successive steps have been transmitted to one sex alone, and some to both sexes, we find in the different breeds of the same species all gradations between great sexual dissimilarity and complete similarity. Instances have already been given with the breeds of the fowl and pigeon, and under nature analogous cases are common. With animals under domestication, but whether in nature I will not venture to say, one sex may lose characters proper to it, and may thus come somewhat to resemble the opposite sex; for instance, the males of some breeds of the fowl have lost their masculine tail-plumes and hackles. On the other hand, the differences between the sexes may be increased under domestication, as with merino sheep, in which the ewes have lost their horns. Again, characters proper to one sex may suddenly appear in the other sex; as in those sub-breeds of the fowl in which the hens acquire spurs whilst young; or, as in certain Polish sub-breeds, in which the females, as there is reason to believe, originally acquired a crest, and subsequently transferred it to the males. All these cases are intelligible on the hypothesis of pangenesis; for they depend on the gemmules of certain parts, although present in both sexes, becoming, through the influence of domestication, either dormant or developed in either sex.

There is one difficult question which it will be convenient to defer to a future chapter; namely, whether a character at first developed in both sexes, could through selection be limited in its development to one sex alone. If, for instance, a breeder observed that some of his pigeons (of which the characters are usually transferred in an equal degree to both sexes) varied into pale blue, could he by long-continued selection make a breed, in which the males alone should be of this tint, whilst the females remained unchanged? I will here only say, that this, though perhaps not impossible, would be extremely difficult; for the natural result of breeding from the pale-blue males would be to change the whole stock of both sexes to this tint. If, however, variations of the desired tint appeared, which were from the first limited in their development to the male sex, there would not be the least difficulty in making a breed with the two sexes of a different colour, as indeed has been effected with a Belgian breed, in which the males alone are streaked with black. In a similar manner, if any variation appeared in a female pigeon, which was from the first sexually limited in its development to the females, it would be easy to make a breed with the females alone thus characterised; but if the variation was not thus originally limited, the process would be extremely difficult, perhaps impossible.[37]

[37] Since the publication of the first edition of this work, it has been highly satisfactory to me to find the following remarks (the 'Field,' Sept. 1872) from so experienced a breeder as Mr. Tegetmeier. After describing some curious cases in pigeons,

On the Relation between the Period of Development of a Character and its Transmission to one Sex or to both Sexes.—Why certain characters should be inherited by both sexes, and other characters by one sex alone, namely by that sex in which the character first appeared, is in most cases quite unknown. We cannot even conjecture why with certain sub-breeds of the pigeon, black striæ, though transmitted through the female, should be developed in the male alone, whilst every other character is equally transferred to both sexes. Why, again, with cats, the tortoise-shell colour should, with rare exceptions, be developed in the female alone. The very same character, such as deficient or supernumerary digits, colour-blindness, &c., may with mankind be inherited by the males alone of one family, and in another family by the females alone, though in both cases transmitted through the opposite as well as through the same sex.[38] Although we are thus ignorant, the two following rules seem often to hold good—that variations which first appear in either sex at a late period of life, tend to be developed in the same sex alone; whilst variations which first appear early in life in either sex tend to be developed in both sexes. I am, however, far from supposing that this is the sole determining cause. As

---

of the transmission of colour by one sex alone, and the formation of a sub-breed with this character, he says: " It is a " singular circumstance that Mr. " Darwin should have suggested " the possibility of modifying " the sexual colours of birds by " a course of artificial selection.

" When he did so, he was in " ignorance of these facts that I " have related; but it is remark- " able how very closely he sug- " gested the right method of " procedure."

[38] References are given in my 'Variation of Animals under Domestication,' vol. ii. p. 72.

I have not elsewhere discussed this subject, and as it has an important bearing on sexual selection, I must here enter into lengthy and somewhat intricate details.

It is in itself probable that any character appearing at an early age would tend to be inherited equally by both sexes, for the sexes do not differ much in constitution before the power of reproduction is gained. On the other hand, after this power has been gained and the sexes have come to differ in constitution, the gemmules (if I may again use the language of pangenesis) which are cast off from each varying part in the one sex would be much more likely to possess the proper affinities for uniting with the tissues of the same sex, and thus becoming developed, than with those of the opposite sex.

I was first led to infer that a relation of this kind exists, from the fact that whenever and in whatever manner the adult male differs from the adult female, he differs in the same manner from the young of both sexes. The generality of this fact is quite remarkable: it holds good with almost all mammals, birds, amphibians, and fishes; also with many crustaceans, spiders, and some few insects, such as certain orthoptera and libellulæ. In all these cases the variations, through the accumulation of which the male acquired his proper masculine characters, must have occurred at a somewhat late period of life; otherwise the young males would have been similarly characterised; and conformably with our rule, the variations are transmitted to and developed in the adult males alone. When, on the other hand, the adult male closely resembles the young of both sexes (these, with rare exceptions, being alike), he generally resembles the adult female; and in most of these cases the variations through which the young and old acquired their present characters, probably occurred, according to our rule, during youth. But there is here room for doubt, for characters are sometimes transferred to the offspring at an earlier age than that at which they first appeared in the parents, so that the parents may have varied when adult, and have transferred their characters to their offspring whilst young. There are, moreover, many animals, in which the two sexes closely resemble each other, and yet both differ from their young; and here the characters of the adults must have been acquired late in life; nevertheless, these characters, in apparent contradiction to our rule, are transferred to both sexes. We must not, however, overlook the possibility or even probability of successive variations of the same nature occurring, under exposure to similar conditions, simultaneously in both sexes at a rather late period of life; and in this case the variations would be transferred to the offspring of both sexes at a corresponding late age; and there would then be no real contradiction to the rule that variations occurring late in life are transferred exclusively to the sex in which they first appeared. This latter rule seems to hold true more generally than the second one, namely, that variations which occur in either sex early in life tend to be transferred to both sexes. As it was obviously impossible even to estimate in how large a number of cases throughout the animal kingdom these two propositions held good, it occurred to me to investigate some striking or crucial instances, and to rely on the result.

An excellent case for investigation is afforded by the

Deer family. In all the species, but one, the horns are developed only in the males, though certainly transmitted through the females, and capable of abnormal development in them. In the reindeer, on the other hand, the female is provided with horns; so that in this species, the horns ought, according to our rule, to appear early in life, long before the two sexes are mature and have come to differ much in constitution. In all the other species the horns ought to appear later in life, which would lead to their development in that sex alone, in which they first appeared in the progenitor of the whole Family. Now in seven species, belonging to distinct sections of the family and inhabiting different regions, in which the stags alone bear horns, I find that the horns first appear at periods, varying from nine months after birth in the roebuck, to ten, twelve or even more months in the stags of the six other and larger species.[39] But with the reindeer the case is widely different; for, as I hear from Prof. Nilsson, who kindly made special enquiries for me in Lapland, the horns appear in the young animals within four or five weeks after birth, and at the same time in both sexes. So that here we have a structure, developed at a most unusually early age in one species of the family, and likewise common to both sexes in this one species alone.

[39] I am much obliged to Mr. Cupples for having made enquiries for me in regard to the Roebuck and Red Deer of Scotland from Mr. Robertson, the experienced head-forester to the Marquis of Breadalbane. In regard to Fallow-deer, I have to thank Mr. Eyton and others for information. For the *Cervus alces* of N. America, see 'Land and Water,' 1868, pp. 221 and 254; and for the *C. Virginianus* and *strongyloceros* of the same continent, see J. D. Caton, in 'Ottawa Acad. of Nat. Sc.' 1868, p. 13. For *Cervus Eldi* of Pegu, see Lieut. Beavan, 'Proc. Zoolog. Soc.' 1867, p. 762.

In several kinds of antelopes, only the males are provided with horns, whilst in the greater number both sexes bear horns. With respect to the period of development, Mr. Blyth informs me that there was at one time in the Zoological Gardens a young koodoo (*Ant. strepsiceros*), of which the males alone are horned, and also the young of a closely-allied species, the eland (*Ant. oreas*), in which both sexes are horned. Now it is in strict conformity with our rule, that in the young male koodoo, although ten months old, the horns were remarkably small, considering the size ultimately attained by them; whilst in the young male eland, although only three months old, the horns were already very much larger than in the koodoo. It is also a noticeable fact that in the prong-horned antelope,[40] only a few of the females, about one in five, have horns, and these are in a rudimentary state, though sometimes above four inches long; so that as far as concerns the possession of horns by the males alone, this species is in an intermediate condition, and the horns do not appear until about five or six months after birth. Therefore in comparison with what little we know of the development of the horns in other antelopes, and from what we do know with respect to the horns of deer, cattle, &c., those of the prong-horned antelope appear at an intermediate period of life,—that is, not very early, as in cattle and sheep, nor very late, as in the larger deer and antelopes. The horns of sheep, goats, and cattle, which are well developed in both sexes, though not quite equal in size, can be felt, or

[40] *Antilocapra Americana.* I have to thank Dr. Canfield for information with respect to the horns of the female : see also his paper in 'Proc. Zoolog. Soc.' 1866, p. 109. Also Owen, 'Anatomy of Vertebrates,' vol. iii. p. 627.

even seen, at birth or soon afterwards.[41] Our rule, however, seems to fail in some breeds of sheep, for instance merinos, in which the rams alone are horned; for I cannot find on enquiry,[42] that the horns are developed later in life in this breed than in ordinary sheep in which both sexes are horned. But with domesticated sheep the presence or absence of horns is not a firmly fixed character; for a certain proportion of the merino ewes bear small horns, and some of the rams are hornless; and in most breeds hornless ewes are occasionally produced.

Dr. W. Marshall has lately made a special study of the protuberances so common on the heads of birds,[43] and he comes to the following conclusion;—that with those species in which they are confined to the males, they are developed late in life; whereas with those species in which they are common to the two sexes, they are developed at a very early period. This is certainly a striking confirmation of my two laws of inheritance.

In most of the species of the splendid family of the

[41] I have been assured that the horns of the sheep in North Wales can always be felt, and are sometimes even an inch in length, at birth. Youatt says ('Cattle,' 1834, p. 277), that the prominence of the frontal bone in cattle penetrates the cutis at birth, and that the horny matter is soon formed over it.

[42] I am greatly indebted to Prof. Victor Carus for having made enquiries for me, from the highest authorities, with respect to the merino sheep of Saxony. On the Guinea coast of Africa there is, however, a breed of sheep in which, as with merinos, the rams alone bear horns; and Mr. Winwood Reade informs me that in one case observed by him, a young ram, born on Feb. 10th, first shewed horns on March 6th, so that in this instance, in conformity with rule, the development of the horns occurred at a later period of life than in Welsh sheep, in which both sexes are horned.

[43] 'Ueber die knöchernen Schädelhöcker der Vögel' in the 'Niederlandischen Archiv für Zoologie,' Band I. Heft 2, 1872.

Pheasants, the males differ conspicuously from the females, and they acquire their ornaments at a rather late period of life. The eared pheasant (*Crossoptilon auritum*), however, offers a remarkable exception, for both sexes possess the fine caudal plumes, the large ear-tufts and the crimson velvet about the head; I find that all these characters appear very early in life in accordance with rule. The adult male can, however, be distinguished from the adult female by the presence of spurs; and conformably with our rule, these do not begin to be developed before the age of six months, as I am assured by Mr. Bartlett, and even at this age, the two sexes can hardly be distinguished.[44] The male and female Peacock differ conspicuously from each other in almost every part of their plumage, except in the elegant head-crest, which is common to both sexes; and this is developed very early in life, long before the other ornaments, which are confined to the male. The wild-duck offers an analogous case, for the beautiful green speculum on the wings is common to both sexes, though duller and somewhat smaller in the female, and it is developed early in life, whilst the curled tail-feathers and other ornaments of the male are developed later.[45] Between such extreme cases of

[44] In the common peacock (*Pavo cristatus*) the male alone possesses spurs, whilst both sexes of the Java Peacock (*P. muticus*) offer the unusual case of being furnished with spurs. Hence I fully expected that in the latter species they would have been developed earlier in life than in the common peacock; but M. Hegt of Amsterdam informs me, that with young birds of the previous year, of both species, compared on April 23rd, 1869, there was no difference in the development of the spurs. The spurs, however, were as yet represented merely by slight knobs or elevations. I presume that I should have been informed if any difference in the rate of development had been observed subsequently.

[45] In some other species of the Duck family the speculum differs in a greater degree in the

close sexual resemblance and wide dissimilarity, as those of the Crossoptilon and peacock, many intermediate ones could be given, in which the characters follow our two rules in their order of development.

As most insects emerge from the pupal state in a mature condition, it is doubtful whether the period of development can determine the transference of their characters to one or to both sexes. But we do not know that the coloured scales, for instance, in two species of butterflies, in one of which the sexes differ in colour, whilst in the other they are alike, are developed at the same relative age in the cocoon. Nor do we know whether all the scales are simultaneously developed on the wings of the same species of butterfly, in which certain coloured marks are confined to one sex, whilst others are common to both sexes. A difference of this kind in the period of development is not so improbable as it may at first appear; for with the Orthoptera, which assume their adult state, not by a single metamorphosis, but by a succession of moults, the young males of some species at first resemble the females, and acquire their distinctive masculine

two sexes; but I have not been able to discover whether its full development occurs later in life in the males of such species, than in the male of the common duck, as ought to be the case according to our rule.   With the allied *Mergus cucullatus* we have, however, a case of this kind : the two sexes differ conspicuously in general plumage, and to a considerable degree in the speculum, which is pure white in the male and greyish-white in the female. Now the young males at first entirely resemble the females, and have a greyish-white speculum, which becomes pure white at an earlier age than that at which the adult male acquires his other and more strongly-marked sexual differences : see Audubon, 'Ornithological Biography,' vol. iii. 1835, pp. 249–250.

characters only at a later moult. Strictly analogous cases occur at the successive moults of certain male crustaceans.

We have as yet considered the transference of characters, relatively to their period of development, only in species in a natural state; we will now turn to domesticated animals, and first touch on monstrosities and diseases. The presence of supernumerary digits, and the absence of certain phalanges, must be determined at an early embryonic period—the tendency to profuse bleeding is at least congenital, as is probably colour-blindness—yet these peculiarities, and other similar ones, are often limited in their transmission to one sex; so that the rule that characters, developed at an early period, tend to be transmitted to both sexes, here wholly fails. But this rule, as before remarked, does not appear to be nearly so general as the converse one, namely, that characters which appear late in life in one sex are transmitted exclusively to the same sex. From the fact of the above abnormal peculiarities becoming attached to one sex, long before the sexual functions are active, we may infer that there must be some difference between the sexes at an extremely early age. With respect to sexually-limited diseases, we know too little of the period at which they originate, to draw any safe conclusion. Gout, however, seems to fall under our rule, for it is generally caused by intemperance during manhood, and is transmitted from the father to his sons in a much more marked manner than to his daughters.

In the various domestic breeds of sheep, goats, and cattle, the males differ from their respective females in the shape or development of their horns, forehead,

mane, dewlap, tail, and hump on the shoulders; and
these peculiarities, in accordance with our rule, are not
fully developed until a rather late period of life.   The
sexes of dogs do not differ, except that in certain
breeds, especially in the Scotch deer-hound, the male
is much larger and heavier than the female ; and, as
we shall see in a future chapter, the male goes on
increasing in size to an unusually late period of life,
which, according to rule, will account for his increased
size being transmitted to his male offspring alone.   On
the other hand, the tortoise-shell colour, which is confined to female cats, is quite distinct at birth, and this
case violates the rule.   There is a breed of pigeons in
which the males alone are streaked with black, and the
streaks can be detected even in the nestlings ; but they
become more conspicuous at each successive moult, so
that this case partly opposes and partly supports the
rule.   With the English Carrier and Pouter pigeons,
the full development of the wattle and the crop occurs
rather late in life, and conformably with the rule,
these characters are transmitted in full perfection to
the males alone. The following cases perhaps come within the class previously alluded to, in which both sexes
have varied in the same manner at a rather late period
of life, and have consequently transferred their new
characters to both sexes at a corresponding late period ;
and if so, these cases are not opposed to our rule :—
there exist sub-breeds of the pigeon, described by
Neumeister,[46] in which both sexes change their colour
during two or three moults (as is likewise the case
with the Almond Tumbler), nevertheless, these changes,

[46] 'Das Ganze der Tauben-
zucht,' 1837, s. 21, 24. For the
case of the streaked pigeons,
see Dr. Chapuis, 'Le pigeon
voyageur Belge,' 1865, p. 87.

though occurring rather late in life, are common to both sexes. One variety of the Canary-bird, namely the London Prize, offers a nearly analogous case.

With the breeds of the Fowl the inheritance of various characters by one or both sexes, seems generally determined by the period at which such characters are developed. Thus in all the many breeds in which the adult male differs greatly in colour from the female, as well as from the wild parent-species, he differs also from the young male, so that the newly-acquired characters must have appeared at a rather late period of life. On the other hand, in most of the breeds in which the two sexes resemble each other, the young are coloured in nearly the same manner as their parents, and this renders it probable that their colours first appeared early in life. We have instances of this fact in all black and white breeds, in which the young and old of both sexes are alike; nor can it be maintained that there is something peculiar in a black or white plumage, which leads to its transference to both sexes; for the males alone of many natural species are either black or white, the females being differently coloured. With the so-called Cuckoo sub-breeds of the fowl, in which the feathers are trans-versely pencilled with dark stripes, both sexes and the chickens are coloured in nearly the same manner. The laced plumage of the Sebright bantam is the same in both sexes, and in the young chickens the wing-feathers are distinctly, though imperfectly laced. Spangled Hamburgs, however, offer a partial excep-tion; for the two sexes, though not quite alike, resemble each other more closely than do the sexes of the aboriginal parent-species; yet they acquire their characteristic plumage late in life, for the chickens are distinctly pencilled. With respect to other characters besides colour, in the wild-parent species and in most of the domestic breeds, the males alone possess a well-developed comb; but in the young of the Spanish fowl it is largely developed at a very early age, and, in accordance with this early development in the male, it is of unusual size in the adult female. In the Game breeds pugnacity is developed at a wonderfully early age, of which curious proofs could be given; and this character is transmitted to both sexes, so that the hens, from their extreme pugnacity, are now generally exhibited in separate pens. With the Polish breeds the bony protuberance of the skull which supports the crest is partially developed even before the chickens are hatched, and the crest itself soon begins to grow, though at first feebly; [47] and in this breed the adults of both sexes are characterised by a great bony protuberance and an immense crest.

Finally, from what we have now seen of the relation which exists in many natural species and domesticated races, between the period of the development of their characters and the manner of their transmission—for example, the striking fact of the early growth of the horns in the reindeer, in which both sexes bear horns, in comparison with their much later growth in the other species in which the male alone bears horns—we may conclude that one, though not the sole cause of

[47] For full particulars and references on all these points respecting the several breeds of the Fowl, see 'Variation of Animals and Plants under Domestication,' vol. i. pp. 250, 256. In regard to the higher animals, the sexual differences which have arisen under domestication are described in the same work under the head of each species.

characters being exclusively inherited by one sex, is their development at a late age. And secondly, that one, though apparently a less efficient cause of characters being inherited by both sexes, is their development at an early age, whilst the sexes differ but little in constitution. It appears, however, that some difference must exist between the sexes even during a very early embryonic period, for characters developed at this age not rarely become attached to one sex.

Summary and concluding remarks.—From the foregoing discussion on the various laws of inheritance, we learn that the characters of the parents often, or even generally, tend to become developed in the offspring of the same sex, at the same age, and periodically at the same season of the year, in which they first appeared in the parents. But these rules, owing to unknown causes, are far from being fixed. Hence during the modification of a species, the successive changes may readily be transmitted in different ways; some to one sex, and some to both; some to the offspring at one age, and some to the offspring at all ages. Not only are the laws of inheritance extremely complex, but so are the causes which induce and govern variability. The variations thus induced are preserved and accumulated by sexual selection, which is in itself an extremely complex affair, depending, as it does, on the ardour in love, the courage, and the rivalry of the males, as well as on the powers of perception, the taste, and will of the female. Sexual selection will also be largely dominated by natural selection tending towards the general welfare of the species. Hence the manner in which the individuals of either or both sexes have been affected through sexual selection cannot fail to be complex in the highest degree.

When variations occur late in life in one sex, and are transmitted to the same sex at the same age, the other sex and the young are left unmodified. When they occur late in life, but are transmitted to both sexes at the same age, the young alone are left unmodified. Variations, however, may occur at any period of life in one sex or in both, and be transmitted to both sexes at all ages, and then all the individuals of the species are similarly modified. In the following chapters it will be seen that all these cases frequently occur in nature.

Sexual selection can never act on any animal before the age for reproduction arrives. From the great eagerness of the male it has generally acted on this sex and not on the females. The males have thus become provided with weapons for fighting with their rivals, with organs for discovering and securely holding the female, and for exciting or charming her. When the sexes differ in these respects, it is also, as we have seen, an extremely general law that the adult male differs more or less from the young male; and we may conclude from this fact that the successive variations, by which the adult male became modified, did not generally occur much before the age for reproduction. Whenever some or many of the variations occurred early in life, the young males would partake more or less of the characters of the adult males; and differences of this kind between the old and young males may be observed in many species of animals.

It is probable that young male animals have often tended to vary in a manner which would not only have been of no use to them at an early age, but would have been actually injurious—as by acquiring bright colours, which would render them conspicuous to their enemies, or by acquiring structures, such as great horns, which would expend much vital force in their development. Variations of this kind occurring in the young males would almost certainly be eliminated through natural selection. With the adult and experienced males, on the other hand, the advantages derived from the acquisition of such characters, would more than counterbalance some exposure to danger, and some loss of vital force.

As variations which give to the male a better chance of conquering other males, or of finding, securing, or charming the opposite sex, would, if they happened to arise in the female, be of no service to her, they would not be preserved in her through sexual selection. We have also good evidence with domesticated animals, that variations of all kinds are, if not carefully selected, soon lost through intercrossing and accidental deaths. Consequently in a state of nature, if variations of the above kind chanced to arise in the female line, and to be transmitted exclusively in this line, they would be extremely liable to be lost. If, however, the females varied and transmitted their newly acquired characters to their offspring of both sexes, the characters which were advantageous to the males would be preserved by them through sexual selection, and the two sexes would in consequence be modified in the same manner, although such characters were of no use to the females : but I shall hereafter have to recur to these more intricate contingencies. Lastly, the females may acquire, and apparently have often acquired by trans-ference, characters from the male sex.

As variations occurring late in life, and transmitted

to one sex alone, have incessantly been taken advantage
of and accumulated through sexual selection in relation
to the reproduction of the species; therefore it appears,
at first sight, an unaccountable fact that similar
variations have not frequently been accumulated
through natural selection, in relation to the ordinary
habits of life. If this had occurred, the two sexes
would often have been differently modified, for the
sake, for instance, of capturing prey or of escaping
from danger. Differences of this kind between the
two sexes do occasionally occur, especially in the lower
classes. But this implies that the two sexes follow
different habits in their struggles for existence, which
is a rare circumstance with the higher animals. The
case, however, is widely different with the reproductive
functions, in which respect the sexes necessarily differ.
For variations in structure which are related to these
functions, have often proved of value to one sex, and
from having arisen at a late period of life, have been
transmitted to one sex alone; and such variations, thus
preserved and transmitted, have given rise to secondary
sexual characters.

In the following chapters, I shall treat of the
secondary sexual characters in animals of all classes,
and shall endeavour in each case to apply the principles
explained in the present chapter. The lowest classes
will detain us for a very short time, but the higher
animals, especially birds, must be treated at considerable length. It should be borne in mind that for
reasons already assigned, I intend to give only a few
illustrative instances of the innumerable structures by
the aid of which the male finds the female, or, when
found, holds her. On the other hand, all structures

and instincts by the aid of which the male conquers other males, and by which he allures or excites the female, will be fully discussed, as these are in many ways the most interesting.

Supplement on the proportional numbers of the two sexes in animals belonging to various classes.

As no one, as far as I can discover, has paid attention to the relative numbers of the two sexes throughout the animal kingdom, I will here give such materials as I have been able to collect, although they are extremely imperfect. They consist in only a few instances of actual enumeration, and the numbers are not very large. As the proportions are known with certainty only in mankind, I will first give them as a standard of comparison.

Man.—In England during ten years (from 1857 to 1866) the average number of children born alive yearly was 707,120, in the proportion of 104·5 males to 100 females. But in 1857 the male births throughout England were as 105·2, and in 1865 as 104 0 to 100. Looking to separate districts, in Buckinghamshire (where about 5000 children are annually born) the *mean* proportion of male to female births, during the whole period of the above ten years, was as 102·8 to 100; whilst in N. Wales (where the average annual births are 12,873) it was as high as 106·2 to 100. Taking a still smaller district, viz., Rutlandshire (where the annual births average only 739), in 1864 the male births were as 114·6, and in 1862 as only 97·0 to 100; but even in this small district the average of the 7385 births during the whole ten years, was as 104·5 to 100:

that is in the same ratio as throughout England.[48]
The proportions are sometimes slightly disturbed by
unknown causes; thus Prof. Faye states " that in some
"districts of Norway there has been during a decennial
"period a steady deficiency of boys, whilst in others
"the opposite condition has existed." In France
during forty-four years the male to the female births
have been as 106·2 to 100; but during this period it
has occurred five times in one department, and six times
in another, that the female births have exceeded the
males. In Russia the average proportion is as high as
108·9, and in Philadelphia in the United States as 110·5
to 100.[49] The average for Europe, deduced by Bickes
from about seventy million births, is 106 males to 100
females. On the other hand, with white children born
at the Cape of Good Hope, the proportion of males is so
low as to fluctuate during successive years between 90
and 99 males for every 100 females. It is a singular
fact that with Jews the proportion of male births is
decidedly larger than with Christians : thus in Prussia
the proportion is as 113, in Breslau as 114, and in
Livonia as 120 to 100; the Christian births in these
countries being the same as usual, for instance, in
Livonia as 104 to 100.[50]

---

[48] 'Twenty-ninth Annual Report of the Registrar-General for 1866.' In this report (p. xii.) a special decennial table is given.

[49] For Norway and Russia, see abstract of Prof. Faye's researches, in ' British and Foreign Medico-Chirurg. Review,' April, 1867, pp. 343, 345. For France, the ' Annuaire pour l'An 1867,' p. 213. For Philadelphia, Dr.

Stockton Hough, ' Social Science Assoc.' 1874. For the Cape of Good Hope, Quetelet as quoted by Dr. H. H. Zouteveen, in the Dutch Translation of this work (vol. i. p. 417), where much information is given on the proportion of the sexes.

[50] In regard to the Jews, see M. Thury, ' La Loi de Production des Sexes,' 1863, p. 25.

Prof. Faye remarks that "a still greater preponder-"ance of males would be met with, if death struck both "sexes in equal proportion in the womb and during "birth. But the fact is, that for every 100 still-born "females, we have in several countries from 134·6 to "144·9 still-born males. During the first four or five "years of life, also, more male children die than females, "for example in England, during the first year, 126 "boys die for every 100 girls—a proportion which in "France is still more unfavourable."[51] Dr. Stockton-Hough accounts for these facts in part by the more frequent defective development of males than of females. We have before seen that the male sex is more variable in structure than the female; and variations in important organs would generally be injurious. But the size of the body, and especially of the head, being greater in male than female infants is another cause: for the males are thus more liable to be injured during parturition. Consequently the still-born males are more numerous; and, as a highly competent judge, Dr. Crichton Browne,[52] believes, male infants often

[51] 'British and Foreign Medico-Chirurg. Review,' April, 1867, p. 343. Dr. Stark also remarks ('Tenth Annual Report of Births, Deaths, &c., in Scotland,' 1867, p. xxviii.) that "These examples may suffice to "show that, at almost every "stage of life, the males in "Scotland have a greater lia-"bility to death and a higher "death-rate than the females. "The fact, however, of this "peculiarity being most strongly "developed at that infantile "period of life when the dress, "food, and general treatment of "both sexes are alike, seems to "prove that the higher male "death-rate is an impressed, "natural, and constitutional "peculiarity due to sex alone."

[52] 'West Riding Lunatic Asylum Reports,' vol. i. 1871, p. 8. Sir J. Simpson has proved that the head of the male infant exceeds that of the female by 3-8ths of an inch in circumference, and by 1-8th in transverse diameter. Quetelet has shown that woman is born smaller than man; see Dr. Duncan, 'Fecundity, Fertility, Sterility,' 1871, p. 382.

suffer in health for some years after birth. Owing to
this excess in the death-rate of male children, both
at birth and for some time subsequently, and owing to
the exposure of grown men to various dangers, and to
their tendency to emigrate, the females in all old-
settled countries, where statistical records have been
kept,[53] are found to preponderate considerably over
the males.

It seems at first sight a mysterious fact that in
different nations, under different conditions and climates, in Naples, Prussia, Westphalia, Holland, France,
England and the United States, the excess of male over
female births is less when they are illegitimate than
when legitimate.[54] This has been explained by
different writers in many different ways, as from the
mothers being generally young, from the large proportion of first pregnancies, &c. But we have seen
that male infants, from the large size of their heads,
suffer more than female infants during parturition ;
and as the mothers of illegitimate children must be
more liable than other women to undergo bad labours,
from various causes, such as attempts at concealment
by tight lacing, hard work, distress of mind, &c., their
male infants would proportionably suffer. And this
probably is the most efficient of all the causes of the
proportion of males to females born alive being less
amongst illegitimate children than amongst the legitimate. With most animals the greater size of the adult

[53] With the savage Guaranys
of Paraguay, according to the
accurate Azara ('Voyages dans
l'Amérique merid.' tom. ii. 1809,
p. 60, 179), the women are to
the men in the proportion of 14
to 13.

[54] Babbage, 'Edinburgh Journal of Science,' 1829, vol. i. p.
88; also p. 90, on still-born
children. On illegitimate children in England, see 'Report of
Registrar-General for 1866,'
p. xv.

male than of the female, is due to the stronger males having conquered the weaker in their struggles for the possession of the females, and no doubt it is owing to this fact that the two sexes of at least some animals differ in size at birth. Thus we have the curious fact that we may attribute the more frequent deaths of male than female infants, especially amongst the illegitimate, at least in part to sexual selection.

It has often been supposed that the relative age of the two parents determines the sex of the offspring; and Prof. Leuckart[55] has advanced what he considers sufficient evidence, with respect to man and certain domesticated animals, that this is one important though not the sole factor in the result. So again the period of impregnation relatively to the state of the female has been thought by some to be the efficient cause; but recent observations discountenance this belief. According to Dr. Stockton-Hough,[56] the season of the year, the poverty or wealth of the parents, residence in the country or in cities, the crossing of foreign immigrants, &c., all influence the proportion of the sexes. With mankind, polygamy has also been supposed to lead to the birth of a greater proportion of female infants; but Dr. J. Campbell[57] carefully attended to this subject in the harems of Siam, and concludes that the proportion of male to female births is the same as from monogamous unions. Hardly any animal has been rendered so highly polygamous as the English race-horse, and we shall immediately see that his male and female offspring are almost exactly equal

[55] Leuckart, in Wagner 'Handwörterbuch der Phys.' B. iv. 1853, s. 774.
[56] Social Science Assoc. of Philadelphia, 1874.
[57] 'Anthropological Review,' April, 1870, p. cviii.

in number. I will now give the facts which I have collected with respect to the proportional numbers of the sexes of various animals; and will then briefly discuss how far selection has come into play in determining the result.

Horses.—Mr. Tegetmeier has been so kind as to tabulate for me from the 'Racing Calendar' the births of race-horses during a period of twenty-one years, viz., from 1846 to 1867; 1849 being omitted, as no returns were that year published. The total births were 25,560,[58] consisting of 12,763 males and 12,797 females, or in the proportion of 99·7 males to 100 females. As these numbers are tolerably large, and as they are drawn from all parts of England, during several years, we may with much confidence conclude that with the domestic horse, or at least with the race-horse, the two sexes are produced in almost equal numbers. The fluctuations in the proportions during successive years are closely like those which occur with mankind, when a small and thinly-populated area is considered; thus in 1856 the male horses were as 107·1, and in 1867 as only 92·6 to 100 females. In the tabulated returns the proportions vary in cycles, for the males exceeded the females during six successive years; and the females exceeded the males during two periods each of four years: this, however, may be accidental; at least I can detect nothing of the kind with man in the decennial table in the Registrar's Report for 1866.

Dogs.—During a period of twelve years, from 1857 to 1868, the births of a large number of greyhounds, throughout England, were sent to the 'Field' newspaper; and I am again indebted to Mr. Tegetmeier for carefully tabulating the results. The recorded births were 6878, consisting of 3605 males and 3273 females, that is, in

---

[58] During eleven years a record was kept of the number of mares which proved barren or prematurely slipped their foals; and it deserves notice, as shewing how infertile these highly-nurtured and rather closely-interbred animals have become, that not far from one-third of the mares failed to produce living foals. Thus during 1866, 809 male colts and 816 female colts were born, and 743 mares failed to produce offspring. During 1867, 836 males and 902 females were born, and 794 mares failed.

the proportion of 110·1 males to 100 females. The greatest fluctuations occurred in 1864, when the proportion was as 95·3 males, and in 1867, as 116·3 males to 100 females. The above average proportion of 110·1 to 100 is probably nearly correct in the case of the greyhound, but whether it would hold with other domesticated breeds is in some degree doubtful. Mr. Cupples has enquired from several great breeders of dogs, and finds that all without exception believe that females are produced in excess; but he suggests that this belief may have arisen from females being less valued, and from the consequent disappointment producing a stronger impression on the mind.

Sheep.—The sexes of sheep are not ascertained by agriculturists until several months after birth, at the period when the males are castrated; so that the following returns do not give the proportions at birth. Moreover, I find that several great breeders in Scotland, who annually raise some thousand sheep, are firmly convinced that a larger proportion of males than of females die during the first year or two. Therefore the proportion of males would be somewhat larger at birth than at the age of castration. This is a remarkable coincidence with what, as we have seen, occurs with mankind, and both cases probably depend on the same cause. I have received returns from four gentlemen in England who have bred Lowland sheep, chiefly Leicesters, during the last ten to sixteen years; they amount altogether to 8965 births, consisting of 4407 males and 4558 females; that is in the proportion of 96·7 males to 100 females. With respect to Cheviot and black-faced sheep bred in Scotland, I have received returns from six breeders, two of them on a large scale, chiefly for the years 1867–1869, but some of the returns extend back to 1862. The total number recorded amounts to 50,685, consisting of 25,071 males and 25,614 females, or in the proportion of 97·9 males to 100 females. If we take the English and Scotch returns together, the total number amounts to 59,650, consisting of 29,478 males and 30,172 females, or as 97·7 to 100. So that with sheep at the age of castration the females are certainly in excess of the males, but probably this would not hold good at birth.[59]

---

[59] I am much indebted to Mr. Cupples for having procured for me the above returns from Scotland, as well as some of the following returns on cattle. Mr. R. Elliot, of Laighwood, first called my attention to the premature deaths of the males,—a statement subsequently confirmed by Mr. Aitchison

Of *Cattle* I have received returns from nine gentlemen of 982 births, too few to be trusted; these consisted of 477 bull-calves and 505 cow-calves; i.e., in the proportion of 94·4 males to 100 females. The Rev. W. D. Fox informs me that in 1867 out of 34 calves born on a farm in Derbyshire only one was a bull.   Mr. Harrison Weir has enquired from several breeders of *Pigs*, and most of them estimate the male to the female births as about 7 to 6.   This same gentleman has bred *Rabbits* for many years, and has noticed that a far greater number of bucks are produced than does.   But estimations are of little value.

Of mammalia in a state of nature I have been able to learn very little.   In regard to the common rat, I have received conflicting statements.   Mr. R. Elliot, of Laighwood, informs me that a rat-catcher assured him that he had always found the males in great excess, even with the young in the nest.   In consequence of this, Mr. Elliot himself subsequently examined some hundred old ones, and found the statement true.   Mr. F. Buckland has bred a large number of white rats, and he also believes that the males greatly " exceed the females.   In regard to Moles, it is said that " the males " are much more numerous than the females; " [60] and as the catching of these animals is a special occupation, the statement may perhaps be trusted.   Sir A. Smith, in describing an antelope of S. Africa [61] (*Kobus ellipsiprymnus*), remarks, that in the herds of this and other species, the males are few in number compared with the females: the natives believe that they are born in this proportion; others believe that the younger males are expelled from the herds, and Sir A. Smith says, that though he has himself never seen herds consisting of young males alone, others affirm that this does occur.   It appears probable that the young when expelled from the herd, would often fall a prey to the many beasts of prey of the country.

BIRDS.

With respect to the *Fowl*, I have received only one account, namely, that out of 1001 chickens of a highly-bred stock of Cochins, reared during eight years by Mr. Stretch, 487 proved males and

---

and others.   To this latter gentleman, and to Mr. Payan, I owe my thanks for large returns as to sheep.

[60] Bell, 'History of British Quadrupeds,' p. 100.

[61] 'Illustrations of the Zoology of S. Africa,' 1849, pl. 29.

514 females; i.e., as 94·7 to 100. In regard to domestic pigeons there is good evidence either that the males are produced in excess, or that they live longer; for these birds invariably pair, and single males, as Mr. Tegetmeier informs me, can always be purchased cheaper than females. Usually the two birds reared from the two eggs laid in the same nest are a male and a female; but Mr. Harrison Weir, who has been so large a breeder, says that he has often bred two cocks from the same nest, and seldom two hens; moreover, the hen is generally the weaker of the two, and more liable to perish.

With respect to birds in a state of nature, Mr. Gould and others [62] are convinced that the males are generally the more numerous; and as the young males of many species resemble the females, the latter would naturally appear to be the more numerous. Large numbers of pheasants are reared by Mr. Baker of Leadenhall from eggs laid by wild birds, and he informs Mr. Jenner Weir that four or five males to one female are generally produced. An experienced observer remarks,[63] that in Scandinavia the broods of the capercailzie and black-cock contain more males than females; and that with the Dal-ripa (a kind of ptarmigan) more males than females attend the *leks* or places of courtship; but this latter circumstance is accounted for by some observers by a greater number of hen birds being killed by vermin. From various facts given by White of Selborne,[64] it seems clear that the males of the partridge must be in considerable excess in the south of England; and I have been assured that this is the case in Scotland. Mr. Weir on enquiring from the dealers, who receive at certain seasons large numbers of ruffs (*Machetes pugnax*), was told that the males are much the more numerous. This same naturalist has also enquired for me from the birdcatchers, who annually catch an astonishing number of various small species alive for the London market, and he was unhesitatingly answered by an old and trustworthy man, that with the chaffinch the males are in large excess; he thought as high as 2 males to 1 female, or at least as high as 5 to 3.[65] The males

---

[62] Brehm ('Illust. Thierleben,' B. iv. s. 990) comes to the same conclusion.

[63] On the authority of L. Lloyd, 'Game Birds of Sweden,' 1867, pp. 12, 132.

[64] 'Nat. Hist. of Selborne,' letter xxix. edit. of 1825, vol. i. p. 139.

[65] Mr. Jenner Weir received similar information, on making enquiries during the following

of the blackbird, he likewise maintained, were by far the more numerous, whether caught by traps or by netting at night. These statements may apparently be trusted, because this same man said that the sexes are about equal with the lark, the twite (*Linaria montana*), and goldfinch. On the other hand, he is certain that with the common linnet, the females preponderate greatly, but unequally during different years; during some years he has found the females to the males as four to one. It should, however, be borne in mind, that the chief season for catching birds does not begin till September, so that with some species partial migrations may have begun, and the flocks at this period often consist of hens alone. Mr. Salvin paid particular attention to the sexes of the humming-birds in Central America, and he is convinced that with most of the species the males are in excess; thus one year he procured 204 specimens belonging to ten species, and these consisted of 166 males and of only 38 females. With two other species the females were in excess: but the proportions apparently vary either during different seasons or in different localities; for on one occasion the males of *Campylopterus hemileucurus* were to the females as 5 to 2, and on another occasion[66] in exactly the reversed ratio. As bearing on this latter point, I may add, that Mr. Powys found in Corfu and Epirus the sexes of the chaffinch keeping apart, and "the females by far the most numerous;" whilst in Palestine Mr. Tristram found "the male flocks appearing greatly to exceed "the female in number."[67] So again with the *Quiscalus major*, Mr. G. Taylor[68] says, that in Florida there were "very few females in "proportion to the males," whilst in Honduras the proportion was the other way, the species there having the character of a polygamist.

---

year. To shew the number of living chaffinches caught, I may mention that in 1869 there was a match between two experts, and one man caught in a day 62, and another 40, male chaffinches. The greatest number ever caught by one man in a single day was 70.

[66] 'Ibis,' vol. ii. p. 260, as quoted in Gould's 'Trochilidæ,' 1861, p. 52. For the foregoing proportions, I am indebted to Mr. Salvin for a table of his results.

[67] 'Ibis,' 1860, p. 137; and 1867, p. 369.

[68] 'Ibis,' 1862, p. 187.

FISH.

With Fish the proportional numbers of the sexes can be ascertained only by catching them in the adult or nearly adult state; and there are many difficulties in arriving at any just conclusion.[69] Infertile females might readily be mistaken for males, as Dr. Günther has remarked to me in regard to trout. With some species the males are believed to die soon after fertilising the ova. With many species the males are of much smaller size than the females, so that a large number of males would escape from the same net by which the females were caught. M. Carbonnier,[70] who has especially attended to the natural history of the pike (*Esox lucius*), states that many males, owing to their small size, are devoured by the larger females; and he believes that the males of almost all fish are exposed from this same cause to greater danger than the females. Nevertheless, in the few cases in which the proportional numbers have been actually observed, the males appear to be largely in excess. Thus Mr. R. Buist, the superintendent of the Stormontfield experiments, says that in 1865, out of 70 salmon first landed for the purpose of obtaining the ova, upwards of 60 were males. In 1867 he again " calls attention " to the vast disproportion of the males to the females. We had at " the outset at least ten males to one female." Afterwards females sufficient for obtaining ova were procured. He adds, "from the " great proportion of the males, they are constantly fighting and " tearing each other on the spawning-beds." [71] This disproportion, no doubt, can be accounted for in part, but whether wholly is doubtful, by the males ascending the rivers before the females. Mr. F. Buckland remarks in regard to trout, that " it is a curious " fact that the males preponderate very largely in number over the " females. It *invariably* happens that when the first rush of fish " is made to the net, there will be at least seven or eight males to " one female found captive. I cannot quite account for this; " either the males are more numerous than the females, or the

---

[69] Leuckart quotes Bloch (Wagner, 'Handwörterbuch der Phys.,' B. iv. 1853, s. 775), that with fish there are twice as many males as females.

[70] Quoted in the 'Farmer,'

March 18, 1869, p. 369.

[71] 'The Stormontfield Piscicultural Experiments,' 1866, p. 23. The 'Field' newspaper, June 29th, 1867.

"latter seek safety by concealment rather than flight." He then adds, that by carefully searching the banks sufficient females for obtaining ova can be found.[72]   Mr. H. Lee informs me that out of 212 trout, taken for this purpose in Lord Portsmouth's park, 150 were males and 62 females.

The males of the Cyprinidæ likewise seem to be in excess; but several members of this Family, viz., the carp, tench, bream and minnow, appear regularly to follow the practice, rare in the animal kingdom, of polyandry; for the female whilst spawning is always attended by two males, one on each side, and in the case of the bream by three or four males.   This fact is so well known, that it is always recommended to stock a pond with two male tenches to one female, or at least with three males to two females.   With the minnow, an excellent observer states, that on the spawning-beds the males are ten times as numerous as the females; when a female comes amongst the males, "she is immediately pressed "closely by a male on each side; and when they have been in that "situation for a time, are superseded by other two males."[73]

INSECTS.

In this great Class, the Lepidoptera almost alone afford means for judging of the proportional numbers of the sexes; for they have been collected with special care by many good observers, and have been largely bred from the egg or caterpillar state.   I had hoped that some breeders of silk-moths might have kept an exact record, but after writing to France and Italy, and consulting various treatises, I cannot find that this has ever been done.   The general opinion appears to be that the sexes are nearly equal, but in Italy, as I hear from Professor Canestrini, many breeders are convinced that the females are produced in excess.   This same naturalist, however, informs me, that in the two yearly broods of the Ailanthus silk-moth (*Bombyx cynthia*), the males greatly preponderate in the first, whilst in the second the two sexes are nearly equal, or the females rather in excess.

In regard to Butterflies in a state of nature, several observers

---

[72] 'Land and Water,' 1868, p. 41.

[73] Yarrell, ' Hist. British Fishes,' vol. i. 1826, p. 307; on the *Cyprinus carpio*, p. 331; on the *Tinca vulgaris*, p. 331; on the *Abramis brama*, p. 336. See, for the minnow (*Leuciscus phoxinus*), 'Loudon's Mag. of Nat. Hist.' vol. v. 1832, p. 682.

have been much struck by the apparently enormous preponderance of the males.[74] Thus Mr. Bates,[75] in speaking of several species, about a hundred in number, which inhabit the Upper Amazons, says that the males are much more numerous than the females, even in the proportion of a hundred to one. In North America, Edwards, who had great experience, estimates in the genus Papilio the males to the females as four to one; and Mr. Walsh, who informed me of this statement, says that with *P. turnus* this is certainly the case. In South Africa, Mr. R. Trimen found the males in excess in 19 species;[76] and in one of these, which swarms in open places, he estimated the number of males as fifty to one female. With another species, in which the males are numerous in certain localities, he collected only five females during seven years. In the island of Bourbon, M. Maillard states that the males of one species of Papilio are twenty times as numerous as the females.[77] Mr. Trimen informs me that as far as he has himself seen, or heard from others, it is rare for the females of any butterfly to exceed the males in number; but three South African species perhaps offer an exception. Mr. Wallace[78] states that the females of *Ornithoptera cræsus*, in the Malay archipelago, are more common and more easily caught than the males; but this is a rare butterfly. I may here add, that in Hyperythra, a genus of moths, Guenée says, that from four to five females are sent in collections from India for one male.

When this subject of the proportional numbers of the sexes of insects was brought before the Entomological Society,[79] it was generally admitted that the males of most Lepidoptera, in the adult or imago state, are caught in greater numbers than the females: but this fact was attributed by various observers to the more retiring habits of the females, and to the males emerging earlier from the cocoon. This latter circumstance is well known to occur

---

[74] Leuckart quotes Meinecke (Wagner, 'Handwörterbuch der Phys.' B. iv. 1853, s. 775) that the males of Butterflies are three or four times as numerous as the females.

[75] 'The Naturalist on the Amazons,' vol. ii. 1863, p. 228, 347.

[76] Four of these cases are given by Mr. Trimen in his 'Rhopalocera Africæ Australis.'

[77] Quoted by Trimen, 'Transact. Ent. Soc.' vol. v. part iv. 1866, p. 330.

[78] 'Transact. Linn. Soc.' vol. xxv. p. 37.

[79] 'Proc. Entomolog. Soc.' Feb. 17th, 1868.

with most Lepidoptera, as well as with other insects. So that, as M. Personnat remarks, the males of the domesticated *Bombyx Yamamai*, are useless at the beginning of the season, and the females at the end, from the want of mates.[80] I cannot, however, persuade myself that these causes suffice to explain the great excess of males, in the above cases of certain butterflies which are extremely common in their native countries. Mr. Stainton, who has paid very close attention during many years to the smaller moths, informs me that when he collected them in the imago state, he thought that the males were ten times as numerous as the females, but that since he has reared them on a large scale from the caterpillar state, he is convinced that the females are the more numerous. Several entomologists concur in this view. Mr. Doubleday, however, and some others, take an opposite view, and are convinced that they have reared from the eggs and caterpillars a larger proportion of males than of females.

Besides the more active habits of the males, their earlier emergence from the cocoon, and in some cases their frequenting more open stations, other causes may be assigned for an apparent or real difference in the proportional numbers of the sexes of Lepidoptera, when captured in the imago state, and when reared from the egg or caterpillar state. I hear from Professor Canestrini, that it is believed by many breeders in Italy, that the female caterpillar of the silk-moth suffers more from the recent disease than the male; and Dr. Staudinger informs me that in rearing Lepidoptera more females die in the cocoon than males. With many species the female caterpillar is larger than the male, and a collector would naturally choose the finest specimens, and thus unintentionally collect a larger number of females. Three collectors have told me that this was their practice; but Dr. Wallace is sure that most collectors take all the specimens which they can find of the rarer kinds, which alone are worth the trouble of rearing. Birds when surrounded by caterpillars would probably devour the largest; and Professor Canestrini informs me that in Italy some breeders believe, though on insufficient evidence, that in the first broods of the Ailanthus silk-moth, the wasps destroy a larger number of the female than of the male caterpillars. Dr. Wallace further remarks that female caterpillars, from being larger than the

---

[80] Quoted by Dr. Wallace in 'Proc. Ent. Soc.' 3rd series, vol. v. 1867, p. 487.

males, require more time for their development, and consume more food and moisture; and thus they would be exposed during a longer time to danger from ichneumons, birds, &c., and in times of scarcity would perish in greater numbers. Hence it appears quite possible that in a state of nature, fewer female Lepidoptera may reach maturity than males; and for our special object we are concerned with their relative numbers at maturity, when the sexes are ready to propagate their kind.

The manner in which the males of certain moths congregate in extraordinary numbers round a single female, apparently indicates a great excess of males, though this fact may perhaps be accounted for by the earlier emergence of the males from their cocoons. Mr. Stainton informs me that from twelve to twenty males, may often be seen congregated round a female *Elachista rufocinerea*. It is well known that if a virgin *Lasiocampa quercus* or *Saturnia carpini* be exposed in a cage, vast numbers of males collect round her, and if confined in a room will even come down the chimney to her. Mr. Doubleday believes that he has seen from fifty to a hundred males of both these species attracted in the course of a single day by a female in confinement. In the Isle of Wight Mr. Trimen exposed a box in which a female of the Lasiocampa had been confined on the previous day, and five males soon endeavoured to gain admittance. In Australia, M. Verreaux, having placed the female of a small Bombyx in a box in his pocket, was followed by a crowd of males, so that about 200 entered the house with him.[81]

Mr. Doubleday has called my attention to M. Staudinger's[82] list of Lepidoptera, which gives the prices of the males and females of 300 species or well-marked varieties of butterflies (Rhopalocera). The prices for both sexes of the very common species are of course the same; but in 114 of the rarer species they differ; the males being in all cases, excepting one, the cheaper. On an average of the prices of the 113 species, the price of the male to that of the female is as 100 to 149; and this apparently indicates that inversely the males exceed the females in the same proportion. About 2000 species or varieties of moths (Heterocera) are catalogued, those with wingless females being here excluded on account of the difference in habits between the two sexes: of these

---

[81] Blanchard, 'Métamorphoses, Mœurs des Insectes,' 1868, pp. 225–226.

[82] 'Lepidopteren - Doubletten Liste,' Berlin, No. x. 1866.

2000 species, 141 differ in price according to sex, the males of 130 being cheaper, and those of only 11 being dearer than the females. The average price of the males of the 130 species, to that of the females, is as 100 to 143.   With respect to the butterflies in this priced list, Mr. Doubleday thinks (and no man in England has had more experience), that there is nothing in the habits of the species which can account for the difference in the prices of the two sexes, and that it can be accounted for only by an excess in the number of the males.   But I am bound to add that Dr. Staudinger informs me, that he is himself of a different opinion.   He thinks that the less active habits of the females and the earlier emergence of the males will account for his collectors securing a larger number of males than of females, and consequently for the lower prices of the former.   With respect to specimens reared from the caterpillar-state, Dr. Staudinger believes, as previously stated, that a greater number of females than of males die whilst confined in the cocoons.   He adds that with certain species one sex seems to pre-ponderate over the other during certain years.

Of direct observations on the sexes of Lepidoptera, reared either from eggs or caterpillars, I have received only the few following cases :—

	Males.	Females.
The Rev. J. Hellins[83] of Exeter reared, during 1868, imagos of 73 species, which consisted of . .	153	137
Mr. Albert Jones of Eltham reared, during 1868, imagos of 9 species, which consisted of . .	159	126
During 1869 he reared imagos from 4 species, consisting of	114	112
Mr. Buckler of Emsworth, Hants, during 1869, reared imagos from 74 species, consisting of .	180	169
Dr. Wallace of Colchester reared from one brood of Bombyx cynthia	52	48
Dr. Wallace raised, from cocoons of Bombyx Pernyi sent from China, during 1869	224	123
Dr. Wallace raised, during 1868 and 1869, from two lots of cocoons of Bombyx yama-mai . .	52	46
Total	934	761

[83] This naturalist has been so kind as to send me some results from former years, in which the females seemed to preponderate;

So that in these eight lots of cocoons and eggs, males were produced in excess. Taken together the proportion of males is as 122·7 to 100 females. But the numbers are hardly large enough to be trustworthy.

On the whole, from these various sources of evidence, all pointing in the same direction, I infer that with most species of Lepidoptera, the mature males generally exceed the females in number, whatever the proportions may be at their first emergence from the egg.

With reference to the other Orders of insects, I have been able to collect very little reliable information. With the stag-beetle (*Lucanus cervus*) "the males appear to be much more numerous "than the females;" but when, as Cornelius remarked during 1867, an unusual number of these beetles appeared in one part of Germany, the females appeared to exceed the males as six to one. With one of the Elateridæ, the males are said to be much more numerous than the females, and "two or three are often found "united with one female;[84] so that here polyandry seems to "prevail." With Siagonium (Staphylinidæ), in which the males are furnished with horns, "the females are far more numerous than "the opposite sex." Mr. Janson stated at the Entomological Society that the females of the bark-feeding *Tomicus villosus* are so common as to be a plague, whilst the males are so rare as to be hardly known.

It is hardly worth while saying anything about the proportion of the sexes in certain species and even groups of insects, for the males are unknown or very rare, and the females are parthenogenetic, that is, fertile without sexual union; examples of this are afforded by several of the Cynipidæ.[85] In all the gall-making Cynipidæ known to Mr. Walsh, the females are four or five times as numerous as the males; and so it is, as he informs me, with the gall-making Cecidomyiidæ (Diptera). With some common species of Saw-flies (Tenthredinæ) Mr. F. Smith has reared hundreds of specimens from larvæ of all sizes, but has never reared a single

---

but so many of the figures were estimates, that I found it impossible to tabulate them.

[84] Günther's 'Record of Zoological Literature,' 1867, p. 260. On the excess of female Lucanus, ibid. p. 250. On the males of Lucanus in England, 'West-wood, 'Modern Class of Insects,' vol. i. p. 187. On the Siagonium, ibid. p. 172.

[85] Walsh, in 'The American Entomologist,' vol. i. 1869, p. 103. F. Smith, 'Record of Zoological Literature,' 1867, p. 328.

male: on the other hand, Curtis says,[86] that with certain species (Athalia), bred by him, the males were to the females as six to one; whilst exactly the reverse occurred with the mature insects of the same species caught in the fields. In the family of Bees, Hermann Müller,[87] collected a large number of specimens of many species, and reared others from the cocoons, and counted the sexes. He found that the males of some species greatly exceeded the females in number; in others the reverse occurred; and in others the two sexes were nearly equal. But as in most cases the males emerge from the cocoons before the females, they are at the commencement of the breeding season practically in excess. Müller also observed that the relative number of the two sexes in some species differed much in different localities. But as H. Müller has himself remarked to me, these remarks must be received with some caution, as one sex might more easily escape observation than the other. Thus his brother Fritz Müller has noticed in Brazil that the two sexes of the same species of bee sometimes frequent different kinds of flowers. With respect to the Orthoptera, I know hardly anything about the relative number of the sexes: Körte,[88] however, says that out of 500 locusts which he examined, the males were to the females as five to six. With the Neuroptera, Mr. Walsh states that in many, but by no means in all the species of the Odonatous group, there is a great overplus of males: in the genus Hetærina, also, the males are generally at least four times as numerous as the females. In certain species in the genus Gomphus the males are equally in excess, whilst in two other species, the females are twice or thrice as numerous as the males. In some European species of Psocus thousands of females may be collected without a single male, whilst with other species of the same genus both sexes are common.[89] In England, Mr. MacLachlan has captured hundreds of the female *Apatania muliebris*, but has never seen the male; and of *Boreus hyemalis* only four or five males have been seen here.[90] With most of these

[86] 'Farm Insects,' pp. 45–46.

[87] 'Anwendung der Darwinschen Lehre Verh. d. n. V. Jahrg. xxiv.'

[88] 'Die Strich, Zug oder Wanderheuschrecke,' 1828, p. 20.

[89] 'Observations on N. American Neuroptera,' by H. Hagen and B. D. Walsh, 'Proc. Ent. Soc. Philadelphia,' Oct. 1863, pp. 168, 223, 239.

[90] 'Proc. Ent. Soc. London,' Feb. 17, 1868.

species (excepting the Tenthredinæ) there is at present no evidence that the females are subject to parthenogenesis; and thus we see how ignorant we are of the causes of the apparent discrepancy in the proportion of the two sexes.

In the other classes of the Articulata I have been able to collect still less information. With spiders, Mr. Blackwall, who has carefully attended to this class during many years, writes to me that the males from their more erratic habits are more commonly seen, and therefore appear more numerous. This is actually the case with a few species; but he mentions several species in six genera, in which the females appear to be much more numerous than the males.[91] The small size of the males in comparison with the females (a peculiarity which is sometimes carried to an extreme degree), and their widely different appearance, may account in some instances for their rarity in collections.[92]

Some of the lower Crustaceans are able to propagate their kind sexually, and this will account for the extreme rarity of the males; thus Von Siebold[93] carefully examined no less than 13,000 specimens of Apus from twenty-one localities, and amongst these he found only 319 males. With some other forms (as Tanais and Cypris), as Fritz Müller informs me, there is reason to believe that the males are much shorter-lived than the females; and this would explain their scarcity, supposing the two sexes to be at first equal in number. On the other hand, Müller has invariably taken far more males than females of the Diastylidæ and of Cypridina on the shores of Brazil: thus with a species in the latter genus, 63 specimens caught the same day included 57 males; but he suggests that this preponderance may be due to some unknown difference in the habits of the two sexes. With one of the higher Brazilian crabs, namely a Gelasimus, Fritz Müller found the males to be more numerous than the females. According to the large experience of Mr. C. Spence Bate, the reverse seems to be the case with six common British crabs, the names of which he has given me.

---

[91] Another great authority with respect to this class, Prof. Thorell of Upsala ('On European Spiders,' 1869–70, part i. p. 205), speaks as if female spiders were generally commoner than the males.

[92] See, on this subject, Mr. O. P. Cambridge, as quoted in 'Quarterly Journal of Science,' 1868, p. 429.

[93] 'Beiträge zur Parthenogenesis,' p. 174.

The proportion of the sexes in relation to natural selection.

There is reason to suspect that in some cases man has by selection indirectly influenced his own sex-producing powers. Certain women tend to produce during their whole lives more children of one sex than of the other: and the same holds good of many animals, for instance, cows and horses; thus Mr. Wright of Yeldersley House informs me that one of his Arab mares, though put seven times to different horses, produced seven fillies. Though I have very little evidence on this head, analogy would lead to the belief, that the tendency to produce either sex would be inherited like almost every other peculiarity, for instance, that of producing twins; and concerning the above tendency a good authority, Mr. J. Downing, has communicated to me facts which seem to prove that this does occur in certain families of short-horn cattle. Col. Marshall [94] has recently found on careful examination that the Todas, a hill-tribe of India, consist of 112 males and 84 females of all ages—that is in a ratio of 133·3 males to 100 females. The Todas, who are polyandrous in their marriages, during former times invariably practised female infanticide; but this practice has now been discontinued for a considerable period. Of the children born within late years, the males are more numerous than the females, in the proportion of 124 to 100. Colonel Marshall accounts for this fact in the following ingenious manner. " Let us for the purpose of illustration take " three families as representing an average of the

[94] 'The Todas,' 1873, pp. 100, 111, 194, 196.

" entire tribe; say that one mother gives birth to six
" daughters and no sons; a second mother has six
" sons only, whilst the third mother has three sons
" and three daughters. The first mother, following
" the tribal custom, destroys four daughters and
" preserves two. The second retains her six sons.
" The third kills two daughters and keeps one, as also
" her three sons. We have then from the three
" families, nine sons and three daughters, with which
" to continue the breed. But whilst the males belong
" to families in which the tendency to produce sons is
" great, the females are of those of a converse inclina-
" tion. Thus the bias strengthens with each genera-
" tion, until, as we find, families grow to have habitually
" more sons than daughters."

That this result would follow from the above form
of infanticide seems almost certain; that is if we
assume that a sex-producing tendency is inherited.
But as the above numbers are so extremely scanty, I
have searched for additional evidence, but cannot
decide whether what I have found is trustworthy;
nevertheless the facts are, perhaps, worth giving.
The Maories of New Zealand have long practised
infanticide; and Mr. Fenton [95] states that he " has met
" with instances of women who have destroyed four,
" six, and even seven children, mostly females. How-
" ever, the universal testimony of those best qualified
" to judge, is conclusive that this custom has for many
" years been almost extinct. Probably the year 1835
" may be named as the period of its ceasing to exist."
Now amongst the New Zealanders, as with the Todas,

[95] ' Aboriginal Inhabitants of New Zealand; Government Report,'
1859, p. 36.

male births are considerably in excess.   Mr. Fenton
remarks (p. 30), " One fact is certain, although the
" exact period of the commencement of this singular
" condition of the disproportion of the sexes cannot be
" demonstratively fixed, it is quite clear that this
" course of decrease was in full operation during the
" years 1830 to 1844, when the non-adult population
" of 1844 was being produced, and has continued with
" great energy up to the present time."   The following
statements are taken from Mr. Fenton (p. 26), but as
the numbers are not large, and as the census was not
accurate, uniform results cannot be expected.   It
should be borne in mind in this and the following
cases, that the normal state of every population is an
excess of women, at least in all civilised countries,
chiefly owing to the greater mortality of the male sex
during youth, and partly to accidents of all kinds later
in life.   In 1858, the native population of New
Zealand was estimated as consisting of 31,667 males
and 24,303 females of all ages, that is in the ratio of
130·3 males to 100 females.   But during this same
year, and in certain limited districts, the numbers
were ascertained with much care, and the males of all
ages were here 753 and the females 616; that is in
the ratio of 122·2 males to 100 females.   It is more
important for us that during this same year of 1858,
the *non-adult* males within the same district were
found to be 178, and the *non-adult* females 142, that is
in the ratio of 125·3 to 100.   It may be added that in
1844, at which period female infanticide had only
lately ceased, the *non-adult* males in one district were
281, and the *non-adult* females only 194, that is in the
ratio of 144·8 males to 100 females.

In the Sandwich Islands, the males exceed the females in number. Infanticide was formerly practised there to a frightful extent, but was by no means confined to female infants, as is shown by Mr. Ellis,[96] and as I have been informed by Bishop Staley and the Rev. Mr. Coan. Nevertheless, another apparently trustworthy writer, Mr. Jarves,[97] whose observations apply to the whole archipelago, remarks:—"Numbers "of women are to be found, who confess to the murder "of from three to six or eight children," and he adds, "females from being considered less useful than males "were more often destroyed." From what is known to occur in other parts of the world, this statement is probable; but must be received with much caution. The practice of infanticide ceased about the year 1819, when idolatry was abolished and missionaries settled in the Islands. A careful census in 1839 of the adult and taxable men and women in the island of Kauai and in one district of Oahu (Jarves, p. 404), gives 4723 males and 3776 females; that is in the ratio of 125·08 to 100. At the same time the number of males under fourteen years in Kauai and under eighteen in Oahu was 1797, and of females of the same ages 1429; and here we have the ratio of 125·75 males to 100 females.

In a census of all the islands in 1850,[98] the males of all ages amount to 36,272, and the females to 33,128, or as 109·49 to 100. The males under seventeen years amounted to 10,773, and the females under the same age to 9593, or as 112·3 to 100. From the census of

[96] 'Narrative of a Tour through Hawaii,' 1826, p. 298.
[97] 'History of the Sandwich Islands,' 1843, p. 93.

[98] This is given in the Rev. H. T. Cheever's 'Life in the Sandwich Islands,' 1851, p. 277.

1872, the proportion of males of all ages (including half-castes) to females, is as 125·36 to 100. It must be borne in mind that all these returns for the Sandwich Islands give the proportion of living males to living females, and not of the births; and judging from all civilised countries the proportion of males would have been considerably higher if the numbers had referred to births.[99]

[99] Dr. Coulter, in describing ('Journal R. Geograph. Soc,' vol. v. 1835, p. 67) the state of California about the year 1830, says that the natives, reclaimed by the Spanish missionaries, have nearly all perished, or are perishing, although well treated, not driven from their native land, and kept from the use of spirits. He attributes this, in great part, to the undoubted fact that the men greatly exceed the women in number; but he does not know whether this is due to a failure of female off-spring, or to more females dying during early youth. The latter alternative, according to all analogy, is very improbable. He adds that " infanticide, pro-" perly so called, is not common, " though very frequent resource " is had to abortion." If Dr. Coulter is correct about infanticide, this case cannot be advanced in support of Colonel Marshall's view. From the rapid decrease of the reclaimed natives, we may suspect that, as in the cases lately given, their fertility has been diminished from changed habits of life.

I had hoped to gain some light on this subject from the breeding of dogs; inasmuch as in most breeds, with the exception, perhaps, of greyhounds, many more female puppies are destroyed than males, just as with the Toda infants. Mr. Cupples assures me that this is usual with Scotch deer-hounds. Unfortunately, I know nothing of the proportion of the sexes in any breed, excepting greyhounds, and there the male births are to the females as 110·1 to 100. Now from enquiries made from many breeders, it seems that the females are in some respects more esteemed, though otherwise troublesome; and it does not appear that the female puppies of the best-bred dogs are systematically destroyed more than the males, though this does sometimes take place to a limited extent. Therefore I am unable to decide whether we can, on the above principles, account for the preponderance of male births in greyhounds. On the other hand, we have seen that with horses, cattle, and sheep, which are too valuable for the young of either sex to be destroyed, if there is any difference, the females are slightly in excess.

From the several foregoing cases we have some reason to believe that infanticide practised in the manner above explained, tends to make a male-producing race; but I am far from supposing that this practice in the case of man, or some analogous process with other species, has been the sole determining cause of an excess of males. There may be some unknown law leading to this result in decreasing races, which have already become somewhat infertile. Besides the several causes previously alluded to, the greater facility of parturition amongst savages, and the less consequent injury to their male infants, would tend to increase the proportion of live-born males to females. There does not, however, seem to be any necessary connection between savage life and a marked excess of males; that is if we may judge by the character of the scanty offspring of the lately existing Tasmanians and of the crossed offspring of the Tahitians now inhabiting Norfolk Island.

As the males and females of many animals differ somewhat in habits and are exposed in different degrees to danger, it is probable that in many cases, more of one sex than of the other are habitually destroyed. But as far as I can trace out the complication of causes, an indiscriminate though large destruction of either sex would not tend to modify the sex-producing power of the species. With strictly social animals, such as bees or ants, which produce a vast number of sterile and fertile females in comparison with the males, and to whom this preponderance is of paramount importance, we can see that those communities would flourish best which contained females having a strong inherited tendency to produce more and more females; and in such cases an unequal sex-producing tendency would be ultimately gained through natural selection. With animals living in herds or troops, in which the males come to the front and defend the herd, as with the bisons of North America and certain baboons, it is conceivable that a male-producing tendency might be gained by natural selection; for the individuals of the better defended herds would leave more numerous descendants. In the case of mankind the advantage arising from having a preponderance of men in the tribe is supposed to be one chief cause of the practice of female infanticide.

In no case, as far as we can see, would an inherited tendency to produce both sexes in equal numbers or to produce one sex in excess, be a direct advantage or disadvantage to certain individuals more than to others; for instance, an individual with a tendency to produce more males than females would not succeed better in the battle for life than an individual with an opposite tendency; and therefore a tendency of this kind could not be gained through natural selection. Nevertheless, there are certain animals (for instance, fishes and cirripedes) in which two or more males appear to be necessary for the fertilisation of the female; and the males accordingly largely preponderate, but it is by no means obvious how this male-producing tendency could have been acquired. I formerly thought that when a tendency to produce the two sexes in equal numbers was advantageous to the species, it would follow from natural selection, but I now see that the whole problem is so intricate that it is safer to leave its solution for the future.

CHAPTER IX.

SECONDARY SEXUAL CHARACTERS IN THE LOWER CLASSES OF THE ANIMAL KINGDOM.

These characters absent in the lowest classes—Brilliant colours—Mollusca—Annelids—Crustacea, secondary sexual characters strongly developed; dimorphism; colour; characters not acquired before maturity—Spiders, sexual colours of; stridulation by the males—Myriapoda.

WITH animals belonging to the lower classes, the two sexes are not rarely united in the same individual, and therefore secondary sexual characters cannot be developed. In many cases where the sexes are separate, both are permanently attached to some support, and the one cannot search or struggle for the other. Moreover it is almost certain that these animals have too imperfect senses and much too low mental powers, to appreciate each other's beauty or other attractions, or to feel rivalry.

Hence in these classes or sub-kingdoms, such as the Protozoa, Cœlenterata, Echinodermata, Scolecida, secondary sexual characters, of the kind which we have to consider, do not occur; and this fact agrees with the belief that such characters in the higher classes have been acquired through sexual selection, which depends on the will, desire, and choice of either sex. Nevertheless some few apparent exceptions occur; thus, as I hear from Dr. Baird, the males of certain Entozoa, or internal parasitic worms, differ slightly in colour from the females; but we have no reason to suppose that such differences have been augmented through sexual selection. Contrivances by which the male holds the female, and which are indispensable for the propagation of the species, are independent of sexual selection, and have been acquired through ordinary selection.

Many of the lower animals, whether hermaphrodites or with separate sexes, are ornamented with the most brilliant tints, or are shaded and striped in an elegant manner; for instance, many corals and sea-anemones (Actiniæ), some jelly-fish (Medusæ, Porpita, &c.), some Planariæ, many star-fishes, Echini, Ascidians, &c.; but we may conclude from the reasons already indicated, namely, the union of the two sexes in some of these animals, the permanently affixed condition of others, and the low mental powers of all, that such colours do not serve as a sexual attraction, and have not been acquired through sexual selection. It should be borne in mind that in no case have we sufficient evidence that colours have been thus acquired, except where one sex is much more brilliantly or conspicuously coloured than the other, and where there is no difference in habits between the sexes sufficient to account for their different colours. But the evidence is rendered as complete as it can ever be, only when the more ornamented individuals, almost always the males, voluntarily display their attractions before the other sex; for we cannot believe that such display is useless, and if it be advantageous, sexual selection will almost inevitably follow. We may, however, extend this conclusion to both sexes, when coloured alike, if their colours are plainly analogous to those of one sex alone in certain other species of the same group.

How, then, are we to account for the beautiful or even gorgeous colours of many animals in the lowest classes? It appears doubtful whether such colours often serve as a protection; but that we may easily err on this head, will be admitted by every one who reads Mr. Wallace's excellent essay on this subject. It would not, for instance, at first occur to any one that the transparency of the Medusæ, or jelly-fish, is of the highest service to them as a protection; but when we are reminded by Häckel that not only the medusæ, but many floating mollusca, crustaceans, and even small oceanic fishes partake of this same glass-like appearance, often accompanied by prismatic colours, we can hardly doubt that they thus escape the notice of pelagic birds and other enemies. M. Giard is also convinced[1] that the bright tints of certain sponges and ascidians serve as a protection. Conspicuous colours are likewise beneficial to many animals as a warning to their would-be devourers that they are distasteful, or that they possess some special means of defence; but this subject will be discussed more conveniently hereafter.

We can, in our ignorance of most of the lowest animals, only say that their bright tints result either from the chemical nature or the minute structure of their tissues, independently of any benefit thus derived. Hardly any colour is finer than that of arterial blood; but there is no reason to suppose that the colour of the blood is in itself any advantage; and though it adds to the beauty of the maiden's cheek, no one will

[1] 'Archives de Zoolog. Expér.,' Oct. 1872, p. 563.

pretend that it has been acquired for this purpose. So again with many animals, especially the lower ones, the bile is richly coloured; thus, as I am informed by Mr. Hancock, the extreme beauty of the Eolidæ (naked sea-slugs) is chiefly due to the biliary glands being seen through the translucent integuments—this beauty being probably of no service to these animals. The tints of the decaying leaves in an American forest are described by every one as gorgeous; yet no one supposes that these tints are of the least advantage to the trees. Bearing in mind how many substances closely analogous to natural organic compounds have been recently formed by chemists, and which exhibit the most splendid colours, it would have been a strange fact if substances similarly coloured had not often originated, independently of any useful end thus gained, in the complex laboratory of living organisms.

The sub-kingdom of the Mollusca.—Throughout this great division of the animal kingdom, as far as I can discover, secondary sexual characters, such as we are here considering, never occur. Nor could they be expected in the three lowest classes, namely, in the Ascidians, Polyzoa, and Brachiopods (constituting the Molluscoida of some authors), for most of these animals are permanently affixed to a support or have their sexes united in the same individual. In the Lamelli-branchiata, or bivalve shells, hermaphroditism is not rare. In the next higher class of the Gasteropoda, or univalve shells, the sexes are either united or separate. But in the latter case the males never possess special organs for finding, securing, or charming the females, or for fighting with other males. As I am informed by Mr. Gwyn Jeffreys, the sole external difference between the sexes consists in the shell sometimes differing a little in form ; for instance, the shell of the male periwinkle (*Littorina littorea*) is narrower and has a more elongated spire than that of the female. But differences of this nature, it may be presumed, are directly connected with the act of reproduction, or with the development of the ova.

The Gasteropoda, though capable of locomotion and furnished with imperfect eyes, do not appear to be endowed with sufficient mental powers for the members of the same sex to struggle together in rivalry, and thus to acquire secondary sexual characters. Nevertheless with the pulmoniferous gasteropods, or land-snails, the pairing is preceded by courtship ; for these animals, though hermaphrodites, are compelled by their structure to pair together. Agassiz remarks,[2] " Quiconque a eu l'occasion d'observer les amours des " limaçons, ne saurait mettre en doute la séduction " déployée dans les mouvements et les allures qui " préparent et accomplissent le double embrassement " de ces hermaphrodites." These animals appear also susceptible of some degree of permanent attachment : an accurate observer, Mr. Lonsdale, informs me that he placed a pair of land-snails, (*Helix pomatia*), one of which was weakly, into a small and ill-provided garden. After a short time the strong and healthy individual disappeared, and was traced by its track of slime over a wall into an adjoining well-stocked garden. Mr. Lonsdale concluded that it had deserted its sickly mate ; but after an absence of twenty-four hours it returned, and apparently communicated the result of

[2] 'De l'Espèce et de la Class.' &c., 1869, p. 106.

its successful exploration, for both then started along the same track and disappeared over the wall.

Even in the highest class of the Mollusca, the Cephalopoda or cuttlefishes, in which the sexes are separate, secondary sexual characters of the present kind do not, as far as I can discover, occur. This is a surprising circumstance, as these animals possess highly-developed sense-organs and have considerable mental powers, as will be admitted by every one who has watched their artful endeavours to escape from an enemy.[3] Certain Cephalopoda, however, are character-ised by one extraordinary sexual character, namely that the male element collects within one of the arms or tentacles, which is then cast off, and clinging by its sucking-discs to the female, lives for a time an independent life. So completely does the cast-off arm resemble a separate animal, that it was described by Cuvier as a parasitic worm under the name of Hectoco-tyle. But this marvellous structure may be classed as a primary rather than as a secondary sexual character.

Although with the Mollusca sexual selection does not seem to have come into play; yet many univalve and bivalve shells, such as volutes, cones, scallops, &c., are beautifully coloured and shaped. The colours do not appear in most cases to be of any use as a pro-tection; they are probably the direct result, as in the lowest classes, of the nature of the tissues; the patterns and the sculpture of the shell depending on its manner of growth. The amount of light seems to be influential to a certain extent; for although, as

[3] See, for instance, the account which I have given in my 'Journal of Researches,' 1845, p. 7.

repeatedly stated by Mr. Gwyn Jeffreys, the shells of some species living at a profound depth are brightly coloured, yet we generally see the lower surfaces, as well as the parts covered by the mantle, less highly-coloured than the upper and exposed surfaces.[4] In some cases, as with shells living amongst corals or brightly-tinted sea-weeds, the bright colours may serve as a protection.[5] But that many of the nudibranch mollusca, or sea-slugs, are as beautifully coloured as any shells, may be seen in Messrs. Alder and Hancock's magnificent work ; and from information kindly given me by Mr. Hancock, it seems extremely doubtful whether these colours usually serve as a protection. With some species this may be the case, as with one kind which lives on the green leaves of algæ, and is itself bright-green. But many brightly-coloured, white, or otherwise conspicuous species, do not seek concealment ; whilst again some equally conspicuous species, as well as other dull-coloured kinds, live under stones and in dark recesses. So that with these nudibranch molluscs, colour apparently does not stand in any close relation to the nature of the places which they inhabit.

These naked sea-slugs are hermaphrodites, yet they pair together, as do land-snails, many of which have extremely pretty shells. It is conceivable that two hermaphrodites, attracted by each other's greater

[4] I have given ('Geolog. Observations on Volcanic Islands,' 1844, p. 53) a curious instance of the influence of light on the colours of a frondescent incrustation, deposited by the surf on the coast-rocks of Ascension, and formed by the solution of triturated sea-shells.

[5] Dr. Morse has lately discussed this subject in his paper on the Adaptive Coloration of Mollusca, 'Proc. Boston Soc. of Nat. Hist.' vol. xiv., April, 1871.

beauty, might unite and leave offspring which would
inherit their parents' greater beauty. But with such
lowly-organised creatures this is extremely improbable.
Nor is it at all obvious how the offspring from the
more beautiful pairs of hermaphrodites would have any
advantage over the offspring of the less beautiful, so as
to increase in number, unless indeed vigour and beauty
generally coincided. We have not here the case of a
number of males becoming mature before the females,
with the more beautiful males selected by the more
vigorous females. If, indeed, brilliant colours were
beneficial to a hermaphrodite animal in relation to its
general habits of life, the more brightly-tinted individuals would succeed best and would increase in
number; but this would be a case of natural and not
of sexual selection.

Sub-kingdom of the Vermes; Class, *Annelida (or Sea-
worms).*—In this class, although the sexes, when
separate, sometimes differ from each other in characters of such importance that they have been placed
under distinct genera or even families, yet the differences do not seem of the kind which can be safely
attributed to sexual selection. These animals are
often beautifully coloured, but as the sexes do not
differ in this respect, we are but little concerned with
them. Even the Nemertians, though so lowly organised, " vie in beauty and variety of colouring with any
" other group in the invertebrate series; " yet Dr.
McIntosh [6] cannot discover that these colours are of
any service. The sedentary annelids become duller-

---

[6] See his beautiful monograph on 'British Annelids,' part i.
1873, p. 3.

coloured, according to M. Quatrefages,[7] after the
period of reproduction; and this I presume may be
attributed to their less vigorous condition at that
time. All these worm-like animals apparently stand
too low in the scale for the individuals of either sex to
exert any choice in selecting a partner, or for the
individuals of the same sex to struggle together in
rivalry.

Sub-kingdom of the Arthropoda: Class, *Crustacea.*—
In this great class we first meet with undoubted
secondary sexual characters, often developed in a
remarkable manner. Unfortunately the habits of
crustaceans are very imperfectly known, and we cannot
explain the uses of many structures peculiar to one
sex. With the lower parasitic species the males are of
small size, and they alone are furnished with perfect
swimming-legs, antennæ and sense-organs; the females
being destitute of these organs, with their bodies often
consisting of a mere distorted mass. But these extraordinary differences between the two sexes are no doubt
related to their widely different habits of life, and consequently do not concern us. In various crustaceans,
belonging to distinct families, the anterior antennæ
are furnished with peculiar thread-like bodies, which
are believed to act as smelling-organs, and these are
much more numerous in the males than in the females.
As the males, without any unusual development of
their olfactory organs, would almost certainly be able
sooner or later to find the females, the increased
number of the smelling-threads has probably been

[7] See M. Perrier, 'l'Origine   'Revue Scientifique,' Feb. 1873,
de l'Homme d'après Darwin,'   p. 866.

acquired through sexual selection, by the better provided males having been the more successful in finding partners and in producing offspring. Fritz Müller has described a remarkable dimorphic species of Tanais, in which the male is represented by two distinct forms, which never graduate into each other. In the one form the male is furnished with more numerous smelling-threads, and in the other form with more powerful and more elongated chelæ or pincers, which serve to hold the female. Fritz Müller suggests that these differences between the two male forms of the same species may have originated in certain individuals having varied in the number of the smelling-threads, whilst other individuals varied in the shape and size of their chelæ; so that of the former, those which were best able to find the female, and of the latter, those which were best able to hold her, have left the greatest number of progeny to inherit their respective advantages.[8]

In some of the lower crustaceans, the right anterior antenna of the male differs greatly in structure from the left, the latter resembling in its simple tapering joints the antennæ of the female. In the male the modified antenna is either swollen in the middle or angularly bent, or converted (fig. 4) into an elegant, and sometimes wonderfully complex, prehensile organ.[9] It serves, as I hear from Sir J. Lubbock, to hold the

[8] 'Facts and Arguments for Darwin,' English translat. 1869, p. 20. See the previous discussion on the olfactory threads. Sars has described a somewhat analogous case (as quoted in 'Nature,' 1870, p. 455) in a Norwegian crustacean, the *Pontoporeia affinis*.

[9] See Sir J. Lubbock in 'Annals and Mag. of Nat. Hist.' vol. xi. 1853, pl. i. and x.; and vol. xii. (1853) pl. vii. See also Lubbock in 'Transact. Ent. Soc.' vol. iv. new series, 1856–1858, p. 8. With respect to the zigzagged antennæ mentioned below, see Fritz Müller, 'Facts and Arguments for Darwin,' 1869, p. 40, foot-note.

female, and for this same purpose one of the two posterior legs (*b*) on the same side of the body is converted into a forceps. In another family the inferior or posterior antennæ are "curiously zigzagged" in the males alone.

Fig. 4.   Labidocera Darwinii
(from Lubbock).

a. Part of right anterior antenna of male, forming a prehensile organ.
b. Posterior pair of thoracic legs of male.
c. Ditto of female.

In the higher crustaceans the anterior legs are developed into chelæ or pincers; and these are generally larger in the male than in the female,—so much so that the market value of the male edible crab (*Cancer pagurus*), according to Mr. C. Spence Bate, is five times as great as that of the female. In many species the chelæ are of unequal size on the opposite side of the body, the right-hand one being, as I am informed by Mr. Bate, generally, though not invariably, the largest. This inequality is also often much greater in the male than in the female. The two chelæ of the male often differ in structure (figs. 5, 6, and 7), the smaller one resembling that of the female. What advantage is gained by their inequality in size on the opposite sides of the body, and by the inequality being much greater in the male than in the female; and why, when they are of equal size, both are often much larger in the male than in the female, is not known. As I hear from Mr. Bate, the chelæ are sometimes of such length and size that they cannot possibly be used for carrying food to the mouth.   In the males of certain fresh-water prawns (Palæmon) the right leg is

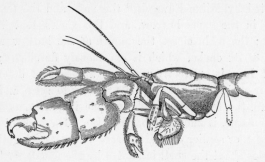

Fig. 5.   Anterior part of body of Callianassa (from Milne-Edwards), showing the unequal and differently-constructed right and left-hand chelæ of the male.

N.B.—The artist by mistake has reversed the drawing, and made the left-hand chela the largest.

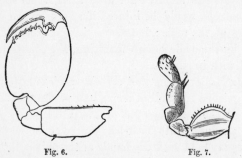

Fig. 6.   Fig. 7.

Fig 6.   Second leg of male Orchestia Tucuratinga (from Fritz Müller).
Fig. 7.   Ditto of female.

actually longer than the whole body.   The great size of the one leg with its chelæ may aid the male in

[10] See a paper by Mr. C. Spence Bate, with figures, in 'Proc. Zoolog. Soc.' 1868, p. 363; and on the nomenclature of the genus, ibid. p. 585.   I am greatly indebted to Mr. Spence Bate for nearly all the above statements with respect to the chelæ of the higher crustaceans.

fighting with his rivals; but this will not account for their inequality in the female on the opposite sides of the body. In Gelasimus, according to a statement quoted by Milne-Edwards,[11] the male and the female live in the same burrow, and this shews that they pair; the male closes the mouth of the burrow with one of its chelæ, which is enormously developed; so that here it indirectly serves as a means of defence. Their main use, however, is probably to seize and to secure the female, and this in some instances, as with Gammarus, is known to be the case. The male of the hermit or soldier crab (*Pagurus*) for weeks together, carries about the shell inhabited by the female.[12] The sexes, however, of the common shore-crab (*Carcinus mænas*), as Mr. Bate informs me, unite directly after the female has moulted her hard shell, when she is so soft that she would be injured if seized by the strong pincers of the male; but as she is caught and carried about by the male before moulting, she could then be seized with impunity.

Fritz Müller states that certain species of Melita are distinguished from all other amphipods by the females having " the coxal lamellæ of the penultimate pair of "feet produced into hook-like processes, of which the "males lay hold with the hands of the first pair." The development of these hook-like processes has probably followed from those females which were the most securely held during the act of reproduction, having left the largest number of offspring. Another Brazilian amphipod (*Orchestia Darwinii*, fig. 8) presents a case

[11] 'Hist. Nat. des Crust.' tom. ii. 1837, p. 50.

[12] Mr. C. Spence Bate, 'Brit. Assoc., Fourth Report on the Fauna of S. Devon.'

of dimorphism, like that of Tanais; for there are two male forms, which differ in the structure of their chelæ.[13]   As either chela would certainly suffice to hold

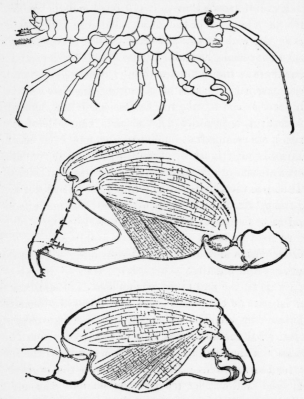

Fig. 8. Orchestia Darwinii (from Fritz Müller), showing the differently-constructed chelæ of the two male forms.

the female,—for both are now used for this purpose,—the two male forms probably originated by some having

[13] Fritz Müller, 'Facts and Arguments for Darwin,' 1869, pp. 25–28.

varied in one manner and some in another; both forms having derived certain special, but nearly equal advantages, from their differently shaped organs.

It is not known that male crustaceans fight together for the possession of the females, but it is probably the case; for with most animals when the male is larger than the female, he seems to owe his greater size to his ancestors having fought with other males during many generations. In most of the orders, especially in the highest or the Brachyura, the male is larger than the female; the parasitic genera, however, in which the sexes follow different habits of life, and most of the Entomostraca must be excepted. The chelæ of many crustaceans are weapons well adapted for fighting. Thus when a Devil-crab (*Portunus puber*) was seen by a son of Mr. Bate fighting with a *Carcinus mænas*, the latter was soon thrown on its back, and had every limb torn from its body. When several males of a Brazilian Gelasimus, a species furnished with immense pincers, were placed together in a glass vessel by Fritz Müller, they mutilated and killed one another. Mr. Bate put a large male *Carcinus mænas* into a pan of water, inhabited by a female which was paired with a smaller male; but the latter was soon dispossessed. Mr. Bate adds, "if they fought, the victory was a bloodless one, "for I saw no wounds." This same naturalist separated a male sand-skipper (so common on our sea-shores), *Gammarus marinus*, from its female, both of whom were imprisoned in the same vessel with many individuals of the same species. The female, when thus divorced, soon joined the others. After a time the male was put again into the same vessel; and he then, after swimming about for a time, dashed into the crowd,

and without any fighting at once took away his wife.
This fact shews that in the Amphipoda, an order low
in the scale, the males and females recognise each
other, and are mutually attached.

The mental powers of the Crustacea are probably
higher than at first sight appears probable. Any one
who tries to catch one of the shore-crabs, so common
on tropical coasts, will perceive how wary and alert
they are. There is a large crab (*Birgus latro*), found
on coral islands, which makes a thick bed of the picked
fibres of the cocoa-nut, at the bottom of a deep burrow.
It feeds on the fallen fruit of this tree by tearing off
the husk, fibre by fibre; and it always begins at that
end where the three eye-like depressions are situated.
It then breaks through one of these eyes by hammering
with its heavy front pincers, and turning round,
extracts the albuminous core with its narrow posterior
pincers. But these actions are probably instinctive, so
that they would be performed as well by a young
animal as by an old one. The following case, however,
can hardly be so considered: a trustworthy naturalist,
Mr. Gardner,[14] whilst watching a shore-crab (Gelasimus)
making its burrow, threw some shells towards the hole.
One rolled in, and three other shells remained within a
few inches of the mouth. In about five minutes the
crab brought out the shell which had fallen in, and
carried it away to a distance of a foot; it then saw the
three other shells lying near, and evidently thinking
that they might likewise roll in, carried them to the
spot where it had laid the first. It would, I think, be

[14] 'Travels in the Interior of
Brazil,' 1846, p. 111. I have
given, in my 'Journal of Researches,' p. 463, an account of
the habits of the Birgus.

difficult to distinguish this act from one performed by man by the aid of reason.

Mr. Bate does not know of any well-marked case of difference of colour in the two sexes of our British crustaceans, in which respect the sexes of the higher animals so often differ. In some cases, however, the males and females differ slightly in tint, but Mr. Bate thinks not more than may be accounted for by their different habits of life, such as by the male wandering more about, and being thus more exposed to the light. Dr. Power tried to distinguish by colour the sexes of the several species which inhabit the Mauritius, but failed, except with one species of Squilla, probably *S. stylifera*, the male of which is described as being " of " a beautiful bluish-green, " with some of the appendages cherry-red, whilst the female is clouded with brown and grey, " with the red about her much less vivid " than in the male." [15] In this case, we may suspect the agency of sexual selection. From M. Bert's observations on Daphnia, when placed in a vessel illuminated by a prism, we have reason to believe that even the lowest crustaceans can distinguish colours. With Saphirina (an oceanic genus of Entomostraca), the males are furnished with minute shields or cell-like bodies, which exhibit beautiful changing colours; these are absent in the females, and in both sexes of one species.[16] It would, however, be extremely rash to conclude that these curious organs serve to attract the females. I am informed by Fritz Müller, that in the female of a Brazilian species of Gelasimus, the whole body is of a

[15] Mr. Ch. Fraser, in 'Proc. Zoolog. Soc.' 1869, p. 3. I am indebted to Mr. Bate for Dr. Power's statement.

[16] Claus, 'Die freilebenden Copepoden,' 1863, s. 35.

nearly uniform greyish-brown. In the male the posterior part of the cephalo-thorax is pure white, with the anterior part of a rich green, shading into dark brown; and it is remarkable that these colours are liable to change in the course of a few minutes—the white becoming dirty grey or even black, the green "losing much of its brilliancy." It deserves especial notice that the males do not acquire their bright colours until they become mature. They appear to be much more numerous than the females; they differ also in the larger size of their chelæ. In some species of the genus, probably in all, the sexes pair and inhabit the same burrow. They are also, as we have seen, highly intelligent animals. From these various considerations it seems probable that the male in this species has become gaily ornamented in order to attract or excite the female.

It has just been stated that the male Gelasimus does not acquire his conspicuous colours until mature and nearly ready to breed. This seems a general rule in the whole class in respect to the many remarkable structural differences between the sexes. We shall hereafter find the same law prevailing throughout the great sub-kingdom of the Vertebrata; and in all cases it is eminently distinctive of characters which have been acquired through sexual selection. Fritz Müller [17] gives some striking instances of this law; thus the male sand-hopper (Orchestia) does not, until nearly full grown, acquire his large claspers, which are very differently constructed from those of the female; whilst young, his claspers resemble those of the female.

Class, *Arachnida* (Spiders).—The sexes do not

[17] 'Facts and Arguments,' &c., p. 79.

generally differ much in colour, but the males are often
darker than the females, as may be seen in Mr. Blackwall's magnificent work.[18] In some species, however,
the difference is conspicuous : thus the female of *Sparassus smaragdulus* is dullish green, whilst the adult
male has the abdomen of a fine yellow, with three longitudinal stripes of rich red. In certain species of
Thomisus the sexes closely resemble each other, in
others they differ much ; and analogous cases occur in
many other genera. It is often difficult to say which
of the two sexes departs most from the ordinary coloration of the genus to which the species belong; but
Mr. Blackwall thinks that, as a general rule, it is the
male; and Canestrini [19] remarks that in certain genera
the males can be specifically distinguished with ease,
but the females with great difficulty. I am informed
by Mr. Blackwall that the sexes whilst young usually
resemble each other ; and both often undergo great
changes in colour during their successive moults,
before arriving at maturity. In other cases the male
alone appears to change colour. Thus the male of the
above bright-coloured Sparassus at first resembles the
female, and acquires his peculiar tints only when nearly
adult. Spiders are possessed of acute senses, and
exhibit much intelligence; as is well known, the
females often shew the strongest affection for their
eggs, which they carry about enveloped in a silken
web. The males search eagerly for the females, and

[18] 'A History of the Spiders
of Great Britain,' 1861–64. For
the following facts, see pp. 77,
88, 102.

[19] This author has recently
published a valuable essay on
the 'Caratteri sessuali secondarii
degli Arachnidi,' in the 'Atti
della Soc. Veneto-Trentina di
Sc. Nat. Padova,' vol. i. Fasc. 3,
1873.

have been seen by Canestrini and others to fight for possession of them. This same author says that the union of the two sexes has been observed in about twenty species; and he asserts positively that the female rejects some of the males who court her, threatens them with open mandibles, and at last after long hesitation accepts the chosen one. From these several considerations, we may admit with some confidence that the well-marked differences in colour between the sexes of certain species are the results of sexual selection; though we have not here the best kind of evidence,—the display by the male of his ornaments. From the extreme variability of colour in the male of some species, for instance of *Theridion lineatum*, it would appear that these sexual characters of the males have not as yet become well fixed. Canestrini draws the same conclusion from the fact that the males of certain species present two forms, differing from each other in the size and length of their jaws; and this reminds us of the above cases of dimorphic crustaceans.

The male is generally much smaller than the female, sometimes to an extraordinary degree,[20] and he is forced to be extremely cautious in making his advances, as the female often carries her coyness to a dangerous pitch. De Geer saw a male that "in the midst of his "preparatory caresses was seized by the object of his "attentions, enveloped by her in a web and then "devoured, a sight which, as he adds, filled him with

[20] Aug. Vinson ('Aranéides des Iles de la Réunion,' pl. vi. figs. 1 and 2) gives a good instance of the small size of the male, in *Epeira nigra*. In this species, as I may add, the male is testaceous and the female black with legs banded with red. Other even more striking cases of inequality in size between the sexes have been recorded ('Quarterly Journal of Science,' 1868, July, p. 429); but I have not seen the original accounts.

"horror and indignation."[21] The Rev. O. P. Cambridge[22] accounts in the following manner for the extreme smallness of the male in the genus Nephila. "M. Vinson gives a graphic account of the agile way "in which the diminutive male escapes from the "ferocity of the female, by gliding about and playing "hide and seek over her body and along her gigantic "limbs : in such a pursuit it is evident that the chances "of escape would be in favour of the smallest males, "while the larger ones would fall early victims ; thus "gradually a diminutive race of males would be selected, "until at last they would dwindle to the smallest "possible size compatible with the exercise of their "generative functions,—in fact probably to the size we "now see them, i.e., so small as to be a sort of parasite "upon the female, and either beneath her notice, or "too agile and too small for her to catch without great "difficulty."

Westring has made the interesting discovery that the males of several species of Theridion[23] have the power of making a stridulating sound, whilst the females are mute. The apparatus consists of a serrated ridge at the base of the abdomen, against which the hard hinder part of the thorax is rubbed ; and of this structure not a trace can be detected in the females. It deserves notice that several writers, including the well-known arachnologist Walckenaer, have declared that

[21] Kirby and Spence, ' Introduction to Entomology,' vol. i. 1818, p. 280.

[22] ' Proc. Zoolog. Soc.' 1871, p. 621.

[23] Theridion (Asagena, Sund.) serratipes, 4-punctatum et guttatum; see Westring, in Kroyer, ' Naturhist. Tidskrift,' vol. iv. 1842–1843, p. 349 ; and vol. ii. 1846–1849, p. 342. See, also, for other species, 'Araneæ Suecicæ,' p. 184.

spiders are attracted by music.[24] From the analogy of
the Orthoptera and Homoptera, to be described in the
next chapter, we may feel almost sure that the stridulation serves, as Westring also believes, to call or to
excite the female; and this is the first case known to
me in the ascending scale of the animal kingdom of
sounds emitted for this purpose.[25]

Class, *Myriapoda.*—In neither of the two orders in
this class, the millipedes and centipedes, can I find any
well-marked instances of such sexual differences as
more particularly concern us. In *Glomeris limbata*,
however, and perhaps in some few other species, the
males differ slightly in colour from the females; but
this Glomeris is a highly variable species. In the
males of the Diplopoda, the legs belonging either to
one of the anterior or of the posterior segments of the
body are modified into prehensile hooks which serve to
secure the female. In some species of Iulus the tarsi
of the male are furnished with membranous suckers for
the same purpose. As we shall see when we treat of
Insects, it is a much more unusual circumstance, that
it is the female in Lithobius, which is furnished with
prehensile appendages at the extremity of her body
for holding the male.[26]

[24] Dr. H. H. van Zouteveen,
in his Dutch translation of this
work (vol. i. p. 444), has collected
several cases.

[25] Hilgendorf, however, has
lately called attention to an
analogous structure in some of
the higher crustaceans, which

seems adapted to produce sound;
see 'Zoological Record,' 1869, p.
603.

[26] Walckenaer et P. Gervais,
'Hist. Nat. des Insectes: Ap-
teres,' tom. iv. 1847, pp. 17, 19,
68.

CHAPTER X.

SECONDARY SEXUAL CHARACTERS OF INSECTS.

Diversified structures possessed by the males for seizing the females
—Differences between the sexes, of which the meaning is not
understood—Difference in size between the sexes—Thysanura
—Diptera—Hemiptera—Homoptera, musical powers possessed
by the males alone—Orthoptera, musical instruments of the
males, much diversified in structure; pugnacity; colours—Neuroptera, sexual differences in colour—Hymenoptera, pugnacity
and colours—Coleoptera, colours; furnished with great horns,
apparently as an ornament; battles; stridulating organs generally
common to both sexes.

IN the immense class of insects the sexes sometimes
differ in their locomotive-organs, and often in their
sense-organs, as in the pectinated and beautifully
plumose antennæ of the males of many species. In
Chloëon, one of the Ephemeræ, the male has great
pillared eyes, of which the female is entirely destitute.[1]
The ocelli are absent in the females of certain insects,
as in the Mutillidæ; and here the females are likewise
wingless. But we are chiefly concerned with structures
by which one male is enabled to conquer another,
either in battle or courtship, through his strength,
pugnacity, ornaments, or music. The innumerable
contrivances, therefore, by which the male is able to

[1] Sir J. Lubbock, 'Transact.
Linnean Soc.' vol. xxv. 1866, p.
484. With respect to the Mutillidæ see Westwood, 'Modern
Class. of Insects,' vol. ii. p. 213.

seize the female, may be briefly passed over. Besides
the complex structures at the apex of the abdomen,
which ought perhaps to be ranked as primary organs,[2]
" it is astonishing," as Mr B. D. Walsh[3] has remarked,
"how many different organs are worked in by nature
"for the seemingly insignificant object of enabling
"the male to grasp the female firmly." The mandibles
or jaws are sometimes used for this purpose; thus the
male *Corydalis cornutus* (a neuropterous insect in some
degree allied to the Dragon flies, &c.) has immense
curved jaws, many times longer than those of the
female; and they are smooth instead of being toothed,
so that he is thus enabled to seize her without injury.[4]
One of the stag-beetles of North America (*Lucanus
elaphus*) uses his jaws, which are much larger than
those of the female, for the same purpose, but probably likewise for fighting. In one of the sand-wasps
(*Ammophila*) the jaws in the two sexes are closely alike,
but are used for widely different purposes: the males,
as Professor Westwood observes, "are exceedingly

[2] These organs in the male
often differ in closely-allied
species, and afford excellent
specific characters. But their
importance, from a functional
point of view, as Mr. R. Mac-
Lachlan has remarked to me,
has probably been overrated. It
has been suggested, that slight
differences in these organs would
suffice to prevent the intercrossing of well-marked varieties or
incipient species, and would thus
aid in their development. That
this can hardly be the case, we
may infer from the many recorded cases (see, for instance,
Bronn, 'Geschichte der Natur,'
B. ii. 1843, s. 164; and Westwood, 'Transact. Ent. Soc.' vol.
iii. 1842, p. 195) of distinct
species having been observed in
union. Mr. MacLachlan in-
forms me (vide 'Stett. Ent.
Zeitung,' 1867, s. 155) that
when several species of Phry-
ganidæ, which present strongly-
pronounced differences of this
kind, were confined together by
Dr. Aug. Meyer, *they coupled*,
and one pair produced fertile
ova.

[3] 'The Practical Entomologist,' Philadelphia, vol. ii.
May, 1867, p. 88.

[4] Mr. Walsh, ibid. p. 107.

"ardent, seizing their partners round the neck with "their sickle-shaped jaws;"[5] whilst the females use these organs for burrowing in sand-banks and making their nests.

The tarsi of the front-legs are dilated in many male

beetles, or are furnished with broad cushions of hairs; and in many genera of water-beetles they are armed with a round flat sucker, so that the male may adhere to the slippery body of the female. It is a much more unusual circumstance that the females of some water-beetles (Dytiscus) have their elytra deeply grooved, and in *Acilius sulcatus* thickly set with hairs, as an aid to the male. The females of some other water-beetles (Hydroporus)

Fig. 9. Crabro cribrarius. Upper figure, male; lower figure, female.

have their elytra punctured for the same purpose.[6] In the male of *Crabro cribrarius* (fig. 9), it is the tibia which is dilated into a broad horny plate, with minute membraneous dots, giving to

[5] 'Modern Classification of Insects,' vol. ii. 1840, pp. 205, 206. Mr. Walsh, who called my attention to the double use of the jaws, says that he has repeatedly observed this fact.

[6] We have here a curious and inexplicable case of dimorphism, for some of the females of four European species of Dysticus, and of certain species of Hydro-porus, have their elytra smooth; and no intermediate gradations between the sulcated or punctured, and the quite smooth elytra have been observed. See Dr. H. Schaum, as quoted in the 'Zoologist,' vol. v.–vi. 1847–48, p. 1896. Also Kirby and Spence, 'Introduction to Entomology,' vol. iii. 1826, p. 305.

it a singular appearance like that of a riddle.[7]   In the
male of Penthe (a genus of beetles) a few of the middle
joints of the antennæ are dilated and
furnished on the inferior surface with
cushions of hair, exactly like those on
the tarsi of the Carabidæ, "and ob-
"viously for the same end."   In male
dragon-flies, "the appendages at the tip
" of the tail are modified in an almost
"infinite variety of curious patterns to
"enable them to embrace the neck of
"the female."   Lastly, in the males of
many insects, the legs are furnished
with peculiar spines, knobs or spurs;
or the whole leg is bowed or thickened,
but this is by no means invariably a
sexual character; or one pair, or all
three pairs are elongated, sometimes to
an extravagant length.[8]

The sexes of many species in all the
orders present differences, of which
the meaning is not understood.   One
curious case is that of a beetle (fig. 10),
the male of which has left mandible
much enlarged; so that the mouth is
greatly distorted.   In another Cara-
bidous beetle, Eurygnathus,[9] we have
the case, unique as far as known to
Mr. Wollaston, of the head of the female

Fig. 10.   Taphroderes
distortus (much en-
larged). Upper figure,
male; lower figure,
female.

[7] Westwood, 'Modern Class.'
vol. ii. p. 193. The following
statement about Penthe, and
others in inverted commas, are
taken from Mr. Walsh, 'Practical Entomologist,' Philadelphia,
vol. iii. p. 88.

[8] Kirby and Spence, 'Introduct.' &c., vol. iii. pp. 332–
336.

[9] 'Insecta Maderensia,' 1854,
p. 20.

being much broader and larger, though in a variable degree, than that of the male. Any number of such cases could be given. They abound in the Lepidoptera: one of the most extraordinary is that certain male butterflies have their fore-legs more or less atrophied, with the tibiæ and tarsi reduced to mere rudimentary knobs. The wings, also, in the two sexes often differ in neuration,[10] and sometimes considerably in outline, as in the *Aricoris epitus,* which was shewn to me in the British Museum by Mr. A. Butler. The males of certain South American butterflies have tufts of hair on the margins of the wings, and horny excrescences on the discs of the posterior pair.[11] In several British butterflies, as shewn by Mr. Wonfor, the males alone are in parts clothed with peculiar scales.

The use of the bright light of the female glow-worm has been subject to much discussion. The male is feebly luminous, as are the larvæ and even the eggs. It has been supposed by some authors that the light serves to frighten away enemies, and by others to guide the male to the female. At last, Mr. Belt[12] appears to have solved the difficulty: he finds that all the Lampyridæ which he has tried are highly distasteful to insectivorous mammals and birds. Hence it is in accordance with Mr. Bates' view, hereafter to be explained, that many insects mimic the Lampyridæ closely, in order to be mistaken for them, and thus to

[10] E. Doubleday, 'Annals and Mag. of Nat. Hist.' vol. i. 1848, p. 379. I may add that the wings in certain Hymenoptera (see Shuckard, 'Fossorial Hymenop.' 1837, pp. 39–43) differ in neuration according to sex.

[11] H. W. Bates, in 'Journal of Proc. Linn. Soc.' vol. vi. 1862,

p. 74. Mr. Wonfor's observations are quoted in 'Popular Science Review,' 1868, p. 343.

[12] 'The Naturalist in Nicaragua,' 1874, pp. 316–320. On the phosphorescence of the eggs, see 'Annals and Mag. of Nat. Hist.' 1871, Nov., p. 372.

escape destruction. He further believes that the luminous species profit by being at once recognised as unpalatable. It is probable that the same explanation may be extended to the Elaters, both sexes of which are highly luminous. It is not known why the wings of the female glow-worm have not been developed; but in her present state she closely resembles a larva, and as larvæ are so largely preyed on by many animals, we can understand why she has been rendered so much more luminous and conspicuous than the male; and why the larvæ themselves are likewise luminous.

Difference in Size between the Sexes.—With insects of all kinds the males are commonly smaller than the females; and this difference can often be detected even in the larval state. So considerable is the difference between the male and female cocoons of the silk-moth (*Bombyx mori*), that in France they are separated by a particular mode of weighing.[13] In the lower classes of the animal kingdom, the greater size of the females seems generally to depend on their developing an enormous number of ova; and this may to a certain extent hold good with insects. But Dr. Wallace has suggested a much more probable explanation. He finds, after carefully attending to the development of the caterpillars of *Bombyx cynthia* and *yamamai*, and especially to that of some dwarfed caterpillars reared from a second brood on unnatural food, " that in proportion as the individual moth is " finer, so is the time required for its metamorphosis " longer; and for this reason the female, which is the " larger and heavier insect, from having to carry her

[13] Robinet, ' Vers à Soie,' 1848, p. 207.

" numerous eggs, will be preceded by the male, which
" is smaller and has less to mature." [14]   Now as most
insects are short-lived, and as they are exposed to
many dangers, it would manifestly be advantageous to
the female to be impregnated as soon as possible.
This end would be gained by the males being first
matured in large numbers ready for the advent of the
females; and this again would naturally follow, as
Mr. A. R. Wallace has remarked,[15] through natural
selection; for the smaller males would be first
matured, and thus would procreate a large number of
offspring which would inherit the reduced size of their
male parents, whilst the larger males from being
matured later would leave fewer offspring.

There are, however, exceptions to the rule of male
insects being smaller than the females: and some of
these exceptions are intelligible. Size and strength
would be an advantage to the males, which fight for
the possession of the females; and in these cases, as
with the stag-beetle (Lucanus), the males are larger
than the females. There are, however, other beetles
which are not known to fight together, of which the
males exceed the females in size; and the meaning of
this fact is not known; but in some of these cases, as
with the huge Dynastes and Megasoma, we can at
least see that there would be no necessity for the
males to be smaller than the females, in order to be
matured before them, for these beetles are not short-
lived, and there would be ample time for the pairing
of the sexes. So again, male dragon-flies (Libellulidæ) are sometimes sensibly larger, and never

[14] 'Transact. Ent. Soc.' 3rd
series, vol. v. p. 486.

[15] 'Journal of Proc. Ent. Soc.'
Feb. 4th, 1867, p. lxxi.

smaller, than the females;[16] and as Mr. MacLachlan believes, they do not generally pair with the females until a week or fortnight has elapsed, and until they have assumed their proper masculine colours. But the most curious case, shewing on what complex and easily-overlooked relations, so trifling a character as difference in size between the sexes may depend, is that of the aculeate Hymenoptera; for Mr. F. Smith informs me that throughout nearly the whole of this large group, the males, in accordance with the general rule, are smaller than the females, and emerge about a week before them; but amongst the Bees, the males of *Apis mellifica*, *Anthidium manicatum*, and *Anthophora acervorum*, and amongst the Fossores, the males of the *Methoca ichneumonides*, are larger than the females. The explanation of this anomaly is that a marriage flight is absolutely necessary with these species, and the male requires great strength and size in order to carry the female through the air. Increased size has here been acquired in opposition to the usual relation between size and the period of development, for the males, though larger, emerge before the smaller females.

We will now review the several Orders, selecting such facts as more particularly concern us. The Lepidoptera (Butterflies and Moths) will be retained for a separate chapter.

Order, *Thysanura.*—The members of this lowly organized order are wingless, dull-coloured, minute

[16] For this and other statements on the size of the sexes, see Kirby and Spence, ibid. vol. iii. p. 300; on the duration of life in insects, see p. 344.

insects, with ugly, almost misshapen heads and bodies.
Their sexes do not differ, but they are interesting as
shewing us that the males pay sedulous court to the
females even low down in the animal scale. Sir J.
Lubbock [17] says: "it is very amusing to see these
"little creatures (*Smynthurus luteus*) coquetting
"together. The male, which is much smaller than the
"female, runs round her, and they butt one another,
"standing face to face and moving backward and
"forward like two playful lambs. Then the female
"pretends to run away and the male runs after her
"with a queer appearance of anger, gets in front and
"stands facing her again; then she turns coyly round,
"but he, quicker and more active, scuttles round too,
"and seems to whip her with his antennæ; then for a
"bit they stand face to face, play with their antennæ,
"and seem to be all in all to one another."

Order, *Diptera* (Flies).—The sexes differ little in
colour. The greatest difference, known to Mr. F.
Walker, is in the genus Bibio, in which the males are
blackish or quite black, and the females obscure
brownish-orange. The genus Elaphomyia, discovered
by Mr. Wallace [18] in New Guinea, is highly remarkable, as the males are furnished with horns, of which
the females are quite destitute. The horns spring
from beneath the eyes, and curiously resemble those of
a stag, being either branched or palmated. In one of
the species, they equal the whole body in length.
They might be thought to be adapted for fighting, but
as in one species they are of a beautiful pink colour,

[17] 'Transact. Linnean Soc.'   [18] 'The Malay Archipelago,'
vol. xxvi. 1868, p. 296.   vol ii. 1869, p. 313.

edged with black, with a pale central stripe, and as these insects have altogether a very elegant appearance, it is perhaps more probable that they serve as ornaments. That the males of some Diptera fight together is certain; Prof. Westwood [19] has several times seen this with the Tipulæ. The males of other Diptera apparently try to win the females by their music: H. Müller [20] watched for some time two males of an Eristalis courting a female; they hovered above her, and flew from side to side, making a high humming noise at the same time. Gnats and mosquitoes (Culicidæ) also seem to attract each other by humming; and Prof. Mayer has recently ascertained that the hairs on the antennæ of the male vibrate in unison with the notes of a tuning-fork, within the range of the sounds emitted by the female. The longer hairs vibrate sympathetically with the graver notes, and the shorter hairs with the higher ones. Landois also asserts that he has repeatedly drawn down a whole swarm of gnats by uttering a particular note. It may be added that the mental faculties of the Diptera are probably higher than in most other insects, in accordance with their highly-developed nervous system. [21]

Order, *Hemiptera* (Field-Bugs).—Mr. J. W. Douglas, who has particularly attended to the British species, has kindly given me an account of their sexual differ-

[19] 'Modern Classification of Insects,' vol. ii. 1840, p. 526.

[20] Anwendung, &c., 'Verh. d. n. V. Jahrg.' xxix. p. 80. Mayer, in 'American Naturalist,' 1874, p. 236.

[21] See Mr. B. T. Lowne's interesting work, 'On the Anatomy of the Blow-fly, Musca vomitoria,' 1870, p. 14. He remarks (p. 33) that, "the "captured flies utter a peculiar "plaintive note, and that this "sound causes other flies to "disappear."

ences. The males of some species are furnished with wings, whilst the females are wingless; the sexes differ in the form of their bodies, elytra, antennæ and tarsi; but as the signification of these differences are unknown, they may be here passed over. The females are generally larger and more robust than the males. With British, and, as far as Mr. Douglas knows, with exotic species, the sexes do not commonly differ much in colour; but in about six British species the male is considerably darker than the female, and in about four other species the female is darker than the male. Both sexes of some species are beautifully coloured; and as these insects emit an extremely nauseous odour, their conspicuous colours may serve as a signal that they are unpalatable to insectivorous animals. In some few cases their colours appear to be directly protective: thus Prof. Hoffmann informs me that he could hardly distinguish a small pink and green species from the buds on the trunks of lime-trees, which this insect frequents.

Some species of Reduvidæ make a stridulating noise; and, in the case of *Pirates stridulus*, this is said [22] to be effected by the movement of the neck within the pro-thoracic cavity. According to Westring, *Reduvius personatus* also stridulates. But I have no reason to suppose that this is a sexual character, excepting that with non-social insects there seems to be no use for sound-producing organs, unless it be as a sexual call.

Order, *Homoptera*.—Every one who has wandered in a tropical forest must have been astonished at the din made by the male Cicadæ. The females are mute; as

[22] Westwood, 'Modern Class. of Insects,' vol. ii. p. 473.

the Grecian poet Xenarchus says, "Happy the Cicadas "live, since they all have voiceless wives." The noise thus made could be plainly heard on board the "Beagle," when anchored at a quarter of a mile from the shore of Brazil; and Captain Hancock says it can be heard at the distance of a mile. The Greeks formerly kept, and the Chinese now keep these insects in cages for the sake of their song, so that it must be pleasing to the ears of some men.[23] The Cicadidæ usually sing during the day, whilst the Fulgoridæ appear to be night-songsters. The sound, according to Landois,[24] is produced by the vibration of the lips of the spiracles, which are set into motion by a current of air emitted from the tracheæ; but this view has lately been disputed. Dr. Powell appears to have proved[25] that it is produced by the vibration of a membrane, set into action by a special muscle. In the living insect, whilst stridulating, this membrane can be seen to vibrate; and in the dead insect the proper sound is heard, if the muscle, when a little dried and hardened, is pulled with the point of a pin. In the female the whole complex musical apparatus is present, but is much less developed than in the male, and is never used for producing sound.

With respect to the object of the music, Dr. Hartman, in speaking of the *Cicada septemdecim* of the United States, says,[26] "the drums are now (June 6th

---

[23] These particulars are taken from Westwood's 'Modern Class. of Insects,' vol. ii. 1840, p. 422. See, also, on the Fulgoridæ Kirby and Spence, 'Introduct.' vol. ii. p. 401.

[24] 'Zeitschrift für wissenschaft Zooiog.' B. xvii. 1867, s. 152–158.

[25] 'Transact. New Zealand Institute,' vol. v. 1873, p. 286.

[26] I am indebted to Mr. Walsh for having sent me this extract from a 'Journal of the Doings of Cicada septemdecim' by Dr. Hartman.

"and 7th, 1851) heard in all directions. This I believe "to be the marital summons from the males. Standing "in thick chestnut sprouts about as high as my head, "where hundreds were around me, I observed the "females coming around the drumming males." He adds, "this season (Aug. 1868) a dwarf pear-tree in "my garden produced about fifty larvæ of *Cic. pruinosa*; "and I several times noticed the females to alight near "a male while he was uttering his clanging notes." Fritz Müller writes to me from S. Brazil that he has often listened to a musical contest between two or three males of a species with a particularly loud voice, seated at a considerable distance from each other: as soon as one had finished his song, another immediately began, and then another. As there is so much rivalry between the males, it is probable that the females not only find them by their sounds, but that, like female birds, they are excited or allured by the male with the most attractive voice.

I have not heard of any well-marked cases of ornamental differences between the sexes of the Homoptera. Mr. Douglas informs me that there are three British species, in which the male is black or marked with black bands, whilst the females are pale-coloured or obscure.

Order, *Orthoptera* (Crickets and Grasshoppers).—The males in the three saltatorial families in this Order are remarkable for their musical powers, namely the Achetidæ or crickets, the Locustidæ for which there is no equivalent English name, and the Acridiidæ or grasshoppers. The stridulation produced by some of the Locustidæ is so loud that it can be heard during the

night at the distance of a mile;[27] and that made by
certain species is not unmusical even to the human ear,
so that the Indians on the Amazons keep them in
wicker cages. All observers agree that the sounds serve
either to call or excite the mute females. With respect
to the migratory locusts of Russia, Körte has given[28]
an interesting case of selection by the female of a male.
The males of this species (*Pachytylus migratorius*)
whilst coupled with the female stridulate from anger
or jealousy, if approached by other males. The house-
cricket when surprised at night uses its voice to warn
its fellows.[29] In North America the Katy-did (*Platyphyllum concavum*, one of the Locustidæ) is described[30]
as mounting on the upper branches of a tree, and in
the evening beginning " his noisy babble, while rival
" notes issue from the neighbouring trees, and the
" groves resound with the call of *Katy-did-she-did* the
" live-long night." Mr. Bates, in speaking of the
European field-cricket (one of the Achetidæ), says
" the male has been observed to place himself in the
" evening at the entrance of his burrow, and stridulate
" until a female approaches, when the louder notes are
" succeeded by a more subdued tone, whilst the success-
" ful musician caresses with his antennæ the mate he
" has won." [31] Dr. Scudder was able to excite one of
these insects to answer him, by rubbing on a file with

[27] L. Guilding, 'Transact.
Linn. Soc.' vol. xv. p. 154.

[28] I state this on the authority
of Köppen, 'Ueber die Heusch-
recken in Südrussland,' 1866,
p. 32, for I have in vain endeavoured to procure Körte's
work.

[29] Gilbert White, 'Nat. Hist.
of Selborne,' vol. ii. 1825, p. 262.

[30] Harris, 'Insects of New
England,' 1842, p. 128.

[31] 'The Naturalist on the
Amazons,' vol. i. 1863, p. 252.
Mr. Bates gives a very interesting discussion on the gradations
in the musical apparatus of the
three families. See also Westwood, 'Modern Class.' vol. ii.
pp. 445 and 453.

a quill.[32] In both sexes a remarkable auditory apparatus has been discovered by Von Siebold, situated in the front legs.[33]

In the three Families the sounds are differently produced. In the males of the Achetidæ both wingcovers have the same apparatus; and this in the field-cricket (*Gryllus campestris*, fig. 11) consists, as described by Landois,[34] of from 131 to 138 sharp, trans-

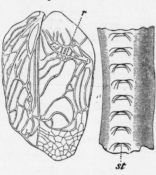

verse ridges or teeth (*st*) on the under side of one of the nervures of the wing-cover. This toothed nervure is rapidly scraped across a projecting, smooth, hard nervure (*r*) on the upper surface of the opposite wing. First one wing is rubbed over the other, and then the movement is reversed. Both wings are raised a little at the same time, so as to increase the reson-

Fig. 11. Gryllus campestris (from Landois).
Right-hand figure, under side of part of a wing-nervure, much magnified, showing the teeth, *st*.
Left-hand figure, upper surface of wing-cover, with the projecting, smooth nervure, *r*, across which the teeth (*st*) are scraped.

ance. In some species the wing-covers of the males are furnished at the base with a talc-like plate.[35] I here give a drawing (fig. 12) of the teeth on the under side of the nervure of another species of Gryllus, viz., *G. domesticus*. With respect to the formation of these teeth, Dr. Gruber has shewn [36] that they have been developed

[32] 'Proc. Boston Soc. of Nat. Hist.' vol. xi. April, 1868.

[33] 'Nouveau Manuel d'Anat. Comp.' (French translat.), tom. 1, 1850, p. 567.

[34] 'Zeitschrift für wissenschaft. Zoolog.' B. xvii. 1867, s. 117.

[35] Westwood, 'Modern Class. of Insects,' vol. i. p. 440.

[36] ' Ueber der Tonapparat der

by the aid of selection, from the minute scales and
hairs with which the wings and body are covered, and
I came to the same conclusion with respect to those of
the Coleoptera. But Dr. Gruber further shews that
their development is in part directly due to the stimulus from the friction of one wing over the other.

In the Locustidæ the opposite wing-
covers differ from each other in structure (fig. 13), and the action cannot, as
in the last family, be reversed. The
left wing, which acts as the bow, lies
over the right wing which serves as
the fiddle. One of the nervures (a)
on the under surface of the former is
finely serrated, and is scraped across
the prominent nervures on the upper
surface of the opposite or right wing.

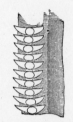

Fig. 12.   Teeth of Ner-
vure of Gryllus domes-
ticus (from Landois).

In our British
Phasgonura viridissima it appeared to me that the
serrated nervure is rubbed against the rounded hind-
corner of the opposite wing, the edge of which is
thickened, coloured brown, and very sharp. In the
right wing, but not in the left, there is a little plate,
as transparent as talc, surrounded by nervures, and
called the speculum. In *Ephippiger vitium*, a member
of this same family, we have a curious subordinate
modification; for the wing-covers are greatly reduced
in size, but " the posterior part of the pro-thorax is
" elevated into a kind of dome over the wing-covers,
" and which has probably the effect of increasing the
" sound." [37]

Locustiden, ein Beitrag zum
Darwinismus,' ' Zeitsch. für wissensch. Zoolog.' B. xxii. 1872,
p. 100.
[37] Westwood, ' Modern Class.
of Insects,' vol. i. p. 453.

We thus see that the musical apparatus is more differentiated or specialised in the Locustidæ (which include, I believe, the most powerful performers in the Order), than in the Achetidæ, in which both wing-

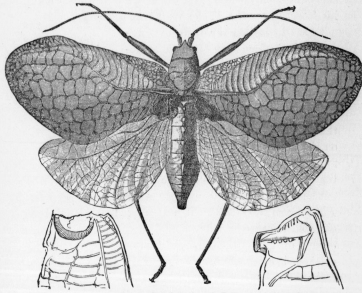

Fig. 13. Chlorocœlus Tanana (from Bates). *a, b.* Lobes of opposite wing-covers.

covers have the same structure and the same function.[38] Landois, however, detected in one of the Locustidæ, namely in Decticus, a short and narrow row of small teeth, mere rudiments, on the inferior surface of the right wing-cover, which underlies the other and is never used as the bow. I observed the same rudimentary structure on the under side of the right wing-cover in *Phasgonura viridissima*. Hence we may infer

[38] Landois. 'Zeitsch. f. wiss. Zoolog.' B. xvii. 1867, s. 121, 122.

with confidence that the Locustidæ are descended from a form, in which, as in the existing Achetidæ, both wing-covers had serrated nervures on the under surface, and could be indifferently used as the bow; but that in the Locustidæ the two wing-covers gradually became differentiated and perfected, on the principle of the division of labour, the one to act exclusively as the bow, and the other as the fiddle. Dr. Gruber takes the same view, and has shown that rudimentary teeth are commonly found on the inferior surface of the right wing. By what steps the more simple apparatus in the Achetidæ originated, we do not know, but it is probable that the basal portions of the wing-covers originally overlapped each other as they do at present; and that the friction of the nervures pro-

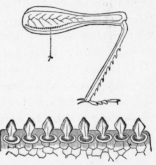

Fig. 14. Hind-leg of Stenobothrus pratorum: *r*, the stridulating ridge; lower figure, the teeth forming the ridge, much magnified (from Landois).

duced a grating sound, as is now the case with the wing-covers of the females.[39] A grating sound thus occasionally and accidentally made by the males, if it served them ever so little as a love-call to the females, might readily have been intensified through sexual selection, by variations in the roughness of the nervures having been continually preserved.

In the last and third Family, namely the Acridiidæ

[39] Mr. Walsh also informs me that he has noticed that the female of the *Platyphyllum con-* *cavum*, "when captured makes "a feeble grating noise by shuf- "fling her wing-covers together."

or grasshoppers, the stridulation is produced in a very different manner, and according to Dr. Scudder, is not so shrill as in the preceding Families. The inner surface of the femur (fig. 14, *r*) is furnished with a longitudinal row of minute, elegant, lancet-shaped, elastic teeth, from 85 to 93 in number; [40] and these are scraped across the sharp, projecting nervures on the wing-covers, which are thus made to vibrate and resound. Harris [41] says that when one of the males begins to play, he first " bends the shank of the hind-" leg beneath the thigh, where it is lodged in a furrow " designed to receive it, and then draws the leg briskly " up and down. He does not play both fiddles together, " but alternately, first upon one and then on the other." In many species, the base of the abdomen is hollowed out into a great cavity which is believed to act as a resounding board. In Pneumora (Fig. 15), a S. African genus belonging to the same family, we meet with a new and remarkable modification; in the males a small notched ridge projects obliquely from each side of the abdomen, against which the hind femora are rubbed. [42] As the male is furnished with wings (the female being wingless), it is remarkable that the thighs are not rubbed in the usual manner against the wing-covers; but this may perhaps be accounted for by the unusually small size of the hind-legs. I have not been able to examine the inner surface of the thighs, which, judging from analogy, would be finely serrated. The species of Pneumora have been more profoundly modified for the sake of stridulation than any other orthopterous

[40] Landois, ibid. s. 113.
[41] 'Insects of New England,' 1842, p. 133.
[42] Westwood, ' Modern Classi-fication,' vol. i. p. 462.

insect; for in the male the whole body has been converted into a musical instrument, being distended with
air, like a great pellucid bladder, so as to increase the
resonance.   Mr. Trimen informs me that at the Cape

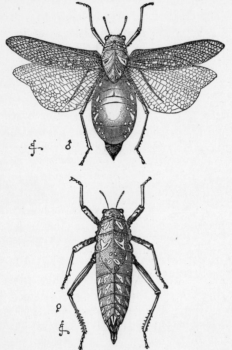

Fig. 15.   Pneumora (from specimens in the British Museum).   Upper figure, male;
lower figure, female.

of Good Hope these insects make a wonderful noise
during the night.

In the three foregoing families, the females are
almost always destitute of an efficient musical
apparatus. But there are a few exceptions to this
rule, for Dr. Gruber has shewn that both sexes of

Ephippiger vitium are thus provided; though the organs differ in the male and female to a certain extent. Hence we cannot suppose that they have been transferred from the male to the female, as appears to have been the case with the secondary sexual characters of many other animals. They must have been independently developed in the two sexes, which no doubt mutually call to each other during the season of love. In most other Locustidæ (but not according to Landois in Decticus) the females have rudiments of the stridulatory organs proper to the male; from whom it is probable that these have been transferred. Landois also found such rudiments on the under surface of the wing-covers of the female Achetidæ, and on the femora of the female Acridiidæ. In the Homoptera, also, the females have the proper musical apparatus in a functionless state; and we shall hereafter meet in other divisions of the animal kingdom with many instances of structures proper to the male being present in a rudimentary condition in the female.

Landois has observed another important fact, namely, that in the females of the Acridiidæ, the stridulating teeth on the femora remain throughout life in the same condition in which they first appear during the larval state in both sexes. In the males, on the other hand, they become further developed, and acquire their perfect structure at the last moult, when the insect is mature and ready to breed.

From the facts now given, we see that the means by which the males of the Orthoptera produce their sounds are extremely diversified, and are altogether different from those employed by the Homoptera.[43] But throughout the animal kingdom we often find the same object gained by the most diversified means; this seems due to the whole organisation having undergone multifarious changes in the course of ages, and as part after part varied different variations were taken advantage of for the same general purpose. The diversity of means for producing sound in the three families of the Orthoptera and in the Homoptera, impresses the mind with the high importance of these structures to the males, for the sake of calling or alluring the females. We need feel no surprise at the amount of modification which the Orthoptera have undergone in this respect, as we now know, from Dr. Scudder's remarkable discovery,[44] that there has been more than ample time. This naturalist has lately found a fossil insect in the Devonian formation of New Brunswick, which is furnished with " the well-" known tympanum or stridulating apparatus of the " male Locustidæ." The insect, though in most respects related to the Neuroptera, appears, as is so often the case with very ancient forms, to connect the two related Orders of the Neuroptera and Orthoptera.

I have but little more to say on the Orthoptera. Some of the species are very pugnacious: when two male field-crickets (*Gryllus campestris*) are confined together, they fight till one kills the other; and the species of Mantis are described as manœuvring with

[43] Landois has recently found in certain Orthoptera rudimentary structures closely similar to the sound-producing organs in the Homoptera; and this is a surprising fact. See 'Zeitschr. für wissensch. Zoolog.' B. xxii. Heft 3, 1871, p. 348.

[44] 'Transact. Ent. Soc.' 3rd series, vol. ii. ('Journal of Proceedings,' p. 117.)

their sword-like front-limbs, like hussars with their sabres. The Chinese keep these insects in little bamboo cages, and match them like game-cocks.[45] With respect to colour, some exotic locusts are beautifully ornamented; the posterior wings being marked with red, blue, and black; but as throughout the Order the sexes rarely differ much in colour, it is not probable that they owe their bright tints to sexual selection. Conspicuous colours may be of use to these insects, by giving notice that they are unpalatable. Thus it has been observed[46] that a bright-coloured Indian locust was invariably rejected when offered to birds and lizards. Some cases, however, are known of sexual differences in colour in this Order. The male of an American cricket[47] is described as being as white as ivory, whilst the female varies from almost white to greenish-yellow or dusky. Mr. Walsh informs me that the adult male of *Spectrum femoratum* (one of the Phasmidæ) "is of a shining brownish-yellow "colour; the adult female being of a dull, opaque, "cinereous brown; the young of both sexes being "green." Lastly, I may mention that the male of one curious kind of cricket[48] is furnished with "a long "membranous appendage, which falls over the face like "a veil; " but what its use may be, is not known.

Order, *Neuroptera.*—Little need here be said, except as to colour. In the Ephemeridæ the sexes often

---

[45] Westwood, 'Modern Class. of Insects,' vol. i. p. 427; for crickets, p. 445.

[46] Mr. Ch. Horne, in 'Proc. Ent. Soc.' May 3, 1869, p. xii.

[47] The *Œcanthus nivalis.* Harris, 'Insects of New England,' 1842, p. 124. The two sexes of *Œ. pellucidus* of Europe differ, as I hear from Victor Carus, in nearly the same manner.

[48] Platyblemnus : Westwood, 'Modern Class.' vol. i. p. 447.

differ slightly in their obscure tints; [49] but it is not
probable that the males are thus rendered attractive
to the females. The Libellulidæ, or dragon flies, are
ornamented with splendid green, blue, yellow, and
vermilion metallic tints; and the sexes often differ.
Thus, as Prof. Westwood remarks,[50] the males of some
of the Agrionidæ, " are of a rich blue with black wings,
" whilst the females are fine green with colourless
" wings." But in *Agrion Ramburii* these colours are
exactly reversed in the two sexes.[51] In the extensive
N. American genus of Hetærina, the males alone have
a beautiful carmine spot at the base of each wing. In
Anax junius the basal part of the abdomen in the male
is a vivid ultramarine blue, and in the female grass-
green. In the allied genus Gomphus, on the other
hand, and in some other genera, the sexes differ but
little in colour. In closely-allied forms throughout
the animal kingdom, similar cases of the sexes differing
greatly, or very little, or not at all, are of frequent
occurrence. Although there is so wide a difference in
colour betweeen the sexes of many Libellulidæ, it is
often difficult to say which is the more brilliant; and
the ordinary coloration of the two sexes is reversed, as
we have just seen, in one species of Agrion. It is not
probable that their colours in any case have been
gained as a protection. Mr. MacLachlan, who has
closely attended to this family, writes to me that
dragon-flies—the tyrants of the insect-world—are the
least liable of any insect to be attacked by birds or

[49] B. D. Walsh, the ' Pseudo-
neuroptera of Illinois,' in ' Proc.
Ent. Soc. of Philadelphia,' 1862,
p. 361.

[50] ' Modern Class.' vol. ii. p. 37.

[51] Walsh, ibid. p. 381. I am
indebted to this naturalist for
the following facts on Hetærina,
Anax, and Gomphus.

other enemies, and he believes that their bright colours serve as a sexual attraction. Certain dragon-flies apparently are attracted by particular colours: Mr. Patterson observed [52] that the Agrionidæ, of which the males are blue, settled in numbers on the blue float of a fishing line; whilst two other species were attracted by shining white colours.

It is an interesting fact, first noticed by Schelver, that, in several genera belonging to two sub-families, the males on first emergence from the pupal state, are coloured exactly like the females; but that their bodies in a short time assume a conspicuous milky-blue tint, owing to the exudation of a kind of oil, soluble in ether and alcohol. Mr. MacLachlan believes that in the male of *Libellula depressa* this change of colour does not occur until nearly a fortnight after the metamorphosis, when the sexes are ready to pair.

Certain species of Neurothemis present, according to Brauer, [53] a curious case of dimorphism, some of the females having ordinary wings, whilst others have them " very richly netted, as in the males of the same "species." Brauer "explains the phenomenon on "Darwinian principles by the supposition that the "close netting of the veins is a secondary sexual "character in the males, which has been abruptly "transferred to some of the females, instead of, as "generally occurs, to all of them." Mr. MacLachlan informs me of another instance of dimorphism in several species of Agrion, in which some individuals are of an orange colour, and these are invariably females. This is probably a case of reversion; for in

[52] 'Transact. Ent. Soc.' vol. i. 1836, p. lxxxi.   [53] See abstract in the 'Zoo-logical Record' for 1867, p. 450.

the true Libellulæ, when the sexes differ in colour, the females are orange or yellow; so that supposing Agrion to be descended from some primordial form which resembled the typical Libellulæ in its sexual characters, it would not be surprising that a tendency to vary in this manner should occur in the females alone.

Although many dragon-flies are large, powerful, and fierce insects, the males have not been observed by Mr. MacLachlan to fight together, excepting, as he believes, in some of the smaller species of Agrion. In another group in this Order, namely, the Termites or white ants, both sexes at the time of swarming may be seen running about, " the male after the female, " sometimes two chasing one female, and contending " with great eagerness who shall win the prize." [54] The *Atropos pulsatorius* is said to make a noise with its jaws, which is answered by other individuals. [55]

Order, *Hymenoptera.*—That inimitable observer, M. Fabre, [56] in describing the habits of Cerceris, a wasp-like insect, remarks that " fights frequently ensue " between the males for the possession of some par- " ticular female, who sits an apparently unconcerned " beholder of the struggle for supremacy, and when " the victory is decided, quietly flies away in company " with the conqueror." Westwood [57] says that the males of one of the saw-flies (Tenthredinæ) " have been found

[54] Kirby and Spence, 'Introduct. to Entomology,' vol. ii, 1818, p. 35.

[55] Houzeau, 'Les Facultés Mentales,' &c. Tom. i. p. 104.

[56] See an interesting article,

'The Writings of Fabre,' in 'Nat. Hist. Review,' April 1862, p. 122.

[57] 'Journal of Proc. of Entomolog. Soc.' Sept. 7th, 1863, p. 169.

" fighting together, with their mandibles locked." As
M. Fabre speaks of the males of Cerceris striving to
obtain a particular female, it may be well to bear in
mind that insects belonging to this Order have the
power of recognising each other after long intervals
of time, and are deeply attached. For instance, Pierre
Huber, whose accuracy no one doubts, separated some
ants, and when, after an interval of four months, they
met others which had formerly belonged to the same
community, they recognised and caressed one another
with their antennæ. Had they been strangers they
would have fought together. Again, when two communities engage in a battle, the ants on the same
side sometimes attack each other in the general con-
fusion, but they soon perceive their mistake, and the
one ant soothes the other.[58]

In this Order slight differences in colour, according
to sex, are common, but conspicuous differences are
rare except in the family of Bees; yet both sexes
of certain groups are so brilliantly coloured—for
instance in Chrysis, in which vermilion and metallic
greens prevail—that we are tempted to attribute the
result to sexual selection. In the Ichneumonidæ,
according to Mr. Walsh,[59] the males are almost universally lighter-coloured than the females. On the
other hand, in the Tenthredinidæ the males are generally darker than the females. In the Siricidæ the
sexes frequently differ; thus the male of *Sirex
juvencus* is banded with orange, whilst the female is
dark purple; but it is difficult to say which sex is the

[58] P. Huber, ' Recherches sur
les Mœurs des Fourmis,' 1810,
pp. 150, 165.

[59] ' Proc. Entomolog. Soc. of
Philadelphia,' 1866 pp. 238,
239.

more ornamented. In *Tremex columbæ* the female is much brighter coloured than the male. I am informed by Mr. F. Smith, that the male ants of several species are black, the females being testaceous.

In the family of Bees, especially in the solitary species, as I hear from the same entomologist, the sexes often differ in colour. The males are generally the brighter, and in Bombus as well as in Apathus, much more variable in colour than the females. In *Anthophora retusa* the male is of a rich fulvous-brown, whilst the female is quite black: so are the females of several species of Xylocopa, the males being bright yellow. On the other hand the females of some species, as of *Andræna fulva*, are much brighter coloured than the males. Such differences in colour can hardly be accounted for by the males being defenceless and thus requiring protection, whilst the females are well defended by their stings. H. Müller,[60] who has particularly attended to the habits of bees, attributes these differences in colour in chief part to sexual selection. That bees have a keen perception of colour is certain. He says that the males search eagerly and fight for the possession of the females; and he accounts through such contests for the mandibles of the males being in certain species larger than those of the females. In some cases the males are far more numerous than the females, either early in the season, or at all times and places, or locally; whereas the females in other cases are apparently in excess. In some species the more beautiful males appear to have been selected by the females; and in others the more beautiful females

<hr>

[60] 'Anwendung der Darwinschen Lehre auf Bienen.' Verh. d. n. Jahrg. xxix.

by the males. Consequently in certain genera (Müller, p. 42), the males of the several species differ much in appearance, whilst the females are almost indistinguishable; in other genera the reverse occurs. H. Müller believes (p. 82) that the colours gained by one sex through sexual selection have often been transferred in a variable degree to the other sex, just as the pollen-collecting apparatus of the female has often been transferred to the male, to whom it is absolutely useless.[61]

Mutilla Europæa makes a stridulating noise; and according to Goureau [62] both sexes have this power. He attributes the sound to the friction of the third and preceding abdominal segments, and I find that these surfaces are marked with very fine concentric ridges; but so is the projecting thoracic collar into which the head articulates, and this collar, when scratched with

[61] M. Perrier in his article 'la Sélection sexuelle d'après Darwin' ('Revue Scientifique,' Feb. 1873, p. 868), without apparently having reflected much on the subject, objects that as the males of social bees are known to be produced from unfertilised ova, they could not transmit new characters to their male offspring. This is an extraordinary objection. A female bee fertilised by a male, which presented some character facilitating the union of the sexes, or rendering him more attractive to the female, would lay eggs which would produce only females; but these young females would next year produce males; and will it be pretended that such males would not in-herit the characters of their male grandfathers? To take a case with ordinary animals as nearly parallel as possible: if a female of any white quadruped or bird were crossed by a male of a black breed, and the male and female offspring were paired together, will it be pretended that the grandchildren would not inherit a tendency to blackness from their male grandfather? The acquirement of new characters by the sterile worker-bees is a much more difficult case, but I have endeavoured to show in my 'Origin of Species,' how these sterile beings are subjected to the power of natural selection.

[62] Quoted by Westwood, 'Modern Class of Insects,' vol. ii. p. 214.

the point of a needle, emits the proper sound. It is
rather surprising that both sexes should have the
power of stridulating, as the male is winged and the
female wingless. It is notorious that Bees express
certain emotions, as of anger, by the tone of their
humming; and according to H. Müller (p. 80), the
males of some species make a peculiar singing noise
whilst pursuing the females.

Order, *Coleoptera* (Beetles). — Many beetles are
coloured so as to resemble the surfaces which they habitually frequent, and they thus escape detection by their
enemies. Other species, for instance diamond-beetles,
are ornamented with splendid colours, which are often
arranged in stripes, spots, crosses, and other elegant
patterns. Such colours can hardly serve directly as a
protection, except in the case of certain flower-feeding
species; but they may serve as a warning or means of
recognition, on the same principle as the phosphorescence of the glow-worm. As with beetles the colours
of the two sexes are generally alike, we have no
evidence that they have been gained through sexual
selection; but this is at least possible, for they may
have been developed in one sex and then transferred
to the other; and this view is even in some degree
probable in those groups which possess other well-
marked secondary sexual characters. Blind beetles,
which cannot of course behold each other's beauty,
never, as I hear from Mr. Waterhouse, jun., exhibit
bright colours, though they often have polished coats;
but the explanation of their obscurity may be that they
generally inhabit caves and other obscure stations.

Some Longicorns, especially certain Prionidæ, offer

an exception to the rule that the sexes of beetles do not differ in colour. Most of these insects are large and splendidly coloured. The males in the genus Pyrodes,[63] which I saw in Mr. Bates's collection, are generally redder but rather duller than the females, the latter being coloured of a more or less splendid golden-green. On the other hand, in one species the male is golden-green, the female being richly tinted with red and purple. In the genus Esmeralda the sexes differ so greatly in colour that they have been ranked as distinct species; in one species both are of a beautiful shining green, but the male has a red thorax. On the whole, as far as I could judge, the females of those Prionidæ, in which the sexes differ, are coloured more richly than the males, and this does not accord with the common rule in regard to colour, when acquired through sexual selection.

A most remarkable distinction between the sexes of many beetles is presented by the great horns which rise from the head, thorax, and clypeus of the males; and in some few cases from the under surface of the

[63] *Pyrodes pulcherrimus*, in which the sexes differ conspicuously, has been described by Mr. Bates in 'Transact. Ent. Soc.' 1869, p. 50. I will specify the few other cases in which I have heard of a difference in colour between the sexes of beetles. Kirby and Spence ('Introduct. to Entomology,' vol. iii. p. 301) mention a Cantharis, Meloe, Rhagium, and the *Leptura testacea*; the male of the latter being testaceous, with a black thorax, and the female of a dull red all over. These two latter beetles belong to the family of Longicorns. Messrs. R. Trimen and Waterhouse, jun., inform me of two Lamellicorns, viz., a Peritrichia and Trichius, the male of the latter being more obscurely coloured then the female. In *Tillus elongatus* the male is black, and the female always, as it is believed, of a dark blue colour, with a red thorax. The male, also, of *Orsodacna atra*, as I hear from Mr. Walsh, is black, the female (the so-called *O. ruficollis*) having a rufous thorax.

body.   These horns, in the great family of the Lamellicorns, resemble those of various quadrupeds, such as
stags, rhinoceroses, &c., and are wonderful both from
their size and diversified shapes.   Instead of describing
them, I have given figures of the males and females of
some of the more remarkable forms.   (Figs. 16 to 20.)
The females generally exhibit rudiments of the horns
in the form of small knobs or ridges; but some are
destitute of even the slightest rudiment.   On the other
hand, the horns are nearly as well developed in the
female as in the male of *Phanæus lancifer;* and only a
little less well developed in the females of some other
species of this genus and of Copris.   I am informed by
Mr. Bates that the horns do not differ in any manner
corresponding with the more important characteristic
differences between the several subdivisions of the

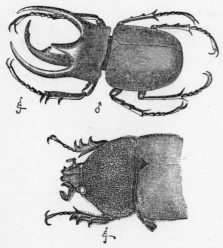

Fig. 16.   Chalcosoma atlas.   Upper figure, male (reduced); lower figure, female
(nat. size).

Fig. 17. Copris isidis. (Left-hand figures, males.)

Fig. 18. Phanæus faunus.

Fig. 19. Dipelicus cantori.

Fig. 20. Onthophagus rangifer, enlarged.

family: thus within the same section of the genus Onthophagus, there are species which have a single horn, and others which have two.

In almost all cases, the horns are remarkable from their excessive variability; so that a graduated series can be formed, from the most highly developed males to others so degenerate that they can barely be distinguished from the females. Mr. Walsh [64] found that in *Phanæus carnifex* the horns were thrice as long in some males as in others. Mr. Bates, after examining above a hundred males of *Onthophagus rangifer* (fig. 20), thought that he had at last discovered a species in which the horns did not vary; but further research proved the contrary.

The extraordinary size of the horns, and their widely different structure in closely-allied forms, indicate that they have been formed for some purpose; but their excessive variability in the males of the same species leads to the inference that this purpose cannot be of a definite nature. The horns do not show marks of friction, as if used for any ordinary work. Some authors suppose [65] that as the males wander about much more than the females, they require horns as a defence against their enemies; but as the horns are often blunt, they do not seem well adapted for defence. The most obvious conjecture is that they are used by the males for fighting together; but the males have never been observed to fight; nor could Mr. Bates, after a careful examination of numerous species, find any sufficient evidence, in their mutilated or broken

[64] 'Proc. Entomolog. Soc. of Philadelphia,' 1864, p. 228.
[65] Kirby and Spence, 'Introduct. Entomolog.' vol. iii. p. 300.

condition, of their having been thus used. If the males had been habitual fighters, the size of their bodies would probably have been increased through sexual selection, so as to have exceeded that of the females; but Mr. Bates, after comparing the two sexes in above a hundred species of the Copridæ, did not find any marked difference in this respect amongst well-developed individuals. In Lethrus, moreover, a beetle belonging to the same great division of the Lamellicorns, the males are known to fight, but are not provided with horns, though their mandibles are much larger than those of the female.

The conclusion that the horns have been acquired as ornaments is that which best agrees with the fact of their having been so immensely, yet not fixedly, developed,—as shewn by their extreme variability in the same species, and by their extreme diversity in closely-allied species. This view will at first appear extremely improbable; but we shall hereafter find with many animals standing much higher in the scale, namely fishes, amphibians, reptiles and birds, that various kinds of crests, knobs, horns and combs have been developed apparently for this sole purpose.

The males of *Onitis furcifer* (fig. 21), and of some other species of the genus, are furnished with singular projections on their anterior femora, and with a great fork or pair of horns on the lower surface of the thorax. Judging from other insects, these may aid the male in clinging to the female. Although the males have not even a trace of a horn on the upper surface of the body, yet the females plainly exhibit a rudiment of a single horn on the head (fig. 22, *a*), and of a crest (*b*) on the thorax. That the slight thoracic crest in

the female is a rudiment of a projection proper to the
male, though entirely absent in the male of this
particular species, is clear: for the female of *Bubas
bison* (a genus which comes next to Onitis) has a

Fig. 21. Onitis furcifer,
male viewed from be-
neath.

Fig. 22. Left-hand figure, male of Onitis furcifer, viewed
laterally. Right-hand figure, female. *a.* Rudiment of
cephalic horn. *b.* Trace of thoracic horn or crest.

similar slight crest on the thorax, and the male bears
a great projection in the same situation. So, again,
there can hardly be a doubt that the little point (*a*) on
the head of the female *Onitis furcifer*, as well as on the
head of the females of two or three allied species,
is a rudimentary representative of the cephalic horn,
which is common to the males of so many Lamellicorn
beetles, as in Phanæus (fig. 18).

The old belief that rudiments have been created to
complete the scheme of nature is here so far from
holding good, that we have a complete inversion of
the ordinary state of things in the family. We may
reasonably suspect that the males originally bore horns
and transferred them to the females in a rudimentary
condition, as in so many other Lamellicorns. Why the
males subsequently lost their horns, we know not; but
this may have been caused through the principle of
compensation, owing to the development of the large
horns and projections on the lower surface; and as

these are confined to the males, the rudiments of the upper horns on the females would not have been thus obliterated.

The cases hitherto given refer to the Lamellicorns, but the males of some few other beetles, belonging to two widely distinct groups, namely, the Curculionidæ and Staphylinidæ, are furnished with horns—in the former on the lower surface of the body,[66] in the latter on the upper surface of the head and thorax. In the Staphylinidæ, the horns of the males are extraordinarily variable in the same species, just as we have seen with the Lamellicorns. In Siagonium we have a case of dimorphism, for the males can be divided into two sets, differing greatly in the size of their bodies and in the

Fig. 23. Bledius taurus, magnified. Left-hand figure, male; right-hand figure, female.

development of their horns, without intermediate gradations. In a species of Bledius (fig. 23), also belonging to the Staphylinidæ, Professor Westwood states that, "male specimens can be found in the same "locality in which the central horn of the thorax is "very large, but the horns of the head quite rudimen- "tal; and others, in which the thoracic horn is much "shorter, whilst the protuberances on the head are "long."[67] Here we apparently have a case of compen-

<hr />

[66] Kirby and Spence, 'Intro-duct. Entomolog.' vol. iii. p. 329.

[67] 'Modern Classification of Insects,' vol. i. p. 172: Siago-nium, p. 172. In the British Museum I noticed one male specimen of Siagonium in an intermediate condition, so that the dimorphism is not strict.

sation, which throws light on that just given, of the
supposed loss of the upper horns by the males of *Onitis*.

Law of Battle.—Some male beetles, which seem ill-
fitted for fighting, nevertheless engage in conflicts for
the possession of the females. Mr. Wallace [68] saw two
males of *Leptorhynchus angustatus*, a linear beetle with
a much elongated rostrum, "fighting for a female, who
"stood close by busy at her boring. They pushed at
"each other with their rostra, and clawed and thumped,
"apparently in the greatest rage." The smaller male,
however, "soon ran away, acknowledging himself
"vanquished." In some few cases male beetles are well
adapted for fighting, by possessing great toothed
mandibles, much larger than those of the females.
This is the case with the common stag-beetle (*Lucanus
cervus*), the males of which emerge from the pupal
state about a week before the other sex, so that several
may often be seen pursuing the same female. At this
season they engage in fierce conflicts. When Mr. A.
H. Davis [69] enclosed two males with one female in a
box, the larger male severely pinched the smaller one,
until he resigned his pretensions. A friend informs
me that when a boy he often put the males together to
see them fight, and he noticed that they were much
bolder and fiercer than the females, as with the higher
animals. The males would seize hold of his finger, if
held in front of them, but not so the females, although
they have stronger jaws. The males of many of the
Lucanidæ, as well as of the above-mentioned Leptorhyn-

[68] 'The Malay Archipelago,'
vol. ii. 1869, p. 276. Riley,
Sixth 'Report on insects of
Missouri,' 1874, p. 115.

[69] 'Entomological Magazine,'
vol. i. 1833, p. 82. See also on
the conflicts of this species,
Kirby and Spence, ibid. vol. iii.
p. 314; and Westwood, ibid.
vol. i. p. 187.

chus, are larger and more powerful insects than the females. The two sexes of *Lethrus cephalotes* (one of the Lamellicorns) inhabit the same burrow; and the male has larger mandibles than the female. If, during the breeding season, a strange male attempts to enter the burrow, he is attacked; the female does not remain passive, but closes the mouth of the burrow, and encourages her mate by continually pushing him on from behind; and the battle lasts until the aggressor is killed or runs away.[70] The two sexes of another Lamellicorn beetle, the *Ateuchus cicatricosus*, live in pairs, and seem much attached to each other; the male excites the females to roll the balls of dung in which the ova are deposited; and if she is removed, he becomes much agitated. If the male is removed the female ceases all work, and as M. Brulerie[71] believes, would remain on the same spot until she died.

The great mandibles of the male Lucanidæ are extremely variable both in size and structure, and in this respect resemble the horns on the head and thorax of many male Lamellicorns and Staphylinidæ. A perfect series can be formed from the best-provided to the worst-provided or degenerate males. Although the mandibles of the common stag-beetle, and probably of many other species, are used as efficient weapons for fighting, it is doubtful whether their great size can thus be accounted for. We have seen that they are used by the *Lucanus elaphus* of N. America for seizing the female. As they are so conspicuous and so elegantly branched, and as owing to their great length

[70] Quoted from Fischer, in 'Dict. Class. d'Hist. Nat.' tom. x. p. 324.

[71] 'Ann. Soc. Entomolog. France,' 1866, as quoted in 'Journal of Travel,' by A. Murray, 1868, p. 135.

they are not well adapted for pinching, the suspicion
has crossed my mind that they may in addition serve
as an ornament, like the horns on
the head and thorax of the various
species above described. The
male *Chiasognathus Grantii* of S.
Chile—a splendid beetle belonging to the same family—has enormously developed mandibles (fig.
24); he is bold and pugnacious;
when threatened he faces round,
opens his great jaws, and at the
same time stridulates loudly. But
the mandibles were not strong
enough to pinch my finger so as
to cause actual pain.

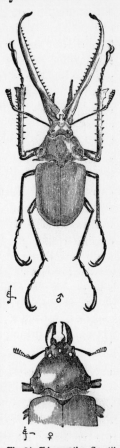

Sexual selection, which implies
the possession of considerable perceptive powers and of strong
passions, seems to have been more
effective with the Lamellicorns
than with any other family of
beetles. With some species the
males are provided with weapons
for fighting ; some live in pairs
and show mutual affection ; many
have the power of stridulating
when excited ; many are furnished
with the most extraordinary
horns, apparently for the sake of
ornament ; and some, which are

Fig. 24. Chiasognathus Grantii,
reduced. Upper figure, male ;
lower figure, female.

diurnal in their habits, are gorgeously coloured.
Lastly, several of the largest beetles in the world

belong to this family, which was placed by Linnæus and Fabricius at the head of the Order.[72]

Stridulating organs.—Beetles belonging to many and widely distinct families possess these organs. The sound thus produced can sometimes be heard at the distance of several feet or even yards,[73] but it is not comparable with that made by the Orthoptera. The rasp generally consists of a narrow, slightly-raised surface, crossed by very fine, parallel ribs, sometimes so fine as to cause iridescent colours, and having a very elegant appearance under the microscope. In some cases, as with Typhœus, minute, bristly or scale-like prominences, with which the whole surrounding surface is covered in approximately parallel lines. could be traced passing into the ribs of the rasp. The transition takes place by their becoming confluent and straight, and at the same time more prominent and smooth. A hard ridge on an adjoining part of the body serves as the scraper for the rasp, but this scraper in some cases has been specially modified for the purpose. It is rapidly moved across the rasp, or conversely the rasp across the scraper.

These organs are situated in widely different positions. In the carrion-beetles (Necrophorus) two parallel rasps (*r*, fig. 25) stand on the dorsal surface of the fifth abdominal segment, each rasp [74] consisting of 126 to 140 fine ribs. These ribs are scraped against the posterior margins of the elytra, a small portion

---

[72] Westwood, 'Modern Class.' vol. i. p. 184.

[73] Wollaston, 'On certain Musical Curculionidæ,' 'Annals and Mag. of Nat. Hist.' vol. vi.

1860, p. 14.

[74] Landois, 'Zeitschrift für wiss. Zoolog.' B. xvii. 1867, s. 127.

of which projects beyond the general outline. In many Crioceridæ, and in *Clythra 4-punctata* (one of the Chrysomelidæ), and in some Tenebrionidæ, &c.,[75] the rasp is seated on the dorsal apex of the abdomen, on the pygidium or pro-pygidium, and is scraped in the same manner by the elytra. In Heterocerus, which belongs to another family, the rasps are placed on the sides of the first abdominal segment, and are scraped by ridges on the femora.[76] In certain Curculionidæ

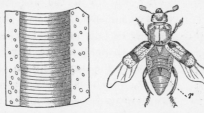

Fig. 25. Necrophorus (from Landois). *r*. The two rasps. Left-hand figure, part of the rasp highly magnified.

and Carabidæ,[77] the parts are completely reversed in position, for the rasps are seated on the inferior surface

[75] I am greatly indebted to Mr. G. R. Crotch for having sent me many prepared specimens of various beetles belonging to these three families and to others, as well as for valuable information. He believes that the power of stridulation in the Clythra has not been previously observed. I am also much indebted to Mr. E. W. Janson, for information and specimens. I may add that my son, Mr. F. Darwin, finds that *Dermestes murinus* stridulates, but he searched in vain for the apparatus. Scolytus has lately been described by Dr. Chapman as a stridulator, in the 'Entomo-

logist's Monthly Magazine,' vol. vi. p. 130.

[76] Schiödte, translated in 'Annals and Mag. of Nat. Hist.' vol. xx. 1867, p. 37.

[77] Westring has described (Kroyer, 'Naturhist. Tidskrift,' B. ii. 1848–49, p. 334) the stridulating organs in these two, as well as in other families. In the Carabidæ I have examined *Elaphrus uliginosus* and *Blethisa multipunctata*, sent to me by Mr. Crotch. In Blethisa the transverse ridges on the furrowed border of the abdominal segment do not, as far as I could judge, come into play in scraping the rasps on the elytra.

of the elytra, near their apices, or along their outer margins, and the edges of the abdominal segments serve as the scrapers. In *Pelobius Hermanni* (one of Dytiscidæ or water-beetles) a strong ridge runs parallel and near to the sutural margin of the elytra, and is crossed by ribs, coarse in the middle part, but becoming gradually finer at both ends, especially at the upper end; when this insect is held under water or in the air, a stridulating noise is produced by the extreme

8

Fig. 26.   Hind-leg of Geotrupes stercorarius (from Landois).
r. Rasp. *c.* Coxa. *f.* Femur. *t.* Tibia. *tr.* Tarsi.

horny margin of the abdomen being scraped against the rasps. In a great number of long-horned beetles (Longicornia) the organs are situated quite otherwise, the rasp being on the mesothorax, which is rubbed against the pro-thorax; Landois counted 238 very fine ribs on the rasp of *Cerambyx heros.*

Many Lamellicorns have the power of stridulating, and the organs differ greatly in position. Some species stridulate very loudly, so that when Mr. F. Smith caught a *Trox sabulosus*, a gamekeeper, who stood by, thought he had caught a mouse; but I failed to discover the proper organs in this beetle. In Geotrupes and Typhœus, a narrow ridge runs obliquely across (*r*, fig. 26) the coxa of each hind-leg (having in *G. stercorarius* 84 ribs), which is scraped by a specially projecting part of one of the abdominal segments. In the nearly allied *Copris lunaris*, an excessively narrow fine rasp runs along the sutural margin of the elytra, with another short rasp near the basal outer margin; but in some other Coprini the rasp is seated, according to Leconte,[78] on the dorsal surface of the abdomen. In Oryctes it is seated on the pro-pygidium; and, according to the same entomologist, in some other Dynastini, on the under surface of the elytra. Lastly, Westring states that in *Omaloplia brunnea* the rasp is placed on the pro-sternum, and the scraper on the meta-sternum, the parts thus occupying the under surface of the body, instead of the upper surface as in the Longicorns.

We thus see that in the different coleopterous families the stridulating organs are wonderfully diversified in position, but not much in structure. Within the same family some species are provided with these organs, and others are destitute of them. This diversity is intelligible, if we suppose that originally various beetles made a shuffling or hissing noise by the rubbing together of any hard and rough parts of their bodies, which happened to be in contact; and that from the noise thus produced being in some way useful, the rough surfaces were gradually de-veloped into regular stridulating organs. Some beetles as they move, now produce, either intention-ally or unintentionally, a shuffling noise, without possessing any proper organs for the purpose. Mr. Wallace informs me that the *Euchirus longimanus* (a Lamellicorn, with the anterior legs wonderfully elongated in the male) " makes, whilst moving, a low " hissing sound by the protrusion and contraction of " the abdomen ; and when seized it produces a grating " sound by rubbing its hind-legs against the edges of

[78] I am indebted to Mr. Walsh, of Illinois, for having sent me extracts from Leconte's 'Introduction to Entomology,' pp. 101, 143.

" the elytra." The hissing sound is clearly due to a narrow rasp running along the sutural margin of each elytron; and I could likewise make the grating sound by rubbing the shagreened surface of the femur against the granulated margin of the corresponding elytron; but I could not here detect any proper rasp; nor is it likely that I could have overlooked it in so large an insect. After examining Cychrus, and reading what Westring has written about this beetle, it seems very doubtful whether it possesses any true rasp, though it has the power of emitting a sound.

From the analogy of the Orthoptera and Homoptera, I expected to find the stridulating organs in the Coleoptera differing according to sex; but Landois, who has carefully examined several species, observed no such difference; nor did Westring; nor did Mr. G. R. Crotch in preparing the many specimens which he had the kindness to send me. Any difference in these organs, if slight, would, however, be difficult to detect, on account of their great variability. Thus, in the first pair of specimens of *Necrophorus humator* and of *Pelobius* which I examined, the rasp was considerably larger in the male than in the female; but not so with succeeding specimens. In *Geotrupes stercorarius* the rasp appeared to me thicker, opaquer, and more prominent in three males than in the same number of females; in order, therefore, to discover whether the sexes differed in their power of stridulating, my son, Mr. F. Darwin, collected fifty-seven living specimens, which he separated into two lots, according as they made a greater or lesser noise, when held in the same manner. He then examined all these specimens, and found that the males were very nearly in the same proportion

to the females in both the lots.   Mr. F. Smith has
kept alive numerous specimens of *Monoynchus pseuda-
cori* (Curculionidæ), and is convinced that both sexes
stridulate, and apparently in an equal degree.

Nevertheless, the power of stridulating is certainly
a sexual character in some few Coleoptera.   Mr. Crotch
discovered that the males alone of two species of
Heliopathes (Tenebrionidæ) possess stridulating organs.
I examined five males of *H. gibbus*, and in all these
there was a well-developed rasp, partially divided into
two, on the dorsal surface of the terminal abdominal
segment; whilst in the same number of females there
was not even a rudiment of the rasp, the membrane of
this segment being transparent, and much thinner
than in the male.   In *H. cribratostriatus* the male has
a similar rasp, excepting that it is not partially divided
into two portions, and the female is completely destitute of this organ; the male in addition has on the
apical margins of the elytra, on each side of the suture,
three or four short longitudinal ridges, which are
crossed by extremely fine ribs, parallel to and resembling those on the abdominal rasp; whether these
ridges serve as an independent rasp, or as a scraper for
the abdominal rasp, I could not decide: the female
exhibits no trace of this latter structure.

Again, in three species of the Lamellicorn genus
Oryctes, we have a nearly parallel case.   In the females
of *O. gryphus* and *nasicornis* the ribs on the rasp of the
pro-pygidium are less continuous and less distinct than
in the males; but the chief difference is that the whole
upper surface of this segment, when held in the proper
light, is seen to be clothed with hairs, which are absent
or are represented by excessively fine down in the

males. It should be noticed that in all Coleoptera the effective part of the rasp is destitute of hairs. In *O. senegalensis* the difference between the sexes is more strongly marked, and this is best seen when the proper abdominal segment is cleaned and viewed as a transparent object. In the female the whole surface is covered with little separate crests, bearing spines; whilst in the male these crests in proceeding towards the apex, become more and more confluent, regular, and naked; so that three-fourths of the segment is covered with extremely fine parallel ribs, which are quite absent in the female. In the females, however, of all three species of Oryctes, a slight grating or stridulating sound is produced, when the abdomen of a softened specimen is pushed backwards and forwards.

In the case of the Heliopathes and Oryctes there can hardly be a doubt that the males stridulate in order to call or to excite the females; but with most beetles the stridulation apparently serves both sexes as a mutual call. Beetles stridulate under various emotions, in the same manner as birds use their voices for many purposes besides singing to their mates. The great Chiasognathus stridulates in anger or defiance; many species do the same from distress or fear, if held so that they cannot escape ; by striking the hollow stems of trees in the Canary Islands, Messrs. Wollaston and Crotch were able to discover the presence of beetles belonging to the genus Acalles by their stridulation. Lastly, the male Ateuchus stridulates to encourage the female in her work, and from distress when she is removed.[79] Some naturalists believe that beetles make

[79] M. P. de la Brulerie, as quoted in 'Journal of Travel,' A. Murray, vol. i. 1868, p. 135.

this noise to frighten away their enemies; but I cannot think that a quadruped or bird, able to devour a large beetle, would be frightened by so slight a sound. The belief that the stridulation serves as a sexual call is supported by the fact that death-ticks (*Anobium tessellatum*) are well known to answer each other's ticking, and, as I have myself observed, a tapping noise artificially made. Mr. Doubleday also informs me that he has sometimes observed a female ticking,[80] and in an hour or two afterwards has found her united with a male, and on one occasion surrounded by several males. Finally, it is probable that the two sexes of many kinds of beetles were at first enabled to find each other by the slight shuffling noise produced by the rubbing together of the adjoining hard parts of their bodies; and that as those males or females which made the greatest noise succeeded best in finding partners, rugosities on various parts of their bodies were gradually developed by means of sexual selection into true stridulating organs.

[80] According to Mr. Doubleday, "the noise is produced by "the insect raising itself on its "legs as high as it can, and then "striking its thorax five or six "times, in rapid succession, "against the substance upon "which it is sitting." For references on this subject see Landois, 'Zeitschrift für wissen. Zoolog.' B. xvii. s. 131. Olivier says (as quoted by Kirby and Spence, 'Introduct.' vol. ii. p. 395) that the female of *Pimelia striata* produces a rather loud sound by striking her abdomen against any hard substance, "and that the male, obedient "to this call, soon attends her, "and they pair."

CHAPTER XI.

INSECTS, *continued*.—ORDER LEPIDOPTERA.

(BUTTERFLIES AND MOTHS.)

Courtship of butterflies—Battles—Ticking noise—Colours common
to both sexes, or more brilliant in the males—Examples—Not
due to the direct action of the conditions of life—Colours adapted
for protection—Colours of moths—Display—Perceptive powers
of the Lepidoptera—Variability—Causes of the difference in
colour between the males and females—Mimicry, female butterflies more brilliantly coloured than the males—Bright colours of
caterpillars—Summary and concluding remarks on the secondary
sexual characters of insects—Birds and insects compared.

IN this great Order the most interesting points for us
are the differences in colour between the sexes of the
same species, and between the distinct species of the
same genus.   Nearly the whole of the following chapter will be devoted to this subject; but I will first
make a few remarks on one or two other points.
Several males may often be seen pursuing and crowding
round the same female.   Their courtship appears to be
a prolonged affair, for I have frequently watched one
or more males pirouetting round a female until I was
tired, without seeing the end of the courtship.   Mr.
A. G. Butler also informs me that he has several times
watched a male courting a female for a full quarter of
an hour; but she pertinaciously refused him, and at

last settled on the ground and closed her wings, so as to escape from his addresses.

Although butterflies are weak and fragile creatures, they are pugnacious, and an Emperor butterfly [1] has been captured with the tips of its wings broken from a conflict with another male. Mr. Collingwood, in speaking of the frequent battles between the butterflies of Borneo, says, " They whirl round each other with " the greatest rapidity, and appear to be incited by the " greatest ferocity."

The *Ageronia feronia* makes a noise like that produced by a toothed wheel passing under a spring catch, and which can be heard at the distance of several yards: I noticed this sound at Rio de Janeiro, only when two of these butterflies were chasing each other in an irregular course, so that it is probably made during the courtship of the sexes.[2]

Some moths also produce sounds; for instance, the males of *Thecophora fovea*. On two occasions Mr. F. Buchanan White [3] heard a sharp quick noise made by the male of *Hylophila prasinana*, and which he believes to be produced, as in Cicada, by an elastic membrane, furnished with a muscle. He quotes, also, Guenée, that Setina produces a sound like the ticking of a watch, apparently by the aid of " two large tympani-

---

[1] *Apatura Iris:* ' The Entomologist's Weekly Intelligence,' 1859, p. 139. For the Bornean Butterflies, see C. Collingwood, ' Rambles of a Naturalist,' 1868, p. 183.

[2] See my ' Journal of Researches,' 1845, p. 33. Mr. Doubleday has detected (' Proc. Ent. Soc.' March 3rd, 1845, p. 123) a peculiar membranous sac at the base of the front wings, which is probably connected with the production of the sound. For the case of Thecophora, see ' Zoological Record,' 1869, p. 401. For Mr. Buchanan White's observations, ' The Scottish Naturalist,' July 1872, p. 214.

[3] ' The Scottish Naturalist,' July 1872, p. 213.

"form vesicles, situated in the pectoral region;" and these "are much more developed in the male than in "the female." Hence the sound-producing organs in the Lepidoptera appear to stand in some relation with the sexual functions. I have not alluded to the well-known noise made by the Death's Head Sphinx, for it is generally heard soon after the moth has emerged from its cocoon.

Giard has always observed that the musky odour, which is emitted by two species of Sphinx moths, is peculiar to the males;[4] and in the higher classes we shall meet with many instances of the males alone being odoriferous.

Every one must have admired the extreme beauty of many butterflies and of some moths; and it may be asked, are their colours and diversified patterns the result of the direct action of the physical conditions to which these insects have been exposed, without any benefit being thus derived? Or have successive variations been accumulated and determined as a protection, or for some unknown purpose, or that one sex may be attractive to the other? And, again, what is the meaning of the colours being widely different in the males and females of certain species, and alike in the two sexes of other species of the same genus? Before attempting to answer these questions a body of facts must be given.

With our beautiful English butterflies, the admiral, peacock, and painted lady (Vanessæ), as well as many others, the sexes are alike. This is also the case with the magnificent Heliconidæ, and most of the Danaidæ in the tropics. But in certain other tropical groups,

[4] 'Zoological Record,' 1869, p. 347.

and in some of our English butterflies, as the purple
emperor, orange-tip, &c. (*Apatura Iris* and *Anthocharis
cardamines*), the sexes differ either greatly or slightly
in colour. No language suffices to describe the splen-
dour of the males of some tropical species. Even
within the same genus we often find species presenting
extraordinary differences between the sexes, whilst
others have their sexes closely alike. Thus in the
South American genus Epicalia, Mr. Bates, to whom I
am indebted for most of the following facts, and for
looking over this whole discussion, informs me that he
knows twelve species, the two sexes of which haunt
the same stations (and this is not always the case with
butterflies), and which, therefore, cannot have been
differently affected by external conditions.[5] In nine
of these twelve species the males rank amongst the most
brilliant of all butterflies, and differ so greatly from
the comparatively plain females that they were formerly
placed in distinct genera. The females of these nine
species resemble each other in their general type of
coloration; and they likewise resemble both sexes of
the species in several allied genera, found in various
parts of the world. Hence we may infer that these
nine species, and probably all the others of the genus,
are descended from an ancestral form which was
coloured in nearly the same manner. In the tenth
species the female still retains the same general
colouring, but the male resembles her, so that he is
coloured in a much less gaudy and contrasted manner
than the males of the previous species. In the eleventh

[5] See also Mr. Bates's paper
in 'Proc. Ent. Soc. of Philadelphia,' 1865, p. 206. Also Mr.
Wallace on the same subject, in
regard to Diadema, in 'Transact.
Entomolog. Soc. of London,
1869, p. 278.

and twelfth species, the females depart from the usual type, for they are gaily decorated almost like the males, but in a somewhat less degree. Hence in these two latter species the bright colours of the males seem to have been transferred to the females; whilst in the tenth species the male has either retained or recovered the plain colours of the female, as well as of the parent-form of the genus. The sexes in these three cases have thus been rendered nearly alike, though in an opposite manner. In the allied genus Eubagis, both sexes of some of the species are plain-coloured and nearly alike; whilst with the greater number the males are decorated with beautiful metallic tints in a diversified manner, and differ much from their females. The females throughout the genus retain the same general style of colouring, so that they resemble one another much more closely than they resemble their own males.

In the genus Papilio, all the species of the Æneas group are remarkable for their conspicuous and strongly contrasted colours, and they illustrate the frequent tendency to gradation in the amount of difference between the sexes. In a few species, for instance in *P. ascanius*, the males and females are alike; in others the males are either a little brighter, or very much more superb than the females. The genus Junonia, allied to our Vanessæ, offers a nearly parallel case, for although the sexes of most of the species resemble each other, and are destitute of rich colours, yet in certain species, as in *J. œnone*, the male is rather more bright-coloured than the female, and in a few (for instance *J. andremiaja*) the male is so different from the female that he might be mistaken for an entirely distinct species.

Another striking case was pointed out to me in the British Museum by Mr. A. Butler, namely, one of the tropical American Theclæ, in which both sexes are nearly alike and wonderfully splendid; in another species the male is coloured in a similarly gorgeous manner, whilst the whole upper surface of the female is of a dull uniform brown. Our common little English blue butterflies of the genus Lycæna, illustrate the various differences in colour between the sexes, almost as well, though not in so striking a manner, as the above exotic genera. In *Lycæna agestis* both sexes have wings of a brown colour, bordered with small ocellated orange spots, and are thus alike. In *L. œgon* the wings of the male are of a fine blue, bordered with black, whilst those of the female are brown, with a similar border, closely resembling the wings of *L. agestis*. Lastly, in *L. arion* both sexes are of a blue colour and are very like, though in the female the edges of the wings are rather duskier, with the black spots plainer; and in a bright blue Indian species both sexes are still more alike.

I have given the foregoing details in order to show, in the first place, that when the sexes of butterflies differ, the male as a general rule is the more beautiful, and departs more from the usual type of colouring of the group to which the species belongs. Hence in most groups the females of the several species resemble each other much more closely than do the males. In some cases, however, to which I shall hereafter allude, the females are coloured more splendidly than the males. In the second place, these details have been given to bring clearly before the mind that within the same genus, the two sexes frequently present every gradation from no difference in colour, to so great a difference that it was long before the two were placed by entomologists in the same genus. In the third place, we have seen that when the sexes nearly resemble each other, this appears due either to the male having transferred his colours to the female, or to the male having retained, or perhaps recovered, the primordial colours of the group. It also deserves notice that in those groups in which the sexes differ, the females usually somewhat resemble the males, so that when the males are beautiful to an extraordinary degree, the females almost invariably exhibit some degree of beauty. From the many cases of gradation in the amount of difference between the sexes, and from the prevalence of the same general type of coloration throughout the whole of the same group, we may conclude that the causes have generally been the same which have determined the brilliant colouring of the males alone of some species, and of both sexes of other species.

As so many gorgeous butterflies inhabit the tropics, it has often been supposed that they owe their colours to the great heat and moisture of these zones; but Mr. Bates[6] has shown by the comparison of various closely-allied groups of insects from the temperate and tropical regions, that this view cannot be maintained; and the evidence becomes conclusive when brilliantly-coloured males and plain-coloured females of the same species inhabit the same district, feed on the same food, and follow exactly the same habits of life. Even when the sexes resemble each other, we can hardly believe that their brilliant and beautifully-arranged colours are the

[6] 'The Naturalist on the Amazons,' vol. i. 1863, p. 19.

purposeless result of the nature of the tissues and of
the action of the surrounding conditions.

With animals of all kinds, whenever colour has been
modified for some special purpose, this has been, as far
as we can judge, either for direct or indirect protection,
or as an attraction between the sexes. With many
species of butterflies the upper surfaces of the wings
are obscure; and this in all probability leads to their
escaping observation and danger. But butterflies
would be particularly liable to be attacked by their
enemies when at rest; and most kinds whilst resting
raise their wings vertically over their backs, so that
the lower surface alone is exposed to view. Hence it
is this side which is often coloured so as to imitate the
objects on which these insects commonly rest. Dr.
Rössler, I believe, first noticed the similarity of the
closed wings of certain Vanessæ and other butterflies
to the bark of trees. Many analogous and striking
facts could be given. The most interesting one is that
recorded by Mr. Wallace [7] of a common Indian and
Sumatran butterfly (Kallima), which disappears like
magic when it settles on a bush; for it hides its head
and antennæ between its closed wings, which, in form,
colour and veining, cannot be distinguished from a
withered leaf with its footstalk. In some other cases
the lower surfaces of the wings are brilliantly coloured,
and yet are protective; thus in *Thecla rubi* the wings
when closed are of an emerald green, and resemble the
young leaves of the bramble, on which in spring this
butterfly may often be seen seated. It is also remark-

[7] See the interesting article in
the ' Westminster Review,' July
1867, p. 10. A woodcut of the
Kallima is given by Mr. Wallace
in ' Hardwicke's Science Gossip,'
Sept. 1867, p. 196.

able that in very many species in which the sexes differ greatly in colour on their upper surface, the lower surface is closely similar or identical in both sexes, and serves as a protection.[8]

Although the obscure tints both of the upper and under sides of many butterflies no doubt serve to conceal them, yet we cannot extend this view to the brilliant and conspicuous colours on the upper surface of such species as our admiral and peacock Vanessæ, our white cabbage-butterflies (Pieris), or the great swallow-tail Papilio which haunts the open fens—for these butterflies are thus rendered visible to every living creature. In these species both sexes are alike; but in the common brimstone butterfly (*Gonepteryx rhamni*), the male is of an intense yellow, whilst the female is much paler; and in the orange-tip (*Anthocharis cardamines*) the males alone have their wings tipped with bright orange. Both the males and females in these cases are conspicuous, and it is not credible that their difference in colour should stand in any relation to ordinary protection. Prof. Weismann remarks,[9] that the female of one of the Lycænæ expands her brown wings when she settles on the ground, and is then almost invisible; the male, on the other hand, as if aware of the danger incurred from the bright blue of the upper surface of his wings, rests with them closed; and this shows that the blue colour cannot be in any way protective. Nevertheless, it is probable that conspicuous colours are indirectly beneficial to many species, as a warning that they are unpalatable. For in certain other cases, beauty has been gained

[8] Mr. G. Fraser, in 'Nature,' April 1871 p. 489.

[9] 'Einfluss der Isolirung au di. Artbildung,' 1872, p. 58.

through the imitation of other beautiful species, which inhabit the same district and enjoy an immunity from attack by being in some way offensive to their enemies; but then we have to account for the beauty of the imitated species.

As Mr. Walsh has remarked to me, the females of our orange-tip butterfly, above referred to, and of an American species (*Anth. genutia*) probably show us the primordial colours of the parent-species of the genus; for both sexes of four or five widely-distributed species are coloured in nearly the same manner. As in several previous cases, we may here infer that it is the males of *Anth. cardamines* and *genutia* which have departed from the usual type of the genus. In the *Anth. sara* from California, the orange-tips to the wings have been partially developed in the female; but they are paler than in the male, and slightly different in some other respects. In an allied Indian form, the *Iphias glaucippe*, the orange-tips are fully developed in both sexes. In this Iphias, as pointed out to me by Mr. A. Butler, the under surface of the wings marvellously resembles a pale-coloured leaf; and in our English orange-tip, the under surface resembles the flower-head of the wild parsley, on which the butterfly often rests at night.[10] The same reason which compels us to believe that the lower surfaces have here been coloured for the sake of protection, leads us to deny that the wings have been tipped with bright orange for the same purpose, especially when this character is confined to the males.

Most Moths rest motionless during the whole or greater part of the day with their wings depressed;

[10] See the interesting observations by Mr. T. W. Wood, 'The Student,' Sept. 1868, p. 81.

and the whole upper surface is often shaded and coloured in an admirable manner, as Mr. Wallace has remarked, for escaping detection. The front-wings of the Bombycidæ and Noctuidæ,[11] when at rest, generally overlap and conceal the hind-wings; so that the latter might be brightly coloured without much risk; and they are in fact often thus coloured. During flight, moths would often be able to escape from their enemies; nevertheless, as the hind-wings are then fully exposed to view, their bright colours must generally have been acquired at some little risk. But the following fact shews how cautious we ought to be in drawing conclusions on this head. The common Yellow Under-wings (Triphæna) often fly about during the day or early evening, and are then conspicuous from the colour of their hind-wings. It would naturally be thought that this would be a source of danger; but Mr. J. Jenner Weir believes that it actually serves them as a means of escape, for birds strike at these brightly coloured and fragile surfaces, instead of at the body. For instance, Mr. Weir turned into his aviary a vigorous specimen of *Triphæna pronuba*, which was instantly pursued by a robin; but the bird's attention being caught by the coloured wings, the moth was not captured until after about fifty attempts, and small portions of the wings were repeatedly broken off. He tried the same experiment, in the open air, with a swallow and *T. fimbria*; but the large size of this moth probably interfered with its capture.[12] We are thus reminded of a statement

[11] Mr. Wallace in 'Hardwicke's Science Gossip,' Sept. 1867, p. 193.

[12] See also, on this subject, Mr. Weir's paper in 'Transact. Ent. Soc.' 1869, p. 23.

made by Mr. Wallace,[13] namely, that in the Brazilian forests and Malayan islands, many common and highly-decorated butterflies are weak flyers, though furnished with a broad expanse of wing; and they "are often "captured with pierced and broken wings, as if they "had been seized by birds, from which they had "escaped: if the wings had been much smaller in "proportion to the body, it seems probable that the "insect would more frequently have been struck or "pierced in a vital part, and thus the increased "expanse of the wings may have been indirectly "beneficial."

Display.—The bright colours of many butterflies and of some moths are specially arranged for display, so that they may be readily seen. During the night colours are not visible, and there can be no doubt that the nocturnal moths, taken as a body, are much less gaily decorated than butterflies, all of which are diurnal in their habits. But the moths of certain families, such as the Zygænidæ, several Sphingidæ, Uraniidæ, some Arctiidæ and Saturniidæ, fly about during the day or early evening, and many of these are extremely beautiful, being far brighter coloured than the strictly nocturnal kinds. A few exceptional cases, however, of bright-coloured nocturnal species have been recorded.[14]

There is evidence of another kind in regard to

[13] 'Westminster Review,' July 1867, p. 16.

[14] For instance, Lithosia; but Prof. Westwood ('Modern Class. of Insects,' vol. ii. p. 390) seems surprised at this case. On the relative colours of diurnal and nocturnal Lepidoptera, see ibid. pp. 333 and 392; also Harris, 'Treatise on the Insects of New England,' 1842, p. 315.

display. Butterflies, as before remarked, elevate their
wings when at rest, but whilst basking in the sunshine
often alternately raise and depress them, thus exposing
both surfaces to full view; and although the lower
surface is often coloured in an obscure manner as a
protection, yet in many species it is as highly decorated
as the upper surface, and sometimes in a very different
manner. In some tropical species the lower surface is
even more brilliantly coloured than the upper.[15] In
the English fritillaries (*Argynnis*) the lower surface
alone is ornamented with shining silver. Nevertheless,
as a general rule, the upper surface, which is probably
more fully exposed, is coloured more brightly and
diversely than the lower. Hence the lower surface
generally affords to entomologists the more useful
character for detecting the affinities of the various
species. Fritz Müller informs me that three species of
Castnia are found near his house in S. Brazil: of two
of them the hind-wings are obscure, and are always
covered by the front-wings when these butterflies are
at rest; but the third species has black hind-wings,
beautifully spotted with red and white, and these are
fully expanded and displayed whenever the butterfly
rests. Other such cases could be added.

If we now turn to the enormous group of moths,
which, as I hear from Mr. Stainton, do not habitually
expose the under surface of their wings to full view,
we find this side very rarely coloured with a brightness
greater than, or even equal to, that of the upper side.

[15] Such differences between
the upper and lower surfaces of
the wings of several species of
Papilio may be seen in the
beautiful plates to Mr. Wallace's
'Memoir on the Papilionidæ of
the Malayan Region,' in 'Transact. Linn. Soc.' vol. xxv. part i.
1865.

Some exceptions to the rule, either real or apparent, must be noticed, as the case of Hypopyra.[16] Mr. Trimen informs me that in Guenée's great work, three moths are figured, in which the under surface is much the more brilliant. For instance, in the Australian Gastrophora the upper surface of the fore-wing is pale greyish-ochreous, while the lower surface is magnificently ornamented by an ocellus of cobalt-blue, placed in the midst of a black mark, surrounded by orange-yellow, and this by bluish-white. But the habits of these three moths are unknown ; so that no explanation can be given of their unusual style of colouring. Mr. Trimen also informs me that the lower surface of the wings in certain other Geometræ[17] and quadrifid Noctuæ are either more variegated or more brightly-coloured than the upper surface ; but some of these species have the habit of " holding their " wings quite erect over their backs, retaining them " in this position for a considerable time," and thus exposing the under surface to view. Other species, when settled on the ground or herbage, now and then suddenly and slightly lift up their wings. Hence the lower surface of the wings being brighter than the upper surface in certain moths is not so anomalous as it at first appears. The Saturniidæ include some of the most beautiful of all moths, their wings being decorated, as in our British Emperor moth, with fine ocelli ; and Mr. T. W. Wood[18] observes that they resemble butterflies in some of their movements ;

---

[16] See Mr. Wormald on this moth : ' Proc. Ent. Soc.' March 2nd, 1868.

[17] See also an account of the S. American genus Erateina

(one of the Geometræ) in ' Transact. Ent. Soc.' new series, vol. v. pl. xv. and xvi.

[18] ' Proc. Ent. Soc. of London,' July 6, 1868, p. xxvii.

" for instance, in the gentle waving up and down of
" the wings as if for display, which is more charac-
" teristic of diurnal than of nocturnal Lepidoptera."

It is a singular fact that no British moths which are
brilliantly coloured, and, as far as I can discover,
hardly any foreign species, differ much in colour
according to sex; though this is the case with many
brilliant butterflies.   The male, however, of one
American moth, the *Saturnia Io,* is described as
having its fore-wings deep yellow, curiously marked
with purplish-red spots; whilst the wings of the
female are purple-brown, marked with grey lines.[19]
The British moths which differ sexually in colour are
all brown, or of various dull yellow tints, or nearly
white.   In several species the males are much darker
than the females,[20] and these belong to groups which
generally fly about during the afternoon.   On the
other hand, in many genera, as Mr. Stainton informs
me, the males have the hind-wings whiter than those
of the female—of which fact *Agrotis exclamationis*
offers a good instance.   In the Ghost Moth (*Hepialus*

[19] Harris, 'Treatise,' &c., edited
by Flint, 1862, p. 395.

[20] For instance, I observe in
my son's cabinet that the males
are darker than the females in
the *Lasiocampa quercus, Odo-
nestis potatoria, Hypogymna
dispar, Dasychira pudibunda,*
and *Cycnia mendica.*   In this
latter species the difference in
colour between the two sexes is
strongly marked; and Mr.
Wallace informs me that we
here have, as he believes, an
instance of protective mimicry
confined to one sex, as will

hereafter be more fully explained.   The white female of
the Cycnia resembles the very
common *Spilosoma menthrasti,*
both sexes of which are white;
and Mr. Stainton observed that
this latter moth was rejected
with utter disgust by a whole
brood of young turkeys, which
were fond of eating other moths;
so that if the Cycnia was commonly mistaken by British birds
for the Spilosoma, it would escape
being devoured, and its white
deceptive colour would thus be
highly beneficial.

humuli) the difference is more strongly marked; the males being white, and the females yellow with darker markings.[21] It is probable that in these cases the males are thus rendered more conspicuous, and more easily seen by the females whilst flying about in the dusk.

From the several foregoing facts it is impossible to admit that the brilliant colours of butterflies, and of some few moths, have commonly been acquired for the sake of protection. We have seen that their colours and elegant patterns are arranged and exhibited as if for display. Hence I am led to believe that the females prefer or are most excited by the more brilliant males; for on any other supposition the males would, as far as we can see, be ornamented to no purpose. We know that ants and certain Lamellicorn beetles are capable of feeling an attachment for each other, and that ants recognise their fellows after an interval of several months. Hence there is no abstract improbability in the Lepidoptera, which probably stand nearly or quite as high in the scale as these insects, having sufficient mental capacity to admire bright colours. They certainly discover flowers by colour. The Humming-bird Sphinx may often be seen to swoop down from a distance on a bunch of flowers in the midst of green foliage; and I have been assured by two persons abroad, that these moths repeatedly visit

[21] It is remarkable, that in the Shetland Islands the male of this moth, instead of differing widely from the female, frequently resembles her closely in colour (see Mr. MacLachlan, 'Transact. Ent. Soc.' vol. ii. 1866, p. 459). Mr. G. Fraser suggests ('Na- ture,' April 1871, p. 489) that at the season of the year when the ghost-moth appears in these northern islands, the whiteness of the males would not be needed to render them visible to the females in the twilight night.

flowers painted on the walls of a room, and vainly endeavour to insert their proboscis into them. Fritz Müller informs me that several kinds of butterflies in S. Brazil shew an unmistakable preference for certain colours over others: he observed that they very often visited the brilliant red flowers of five or six genera of plants, but never the white or yellow flowering species of the same and other genera, growing in the same garden; and I have received other accounts to the same effect. As I hear from Mr. Doubleday, the common white butterfly often flies down to a bit of paper on the ground, no doubt mistaking it for one of its own species. Mr. Collingwood [22] in speaking of the difficulty in collecting certain butterflies in the Malay Archipelago, states that "a dead specimen pinned upon "a conspicuous twig will often arrest an insect of the "same species in its headlong flight, and bring it down "within easy reach of the net, especially if it be of "the opposite sex."

The courtship of butterflies is, as before remarked, a prolonged affair. The males sometimes fight together in rivalry; and many may be seen pursuing or crowding round the same female. Unless, then, the females prefer one male to another, the pairing must be left to mere chance, and this does not appear probable. If, on the other hand, the females habitually, or even occasionally, prefer the more beautiful males, the colours of the latter will have been rendered brighter by degrees, and will have been transmitted to both sexes or to one sex, according to the law of inheritance which has prevailed. The process of sexual selection will have been much facilitated, if the conclusion can

[22] 'Rambles of a Naturalist in the Chinese Seas,' 1868, p. 182.

be trusted, arrived at from various kinds of evidence
in the supplement to the ninth chapter; namely, that
the males of many Lepidoptera, at least in the imago
state, greatly exceed the females in number.

Some facts, however, are opposed to the belief that
female butterflies prefer the more beautiful males;
thus, as I have been assured by several collectors,
fresh females may frequently be seen paired with
battered, faded, or dingy males; but this is a circumstance which could hardly fail often to follow from the
males emerging from their cocoons earlier than the
females. With moths of the family of the Bombycidæ,
the sexes pair immediately after assuming the imago
state; for they cannot feed, owing to the rudimentary
condition of their mouths. The females, as several
entomologists have remarked to me, lie in an almost
torpid state, and appear not to evince the least choice
in regard to their partners. This is the case with the
common silk-moth (*B. mori*), as I have been told by
some continental and English breeders. Dr. Wallace,
who has had great experience in breeding *Bombyx
cynthia*, is convinced that the females evince no choice
or preference. He has kept above 300 of these moths
together, and has often found the most vigorous
females mated with stunted males. The reverse
appears to occur seldom; for, as he believes, the
more vigorous males pass over the weakly females,
and are attracted by those endowed with most vitality. Nevertheless, the Bombycidæ, though obscurely-
coloured, are often beautiful to our eyes from their
elegant and mottled shades.

I have as yet only referred to the species in which
the males are brighter coloured than the females, and

I have attributed their beauty to the females for many generations having chosen and paired with the more attractive males. But converse cases occur, though rarely, in which the females are more brilliant than the males; and here, as I believe, the males have selected the more beautiful females, and have thus slowly added to their beauty. We do not know why in various classes of animals the males of some few species have selected the more beautiful females instead of having gladly accepted any female, as seems to be the general rule in the animal kingdom; but if, contrary to what generally occurs with the Lepidoptera, the females were much more numerous than the males, the latter would be likely to pick out the more beautiful females. Mr. Butler shewed me several species of Callidryas in the British Museum, in some of which the females equalled, and in others greatly surpassed the males in beauty; for the females alone have the borders of their wings suffused with crimson and orange, and spotted with black. The plainer males of these species closely resemble each other, shewing that here the females have been modified; whereas in those cases, where the males are the more ornate, it is these which have been modified, the females remaining closely alike.

In England we have some analogous cases, though not so marked. The females alone of two species of Thecla have a bright-purple or orange patch on their fore-wings. In Hipparchia the sexes do not differ much; but it is the female of *H. janira* which has a conspicuous light-brown patch on her wings; and the females of some of the other species are brighter coloured than their males. Again, the females of

Colias edusa and *hyale* have " orange or yellow spots " on the black marginal border, represented in the males "only by thin streaks; " and in Pieris it is the females which "are ornamented with black spots on the fore- "wings, and these are only partially present in the "males." Now the males of many butterflies are known to support the females during their marriage flight; but in the species just named it is the females which support the males; so that the part which the two sexes play is reversed, as is their relative beauty. Throughout the animal kingdom the males commonly take the more active share in wooing, and their beauty seems to have been increased by the females having accepted the more attractive individuals; but with these butterflies, the females take the more active part in the final marriage ceremony, so that we may suppose that they likewise do so in the wooing; and in this case we can understand how it is that they have been rendered the more beautiful. Mr. Meldola, from whom the foregoing statements have been taken, says in conclusion; "Though I am not convinced of "the action of sexual selection in producing the colours "of insects, it cannot be denied that these facts are "strikingly corroborative of Mr. Darwin's views." [23]

As sexual selection primarily depends on variability, a few words must be added on this subject. In respect to colour there is no difficulty, for any number of highly variable Lepidoptera could be named. One

[23] 'Nature,' April 27th, 1871, p. 508. Mr. Meldola quotes Donzel, in 'Soc. Ent. de France,' 1837, p. 77, on the flight of butterflies whilst pairing. See also Mr. G. Fraser, in 'Nature,' April 20th, 1871, p. 489, on the sexual differences of several British butterflies.

good instance will suffice. Mr. Bates shewed me a whole series of specimens of *Papilio sesostris* and *P. childrenæ;* in the latter the males varied much in the extent of the beautifully enamelled green patch on the fore-wings, and in the size of the white mark, and of the splendid crimson stripe on the hind-wings; so that there was a great contrast amongst the males between the most and the least gaudy. The male of *Papilio sesostris* is much less beautiful than of *P. childrenæ;* and it likewise varies a little in the size of the green patch on the fore-wings, and in the occasional appearance of the small crimson stripe on the hind-wings, borrowed, as it would seem, from its own female; for the females of this and of many other species in the Æneas group possess this crimson stripe. Hence between the brightest specimens of *P. sesostris* and the dullest of *P. childrenæ,* there was but a small interval; and it was evident that as far as mere variability is concerned, there would be no difficulty in permanently increasing the beauty of either species by means of selection. The variability is here almost confined to the male sex; but Mr. Wallace and Mr. Bates have shewn [24] that the females of some species are extremely variable, the males being nearly constant. In a future chapter I shall have occasion to shew that the beautiful eye-like spots, or ocelli, found on the wings of many Lepidoptera, are eminently variable. I may

[24] Wallace on the Papilionidæ of the Malayan Region, in 'Transact. Linn. Soc.' vol. xxv. 1865, pp. 8, 36. A striking case of a rare variety, strictly intermediate between two other well-marked female varieties, is given by Mr. Wallace. See also Mr. Bates, in 'Proc. Entomolog. Soc.' Nov. 19th, 1866, p. xl.

here add that these ocelli offer a difficulty on the
theory of sexual selection; for though appearing to us
so ornamental, they are never present in one sex and
absent in the other, nor do they ever differ much in
the two sexes.[25] This fact is at present inexplicable;
but if it should hereafter be found that the formation
of an ocellus is due to some change in the tissues of
the wings, for instance, occurring at a very early
period of development, we might expect, from what
we know of the laws of inheritance, that it would be
transmitted to both sexes, though arising and perfected in one sex alone.

On the whole, although many serious objections may
be urged, it seems probable that most of the brilliantly-
coloured species of Lepidoptera owe their colours to
sexual selection, excepting in certain cases, presently to
be mentioned, in which conspicuous colours have been
gained through mimicry as a protection. From the
ardour of the male throughout the animal kingdom, he
is generally willing to accept any female; and it is the
female which usually exerts a choice. Hence, if sexual
selection has been efficient with the Lepidoptera, the
male, when the sexes differ, ought to be the more
brilliantly coloured, and this undoubtedly is the case.
When both sexes are brilliantly coloured and resemble
each other, the characters acquired by the males
appear to have been transmitted to both. We are led
to this conclusion by cases, even within the same
genus, of gradation from an extraordinary amount of
difference to identity in colour between the two sexes.

[25] Mr. Bates was so kind as
to lay this subject before the
Entomological Society, and I
have received answers to this
effect from several entomologists.

But it may be asked whether the differences in colour between the sexes may not be accounted for by other means besides sexual selection. Thus the males and females of the same species of butterfly are in several cases known[26] to inhabit different stations, the former commonly basking in the sunshine, the latter haunting gloomy forests. It is therefore possible that different conditions of life may have acted directly on the two sexes; but this is not probable [27] as in the adult state they are exposed to different conditions during a very short period; and the larvæ of both are exposed to the same conditions. Mr. Wallace believes that the difference between the sexes is due not so much to the males having been modified, as to the females having in all or almost all cases acquired dull colours for the sake of protection. It seems to me, on the contrary, far more probable that it is the males which have been chiefly modified through sexual selection, the females having been comparatively little changed. We can thus understand how it is that the females of allied species generally resemble one another so much more closely than do the males. They thus shew us approximately the primordial colouring of the parent-species of the group to which they belong. They have, however, almost always been somewhat modified by the transfer to them of some of the successive variations, through the accumulation of which the males were rendered beautiful. But I do not wish to deny that the females alone of some species

[26] H. W. Bates, 'The Naturalist on the Amazons,' vol. ii. 1863, p. 228. A. R. Wallace, in 'Transact. Linn. Soc.' vol. xxv. 1865, p. 10.

[27] On this whole subject see 'The Variation of Animals and Plants under Domestication,' 1868, vol. ii. chap. xxiii.

may have been specially modified for protection. In most cases the males and females of distinct species will have been exposed during their prolonged larval state to different conditions, and may have been thus affected; though with the males any slight change of colour thus caused will generally have been masked by the brilliant tints gained through sexual selection. When we treat of Birds, I shall have to discuss the whole question, as to how far the differences in colour between the sexes are due to the males having been modified through sexual selection for ornamental purposes, or to the females having been modified through natural selection for the sake of protection, so that I will here say but little on the subject.

In all the cases in which the more common form of equal inheritance by both sexes has prevailed, the selection of bright-coloured males would tend to make the females bright-coloured ; and the selection of dull-coloured females would tend to make the males dull. If both processes were carried on simultaneously, they would tend to counteract each other; and the final result would depend on whether a greater number of females from being well protected by obscure colours, or a greater number of males by being brightly-coloured and thus finding partners, succeeded in leaving more numerous offspring.

In order to account for the frequent transmission of characters to one sex alone, Mr. Wallace expresses his belief that the more common form of equal inheritance by both sexes can be changed through natural selection into inheritance by one sex alone, but in favour of this view I can discover no evidence. We know from what occurs under domestication that new characters often appear, which from the first are transmitted to one sex alone; and by the selection of such variations there would not be the slightest difficulty in giving bright colours to the males alone, and at the same time or subsequently, dull colours to the females alone. In this manner the females of some butterflies and moths have, it is probable, been rendered inconspicuous for the sake of protection, and widely different from their males.

I am, however, unwilling without distinct evidence to admit that two complex processes of selection, each requiring the transference of new characters to one sex alone, have been carried on with a multitude of species,—that the males have been rendered more brilliant by beating their rivals, and the females more dull-coloured by having escaped from their enemies. The male, for instance, of the common brimstone butterfly (Gonepteryx), is of a far more intense yellow than the female, though she is equally conspicuous; and it does not seem probable that she specially acquired her pale tints as a protection, though it is probable that the male acquired his bright colours as a sexual attraction. The female of *Anthocharis cardamines* does not possess the beautiful orange wing-tips of the male; consequently she closely resembles the white butterflies (Pieris) so common in our gardens; but we have no evidence that this resemblance is beneficial to her. As, on the other hand, she resembles both sexes of several other species of the genus inhabiting various quarters of the world, it is probable that she has simply retained to a large extent her primordial colours.

Finally, as we have seen, various considerations lead

to the conclusion that with the greater number of brilliantly-coloured Lepidoptera it is the male which has been chiefly modified through sexual selection; the amount of difference between the sexes mostly depending on the form of inheritance which has prevailed. Inheritance is governed by so many unknown laws or conditions, that it seems to us to act in a capricious manner;[28] and we can thus, to a certain extent, understand how it is that with closely allied species the sexes either differ to an astonishing degree, or are identical in colour. As all the successive steps in the process of variation are necessarily transmitted through the female, a greater or less number of such steps might readily become developed in her; and thus we can understand the frequent gradations from an extreme difference to none at all between the sexes of allied species. These cases of gradation, it may be added, are much too common to favour the supposition that we here see females actually undergoing the process of transition and losing their brightness for the sake of protection; for we have every reason to conclude that at any one time the greater number of species are in a fixed condition.

Mimicry.—This principle was first made clear in an admirable paper by Mr. Bates,[29] who thus threw a flood of light on many obscure problems. It had previously been observed that certain butterflies in S. America belonging to quite distinct families, resembled the Heliconidæ so closely in every stripe and shade of colour, that they could not be distinguished save by

[28] 'The Variation of Animals and Plants under Domestication,' vol. ii. chap. xii. p. 17.

[29] 'Transact. Linn. Soc.' vol. xxiii. 1862, p. 495.

an experienced entomologist. As the Heliconidæ are
coloured in their usual manner, whilst the others
depart from the usual colouring of the groups to which
they belong, it is clear that the latter are the imitators,
and the Heliconidæ the imitated. Mr. Bates further
observed that the imitating species are comparatively
rare, whilst the imitated abound, and that the two sets
live mingled together. From the fact of the Heliconidæ being conspicuous and beautiful insects, yet so
numerous in individuals and species, he concluded that
they must be protected from the attacks of enemies
by some secretion or odour; and this conclusion has
now been amply confirmed,[30] especially by Mr. Belt.
Hence Mr. Bates inferred that the butterflies which
imitate the protected species have acquired their
present marvellously deceptive appearance through
variation and natural selection, in order to be mistaken
for the protected kinds, and thus to escape being
devoured. No explanation is here attempted of the
brilliant colours of the imitated, but only of the imitating butterflies. We must account for the colours of the
former in the same general manner, as in the cases
previously discussed in this chapter. Since the publication of Mr. Bates' paper, similar and equally striking
facts have been observed by Mr. Wallace in the Malayan
region, by Mr. Trimen in South Africa, and by Mr.
Riley in the United States.[31]

[30] 'Proc. Ent. Soc.' Dec. 3rd,
1866, p. xlv.
[31] Wallace, 'Transact. Linn.
Soc.' vol. xxv. 1865, p. 1; also
'Transact. Ent. Soc.' vol. iv.
(3rd series), 1867, p. 301.
Trimen, 'Linn. Transact.' vol.
xxvi. 1869, p. 497. Riley,
'Third Annual Report on the
Noxious Insects of Missouri,
1871, pp. 163–168. This latter
essay is valuable, as Mr. Riley
here discusses all the objections
which have been raised against
Mr. Bates' theory.

As some writers have felt much difficulty in understanding how the first steps in the process of mimicry could have been effected through natural selection, it may be well to remark that the process probably commenced long ago between forms not widely dissimilar in colour. In this case even a slight variation would be beneficial, if it rendered the one species more like the other; and afterwards the imitated species might be modified to an extreme degree through sexual selection or other means, and if the changes were gradual, the imitators might easily be led along the same track, until they differed to an equally extreme degree from their original condition; and they would thus ultimately assume an appearance or colouring wholly unlike that of the other members of the group to which they belonged. It should also be remembered that many species of Lepidoptera are liable to considerable and abrupt variations in colour. A few instances have been given in this chapter; and many more may be found in the papers of Mr. Bates and Mr. Wallace.

With several species the sexes are alike, and imitate the two sexes of another species. But Mr. Trimen gives, in the paper already referred to, three cases in which the sexes of the imitated form differ from each other in colour, and the sexes of the imitating form differ in a like manner. Several cases have also been recorded where the females alone imitate brilliantly-coloured and protected species, the males retaining " the normal " aspect of their immediate congeners." It is here obvious that the successive variations by which the female has been modified have been transmitted to her alone. It is, however, probable that some of the many successive variations would have been transmitted to,

and developed in, the males had not such males been
eliminated by being thus rendered less attractive to
the females; so that only those variations were preserved which were from the first strictly limited in
their transmission to the female sex. We have a partial
illustration of these remarks in a statement by Mr.
Belt;[32] that the males of some of the Leptalides, which
imitate protected species, still retain in a concealed
manner some of their original characters. Thus in
the males " the upper half of the lower wing is of a
" pure white, whilst all the rest of the wings is barred
" and spotted with black, red and yellow, like the
" species they mimic. The females have not this white
" patch, and the males usually conceal it by covering
" it with the upper wing, so that I cannot imagine its
" being of any other use to them than as an attraction
" in courtship, when they exhibit it to the females, and
" thus gratify their deep-seated preference for the
" normal colour of the Order to which the Leptalides
" belong."

Bright Colours of Caterpillars.—Whilst reflecting on
the beauty of many butterflies, it occurred to me that
some caterpillars were splendidly coloured; and as
sexual selection could not possibly have here acted, it
appeared rash to attribute the beauty of the mature
insect to this agency, unless the bright colours of their
larvæ could be somehow explained. In the first place,
it may be observed that the colours of caterpillars do
not stand in any close correlation with those of the
mature insect. Secondly, their bright colours do not
serve in any ordinary manner as a protection. Mr.

[32] 'The Naturalist in Nicaragua,' 1874, p. 385.

Bates informs me, as an instance of this, that the most conspicuous caterpillar which he ever beheld (that of a Sphinx) lived on the large green leaves of a tree on the open llanos of South America; it was about four inches in length, transversely banded with black and yellow, and with its head, legs, and tail of a bright red. Hence it caught the eye of any one who passed by, even at the distance of many yards, and no doubt that of every passing bird.

I then applied to Mr. Wallace, who has an innate genius for solving difficulties. After some consideration he replied: "Most caterpillars require protection, "as may be inferred from some kinds being furnished "with spines or irritating hairs, and from many being "coloured green like the leaves on which they feed, or "being curiously like the twigs of the trees on which "they live." Another instance of protection, furnished me by Mr. J. Mansel Weale, may be added, namely, that there is a caterpillar of a moth which lives on the mimosas in South Africa, and fabricates for itself a case quite indistinguishable from the surrounding thorns. From such considerations Mr. Wallace thought it probable that conspicuously coloured caterpillars were protected by having a nauseous taste; but as their skin is extremely tender, and as their intestines readily protrude from a wound, a slight peck from the beak of a bird would be as fatal to them as if they had been devoured. Hence, as Mr. Wallace remarks, "distastefulness alone would be insufficient to protect "a caterpillar unless some outward sign indicated to "its would-be destroyer that its prey was a disgusting "morsel." Under these circumstances it would be highly advantageous to a caterpillar to be instantaneously and certainly recognised as unpalatable by all birds and other animals. Thus the most gaudy colours would be serviceable, and might have been gained by variation and the survival of the most easily-recognised individuals.

This hypothesis appears at first sight very bold, but when it was brought before the Entomological Society[33] it was supported by various statements; and Mr. J. Jenner Weir, who keeps a large number of birds in an aviary, informs me that he has made many trials, and finds no exception to the rule, that all caterpillars of nocturnal and retiring habits with smooth skins, all of a green colour, and all which imitate twigs, are greedily devoured by his birds. The hairy and spinose kinds are invariably rejected, as were four conspicuously-coloured species. When the birds rejected a caterpillar, they plainly shewed, by shaking their heads, and cleansing their beaks, that they were disgusted by the taste.[34] Three conspicuous kinds of caterpillars and moths were also given to some lizards and frogs, by Mr. A. Butler, and were rejected, though other kinds were eagerly eaten. Thus the probability of Mr. Wallace's view is confirmed, namely, that certain caterpillars have been made conspicuous for their own good, so as to be easily recognised by their enemies, on nearly the same principle that poisons are sold in coloured bottles by druggists for the good of

[33] 'Proc. Entomolog. Soc.' Dec. 3rd, 1866, p. xlv., and March 4th, 1867, p. lxxx.

[34] See Mr. J. Jenner Weir's paper on Insects and Insectivorous Birds, in 'Transact. Ent. Soc.' 1869, p. 21; also Mr. Butler's paper, ibid. p. 27. Mr. Riley has given analogous facts in the 'Third Annual Report on the Noxious Insects of Missouri,' 1871, p. 148. Some opposed cases are, however, given by Dr. Wallace and M. H. d'Orville; see 'Zoological Record,' 1869, p. 349.

man. We cannot, however, at present thus explain the elegant diversity in the colours of many caterpillars; but any species which had at some former period acquired a dull, mottled, or striped appearance, either in imitation of surrounding objects, or from the direct action of climate, &c., almost certainly would not become uniform in colour, when its tints were rendered intense and bright; for in order to make a caterpillar merely conspicuous, there would be no selection in any definite direction.

Summary and Concluding Remarks on Insects.— Looking back to the several Orders, we see that the sexes often differ in various characters, the meaning of which is not in the least understood. The sexes, also, often differ in their organs of sense and means of locomotion, so that the males may quickly discover and reach the females. They differ still oftener in the males possessing diversified contrivances for retaining the females when found. We are, however, here concerned only in a secondary degree with sexual differences of these kinds.

In almost all the Orders, the males of some species, even of weak and delicate kinds, are known to be highly pugnacious; and some few are furnished with special weapons for fighting with their rivals. But the law of battle does not prevail nearly so widely with insects as with the higher animals. Hence it probably arises, that it is in only a few cases that the males have been rendered larger and stronger than the females. On the contrary, they are usually smaller, so that they may be developed within a shorter time, to be ready in large numbers for the emergence of the females.

In two families of the Homoptera and in three of the Orthoptera, the males alone possess sound-producing organs in an efficient state. These are used incessantly during the breeding-season, not only for calling the females, but apparently for charming or exciting them in rivalry with other males. No one who admits the agency of selection of any kind, will, after reading the above discussion, dispute that these musical instruments have been acquired through sexual selection. In four other Orders the members of one sex, or more commonly of both sexes, are provided with organs for producing various sounds, which apparently serve merely as call-notes. When both sexes are thus provided, the individuals which were able to make the loudest or most continuous noise would gain partners before those which were less noisy, so that their organs have probably been gained through sexual selection. It is instructive to reflect on the wonderful diversity of the means for producing sound, possessed by the males alone, or by both sexes, in no less than six Orders. We thus learn how effectual sexual selection has been in leading to modifications which sometimes, as with the Homoptera, relate to important parts of the organisation.

From the reasons assigned in the last chapter, it is probable that the great horns possessed by the males of many Lamellicorn, and some other beetles, have been acquired as ornaments. From the small size of insects, we are apt to undervalue their appearance. If we could imagine a male Chalcosoma (fig. 16), with its polished bronzed coat of mail, and its vast complex horns, magnified to the size of a horse, or even of a dog, it would be one of the most imposing animals in the world.

The colouring of insects is a complex and obscure subject. When the male differs slightly from the female, and neither are brilliantly-coloured, it is probable that the sexes have varied in a slightly different manner, and that the variations have been transmitted by each sex to the same, without any benefit or evil thus accruing. When the male is brilliantly-coloured and differs conspicuously from the female, as with some dragon-flies and many butterflies, it is probable that he owes his colours to sexual selection; whilst the female has retained a primordial or very ancient type of colouring, slightly modified by the agencies before explained. But in some cases the female has apparently been made obscure by variations transmitted to her alone, as a means of direct protection; and it is almost certain that she has sometimes been made brilliant, so as to imitate other protected species inhabiting the same district. When the sexes resemble each other and both are obscurely coloured there is no doubt that they have been in a multitude of cases so coloured for the sake of protection. So it is in some instances when both are brightly-coloured, for they thus imitate protected species, or resemble surrounding objects such as flowers; or they give notice to their enemies that they are unpalatable. In other cases in which the sexes resemble each other and are both brilliant, especially when the colours are arranged for display, we may conclude that they have been gained by the male sex as an attraction, and have been transferred to the female. We are more especially led to this conclusion whenever the same type of coloration prevails throughout a whole group, and we find that the males of some species differ widely in colour from the females, whilst others differ slightly or not at all with intermediate gradations connecting these extreme states.

In the same manner as bright colours have often been partially transferred from the males to the females, so it has been with the extraordinary horns of many Lamellicorn and some other beetles. So again, the sound-producing organs proper to the males of the Homoptera and Orthoptera have generally been transferred in a rudimentary, or even in a nearly perfect condition, to the females; yet not sufficiently perfect to be of any use. It is also an interesting fact, as bearing on sexual selection, that the stridulating organs of certain male Orthoptera are not fully developed until the last moult; and that the colours of certain male dragon-flies are not fully developed until some little time after their emergence from the pupal state, and when they are ready to breed.

Sexual selection implies that the more attractive individuals are preferred by the opposite sex; and as with insects, when the sexes differ, it is the male which, with some rare exceptions, is the more ornamented, and departs more from the type to which the species belongs;—and as it is the male which searches eagerly for the female, we must suppose that the females habitually or occasionally prefer the more beautiful males, and that these have thus acquired their beauty. That the females in most or all the Orders would have the power of rejecting any particular male, is probable from the many singular contrivances possessed by the males, such as great jaws, adhesive cushions, spines, elongated legs, &c., for seizing the female; for these contrivances shew that there is some difficulty in the act, so that her concurrence would seem necessary. Judging from what we know of the perceptive powers and affections of various insects, there is no antecedent improbability in sexual selection having come largely into play; but we have as yet no direct evidence on this head, and some facts are opposed to the belief. Nevertheless, when we see many males pursuing the same female, we can hardly believe that the pairing is left to blind chance—that the female exerts no choice, and is not influenced by the gorgeous colours or other ornaments with which the male is decorated.

If we admit that the females of the Homoptera and Orthoptera appreciate the musical tones of their male partners, and that the various instruments have been perfected through sexual selection, there is little improbability in the females of other insects appreciating beauty in form or colour, and consequently in such characters having been thus gained by the males. But from the circumstance of colour being so variable, and from its having been so often modified for the sake of protection, it is difficult to decide in how large a proportion of cases sexual selection has played a part. This is more especially difficult in those Orders, such as Orthoptera, Hymenoptera, and Coleoptera, in which the two sexes rarely differ much in colour; for we are then left to mere analogy. With the Coleoptera, however, as before remarked, it is in the great Lamellicorn group, placed by some authors at the head of the Order, and in which we sometimes see a mutual attachment between the sexes, that we find the males of some species possessing weapons for sexual strife, others furnished with wonderful horns, many with stridulating organs, and others ornamented with splendid metallic tints. Hence it seems probable that all these characters have been gained through the same means, namely sexual selection. With butterflies we have the best evidence, as the males sometimes take pains to display their beautiful colours; and we cannot believe that they would act thus, unless the display was of use to them in their courtship.

When we treat of Birds, we shall see that they present in their secondary sexual characters the closest analogy with insects. Thus, many male birds are highly pugnacious, and some are furnished with special weapons for fighting with their rivals. They possess organs which are used during the breeding-season for producing vocal and instrumental music. They are frequently ornamented with combs, horns, wattles and plumes of the most diversified kinds, and are decorated with beautiful colours, all evidently the sake of display. We shall find that, as with insects, both sexes in certain groups are equally beautiful, and are equally provided with ornaments which are usually confined to the male sex. In other groups both sexes are equally plain-coloured and unornamented. Lastly, in some few anomalous cases, the females are more beautiful than the males. We shall often find, in the same group of birds, every gradation from no difference between the sexes, to an extreme difference. We shall see that female birds, like female insects, often possess more or less plain traces or rudiments of characters which properly belong to the males and are of use only to them.

The analogy, indeed, in all these respects between birds and insects is curiously close. Whatever explanation applies to the one class probably applies to the other; and this explanation, as we shall hereafter attempt to shew in further detail, is sexual selection.

END OF VOL. I.

LONDON:
PRINTED BY WILLIAM CLOWES AND SONS, LIMITED,
STAMFORD STREET AND CHARING CROSS.